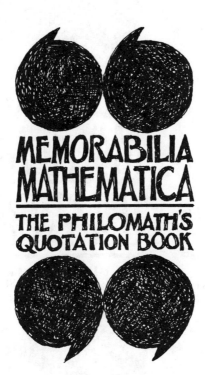

MEMORABILIA MATHEMATICA

THE PHILOMATH'S QUOTATION BOOK

MEMORABILIA MATHEMATICA

THE PHILOMATH'S QUOTATION BOOK

ROBERT EDOUARD MORITZ

1140 ANECDOTES,
APHORISMS AND PASSAGES
BY FAMOUS
MATHEMATICIANS,
SCIENTISTS & WRITERS

MAA
SPECTRUM

THE MATHEMATICAL ASSOCIATION OF AMERICA

PREFACE

EVERY one knows that the fine phrase "God geometrizes" is attributed to Plato, but few know where this famous passage is found, or the exact words in which it was first expressed. Those who, like the author, have spent hours and even days in the search of the exact statements, or the exact references, of similar famous passages, will not question the timeliness and usefulness of a book whose distinct purpose it is to bring together into a single volume exact quotations, with their exact references, bearing on one of the most time-honored, and even today the most active and most fruitful of all the sciences, the queen-mother of all the sciences, that is, mathematics.

It is hoped that the present volume will prove indispensable to every teacher of mathematics, to every writer on mathematics, and that the student of mathematics and the related sciences will find its perusal not only a source of pleasure but of encouragement and inspiration as well. The layman will find it a repository of useful information covering a field of knowledge which, owing to the unfamiliar and hence repellant character of the language employed by mathematicians, is peculiarly inaccessible to the general reader. No technical processes or technical facility is required to understand and appreciate the wealth of ideas here set forth in the words of the world's great thinkers.

No labor has been spared to make the present volume worthy of a place among collections of a like kind in other fields. Ten years have been devoted to its preparation, years, which if they could have been more profitably, could scarcely have been more pleasurably employed. As a result there have been brought together over one thousand more or less familiar passages pertaining to mathematics, by poets, philosophers, historians, statesmen, scientists, and mathematicians. These have been gathered from over three hundred authors, and have been grouped under twenty heads, and cross indexed under nearly seven hundred topics.

The author's original plan was to give foreign quotations both in the original and in translation, but with the growth of material this plan was abandoned as infeasible. It was thought to serve the best interest of the greater number of English readers to give translations only, while preserving the references to the original sources, so that the student or critical reader may readily consult the original of any given extract. In cases where the translation is borrowed the translator's name is inserted in brackets [ ] immediately after the author's name. Brackets are also used to indicate inserted words or phrases made necessary to bring out the context.

The absence of similar English works has made the author's work largely that of the pioneer. Rebière's "Mathématiques et Mathématiciens" and Ahrens' "Scherz und Ernst in der Mathematik" have indeed been frequently consulted but rather with a view to avoid overlapping than to receive aid. Thus certain topics as the correspondence of German and French mathematicians, so excellently treated by Ahrens, have purposely been omitted. The repetitions are limited to a small number of famous utterances whose absence from a work of this kind could scarcely be defended on any grounds.

No one can be more keenly aware of the shortcomings of a work than its author, for none can have so intimate an acquaintance with it. Among those of the present work is its incompleteness, but it should be borne in mind that incompleteness is a necessary concomitant of every collection of whatever kind. Much less can completeness be expected in a first collection, made by a single individual, in his leisure hours, and in a field which is already boundless and is yet expanding day by day. A collection of great thoughts, even if complete today, would be incomplete tomorrow. Again, if some authors are quoted more frequently than others of greater fame and authority, the reason may be sought not only in the fact that the writings of some authors peculiarly lent themselves to quotation, a quality singularly absent in other writers of the greatest merit and authority, but also in this, that the greatest freedom has been exercised in the choice of selections. The author has followed the bent of his own fancy in collecting whatever seemed to him sufficiently valuable because of its content, its beauty, its originality, or its terseness, to deserve a place in a "Memorabilia."

Great pains has been taken to furnish exact readings and references. In some cases where a passage could not be traced to its first source, the secondary source has been given rather than the reputed source. For the same reason many references are to later editions rather than to inaccessible first editions.

The author feels confident that this work will be of assistance to his co-workers in the field of mathematics and allied fields. If in addition it should aid in a better appreciation of mathematicians and their work on the part of laymen and students in other fields, the author's foremost aim in the preparation of this work will have been achieved.

ROBERT EDOUARD MORITZ,
September, 1913.

SPECTRUM SERIES

The Spectrum Series of the Mathematical Association of America was so named to reflect its purpose: to publish a broad range of books including biographies, accessible expositions of old or new mathematical ideas, reprints and revisions of excellent out-of-print books, popular works, and other monographs of high interest that will appeal to a broad range of readers, including students and teachers of mathematics, mathematical amateurs, and researchers.

Mathematical Association of America
1529 Eighteenth Street, NW
Washington, DC 20036
800-331-1MAA   FAX 202-265-2384

CONTENTS

Alles Gescheite ist schon gedacht worden; man muss nur versuchen, es noch einmal zu denken.—GOETHE.

Sprüche in Prosa, Ethisches, I. 1.

A great man quotes bravely, and will not draw on his invention when his memory serves him with a word as good.—EMERSON.

Letters and Social Aims, Quotation and Originality.

R. E. MORITZ

MEMORABILIA MATHEMATICA

CHAPTER I

DEFINITIONS AND OBJECT OF MATHEMATICS

101. I think it would be desirable that this form of word [mathematics] should be reserved for the applications of the science, and that we should use mathematic in the singular to denote the science itself, in the same way as we speak of logic, rhetoric, or (own sister to algebra) music.—SYLVESTER, J. J.

Presidential Address to the British Association, Exeter British Association Report (1869); Collected Mathematical Papers, Vol. 2, p. 659.

102. . . . . all the sciences which have for their end investigations concerning order and measure, are related to mathematics, it being of small importance whether this measure be sought in numbers, forms, stars, sounds, or any other object; that, accordingly, there ought to exist a general science which should explain all that can be known about order and measure, considered independently of any application to a particular subject, and that, indeed, this science has its own proper name, consecrated by long usage, to wit, *mathematics.* And a proof that it far surpasses in facility and importance the sciences which depend upon it is that it embraces at once all the objects to which these are devoted and a great many others besides; . . .

DESCARTES.
Rules for the Direction of the Mind, Philosophy of D. [Torrey] (New York, 1892), p. 72.

103. [Mathematics] has for its object the *indirect* measurement of magnitudes, and it *purposes to determine magnitudes by each other, according to the precise relations which exist between them.*—COMTE.

Positive Philosophy [Martineau], Bk. 1, chap. 1.

1

104. The business of concrete mathematics is to discover the equations which express the mathematical laws of the phenomenon under consideration; and these equations are the starting-point of the calculus, which must obtain from them certain quantities by means of others.—COMTE.

Positive Philosophy [Martineau], Bk. 1, chap. 2.

105. Mathematics is the science of the connection of magnitudes. Magnitude is anything that can be put equal or unequal to another thing. Two things are equal when in every assertion each may be replaced by the other.—GRASSMANN, HERMANN.

Stücke aus dem Lehrbuche der Arithmetik,
Werke (Leipzig, 1904), Bd. 2, p. 298.

106. Mathematic is either Pure or Mixed: To Pure Mathematic belong those sciences which handle Quantity entirely severed from matter and from axioms of natural philosophy. These are two, Geometry and Arithmetic; the one handling quantity continued, the other dissevered. . . . Mixed Mathematic has for its subject some axioms and parts of natural philosophy, and considers quantity in so far as it assists to explain, demonstrate and actuate these.—BACON, FRANCIS.

De Augmentis, Bk. 3; Advancement
of Learning, Bk. 2.

107. The ideas which these sciences, Geometry, Theoretical Arithmetic and Algebra involve extend to all objects and changes which we observe in the external world; and hence the consideration of mathematical relations forms a large portion of many of the sciences which treat of the phenomena and laws of external nature, as Astronomy, Optics, and Mechanics. Such sciences are hence often termed *Mixed Mathematics*, the relations of space and number being, in these branches of knowledge, combined with principles collected from special observation; while Geometry, Algebra, and the like subjects, which involve no result of experience, are called *Pure Mathematics*.

WHEWELL, WILLIAM.
The Philosophy of the Inductive Sciences,
Part 1, Bk. 2, chap. I, sect. 4. (London, 1858).

108. Higher Mathematics is the art of reasoning about numerical relations between natural phenomena; and the several sections of Higher Mathematics are different modes of viewing these relations.—MELLOR, J. W.

Higher Mathematics for Students of Chemistry and Physics (New York, 1902), Prologue.

109. Number, place, and combination . . . the three intersecting but distinct spheres of thought to which all mathematical ideas admit of being referred.—SYLVESTER, J. J.

Philosophical Magazine, Vol. 24 (1844), p. 285; Collected Mathematical Papers, Vol. 1, p. 91.

110. There are three ruling ideas, three so to say, spheres of thought, which pervade the whole body of mathematical science, to some one or other of which, or to two or all three of them combined, every mathematical truth admits of being referred; these are the three cardinal notions, of Number, Space and Order.

Arithmetic has for its object the properties of number in the abstract. In algebra, viewed as a science of operations, order is the predominating idea. The business of geometry is with the evolution of the properties of space, or of bodies viewed as existing in space.—SYLVESTER, J. J.

A Probationary Lecture on Geometry, York British Association Report (1844), Part 2; Collected Mathematical Papers, Vol. 2, p. 5.

111. The object of pure mathematics is those relations which may be conceptually established among any conceived elements whatsoever by assuming them contained in some ordered manifold; the law of order of this manifold must be subject to our choice; the latter is the case in both of the only conceivable kinds of manifolds, in the discrete as well as in the continuous.

PAPPERITZ, E.

Über das System der rein mathematischen Wissenschaften, Jahresbericht der Deutschen Mathematiker-Vereinigung, Bd. 1, p. 36.

112. Pure mathematics is not concerned with magnitude. It is merely the doctrine of notation of relatively ordered thought operations which have become mechanical.—NOVALIS.

Schriften (Berlin, 1901), Zweiter Teil, p. 282.

113. Any conception which is definitely and completely determined by means of a finite number of specifications, say by assigning a finite number of elements, is a mathematical conception. Mathematics has for its function to develop the consequences involved in the definition of a group of mathematical conceptions. Interdependence and mutual logical consistency among the members of the group are postulated, otherwise the group would either have to be treated as several distinct groups, or would lie beyond the sphere of mathematics.

CHRYSTAL, GEORGE.
Encyclopedia Britannica (9th edition), Article "Mathematics."

114. The purely formal sciences, logic and mathematics, deal with those relations which are, or can be, independent of the particular content or the substance of objects. To mathematics in particular fall those relations between objects which involve the concepts of magnitude, of measure and of number.

HANKEL, HERMANN.
Theorie der Complexen Zahlensysteme, (Leipzig, 1867), p. 1.

115. *Quantity is that which is operated with according to fixed mutually consistent laws.* Both operator and operand must derive their meaning from the laws of operation. In the case of ordinary algebra these are the three laws already indicated [the commutative, associative, and distributive laws], in the algebra of quaternions the same save the law of commutation for multiplication and division, and so on. It may be questioned whether this definition is sufficient, and it may be objected that it is vague; but the reader will do well to reflect that any definition must include the linear algebras of Peirce, the algebra of logic, and others that may be easily imagined, although they have not yet been developed. This general definition of quantity enables us to see how operators may be treated as quantities, and thus to understand the rationale of the so called symbolical methods.—CHRYSTAL, GEORGE.

*Encyclopedia Britannica (9th edition), Article
"Mathematics."*

116. Mathematics—in a strict sense—is the abstract science which investigates deductively the conclusions implicit in the elementary conceptions of spatial and numerical relations.

MURRAY, J. A. H.

A New English Dictionary.

117. Everything that the greatest minds of all times have accomplished toward the *comprehension of forms* by means of concepts is gathered into one great science, *mathematics*.

HERBART, J. F.

*Pestalozzi's Idee eines A B C der Anschauung,
Werke [Kehrbach], (Langensalza, 1890), Bd. 1,
p. 163.*

118. Perhaps the least inadequate description of the general scope of modern Pure Mathematics—I will not call it a definition—would be to say that it deals with *form*, in a very general sense of the term; this would include algebraic form, functional relationship, the relations of order in any ordered set of entities such as numbers, and the analysis of the peculiarities of form of groups of operations.—HOBSON, E. W.

*Presidential Address British Association for
the Advancement of Science (1910); Nature,
Vol. 84, p. 287.*

119. The ideal of mathematics should be to erect a calculus to facilitate reasoning in connection with every province of thought, or of external experience, in which the succession of thoughts, or of events can be definitely ascertained and precisely stated. So that all serious thought which is not philosophy, or inductive reasoning, or imaginative literature, shall be mathematics developed by means of a calculus.

WHITEHEAD, A. N.

Universal Algebra (Cambridge, 1898), Preface.

120. Mathematics is the science which draws necessary conclusions.—PEIRCE, BENJAMIN.
> *Linear Associative Algebra, American Journal of Mathematics, Vol. 4 (1881), p. 97.*

121. Mathematics is the universal art apodictic.
> SMITH, W. B.
> *Quoted by Keyser, C. J. in Lectures on Science, Philosophy and Art (New York, 1908), p. 13.*

122. Mathematics in its widest signification is the development of all types of formal, necessary, deductive reasoning.
> WHITEHEAD, A. N.
> *Universal Algebra (Cambridge, 1898), Preface, p. vi.*

123. Mathematics in general is fundamentally the science of self-evident things.—KLEIN, FELIX.
> *Anwendung der Differential-und Integralrechnung auf Geometrie (Leipzig, 1902), p. 26.*

124. A mathematical science is any body of propositions which is capable of an abstract formulation and arrangement in such a way that every proposition of the set after a certain one is a formal logical consequence of some or all the preceding propositions. Mathematics consists of all such mathematical sciences.—YOUNG, CHARLES WESLEY.
> *Fundamental Concepts of Algebra and Geometry (New York, 1911), p. 222.*

125. Pure mathematics is a collection of hypothetical, deductive theories, each consisting of a definite system of primitive, *undefined*, concepts or symbols and primitive, *unproved*, but self-consistent assumptions (commonly called axioms) together with their logically deducible consequences following by rigidly deductive processes without appeal to intuition.—FITCH, G. D.
> *The Fourth Dimension simply Explained (New York, 1910), p. 58.*

126. The whole of Mathematics consists in the organization of a series of aids to the imagination in the process of reasoning.
> WHITEHEAD, A. N.
> *Universal Algebra (Cambridge, 1898), p. 12.*

127. Pure mathematics consists entirely of such asseverations as that, if such and such a proposition is true of *anything*, then such and such another proposition is true of that thing. It is essential not to discuss whether the first proposition is really true, and not to mention what the anything is of which it is supposed to be true. . . . If our hypothesis is about *anything* and not about some one or more particular things, then our deductions constitute mathematics. Thus mathematics may be defined as the subject in which we never know what we are talking about, nor whether what we are saying is true.

RUSSELL, BERTRAND.
Recent Work on the Principles of Mathematics,
International Monthly, Vol. 4 (1901), p. 84.

128. Pure Mathematics is the class of all propositions of the form "*p* implies *q*," where *p* and *q* are propositions containing one or more variables, the same in the two propositions, and neither *p* nor *q* contains any constants except logical constants. And logical constants are all notions definable in terms of the following: Implication, the relation of a term to a class of which it is a member, the notion of *such that*, the notion of relation, and such further notions as may be involved in the general notion of propositions of the above form. In addition to these, Mathematics *uses* a notion which is not a constituent of the propositions which it considers—namely, the notion of truth.

RUSSELL, BERTRAND.
Principles of Mathematics (Cambridge, 1903),
p. 1.

129. The object of pure Physic is the unfolding of the laws of the intelligible world; the object of pure Mathematic that of unfolding the laws of human intelligence.—SYLVESTER, J. J.
On a theorem connected with Newton's Rule,
etc., Collected Mathematical Papers, Vol. 3,
p. 424.

130. First of all, we ought to observe, that mathematical propositions, properly so called, are always judgments *a priori*, and not empirical, because they carry along with them necessity, which can never be deduced from experience. If people should object to this, I am quite willing to confine my statements to pure mathematics, the very concept of which implies that it does not contain empirical, but only pure knowledge *a priori*.

KANT, IMMANUEL.
Critique of Pure Reason [*Müller*], (*New York,*
1900), *p. 720.*

131. Mathematics, the science of the ideal, becomes the means of investigating, understanding and making known the world of the real. The complex is expressed in terms of the simple. From one point of view mathematics may be defined as the science of successive substitutions of simpler concepts for more complex. . . .—WHITE, WILLIAM F.

A Scrap-book of Elementary Mathematics,
(*Chicago, 1908*), *p. 215.*

132. The critical mathematician has abandoned the search for truth. He no longer flatters himself that his propositions are or can be known to him or to any other human being to be true; and he contents himself with aiming at the correct, or the consistent. The distinction is not annulled nor even blurred by the reflection that consistency contains immanently a kind of truth. He is not absolutely certain, but he believes profoundly that it is possible to find various sets of a few propositions each such that the propositions of each set are compatible, that the propositions of each such set imply other propositions, and that the latter can be deduced from the former with certainty. That is to say, he believes that there are systems of coherent or consistent propositions, and he regards it his business to discover such systems. Any such system is a branch of mathematics.—KEYSER, C. J.

Science, New Series, Vol. 35, p. 107.

133. [Mathematics is] the study of ideal constructions (often applicable to real problems), and the discovery thereby of relations between the parts of these constructions, before unknown.

PEIRCE, C. S.
Century Dictionary, Article "Mathematics."

134. Mathematics is that form of intelligence in which we bring the objects of the phenomenal world under the control of the conception of quantity. [Provisional definition.]

HOWISON, G. H.
The Departments of Mathematics, and their Mutual Relations; Journal of Speculative Philosophy, Vol. 5, p. 164.

135. Mathematics is the science of the functional laws and transformations which enable us to convert figured extension and rated motion into number.—HOWISON, G. H.

The Departments of Mathematics, and their Mutual Relations; Journal of Speculative Philosophy, Vol. 5, p. 170.

CHAPTER II

THE NATURE OF MATHEMATICS

201. Mathematics, from the earliest times to which the history of human reason can reach, has followed, among that wonderful people of the Greeks, the safe way of science. But it must not be supposed that it was as easy for mathematics as for logic, in which reason is concerned with itself alone, to find, or rather to make for itself that royal road. I believe, on the contrary, that there was a long period of tentative work (chiefly still among the Egyptians), and that the change is to be ascribed to a *revolution*, produced by the happy thought of a single man, whose experiments pointed unmistakably to the path that had to be followed, and opened and traced out for the most distant times the safe way of a science. The history of that intellectual revolution, which was far more important than the passage round the celebrated Cape of Good Hope, and the name of its fortunate author, have not been preserved to us. . . . A new light flashed on the first man who demonstrated the properties of the isosceles triangle (whether his name was *Thales* or any other name), for he found that he had not to investigate what he saw in the figure, or the mere concepts of that figure, and thus to learn its properties; but that he had to produce (by construction) what he had himself, according to concepts *a priori*, placed into that figure and represented in it, so that, in order to know anything with certainty *a priori*, he must not attribute to that figure anything beyond what necessarily follows from what he has himself placed into it, in accordance with the concept.—KANT, IMMANUEL.

Critique of Pure Reason, Preface to the Second Edition [*Müller*], (*New York, 1900*), *p. 690.*

202. [When followed in the proper spirit], there is no study in the world which brings into more harmonious action all the faculties of the mind than the one [mathematics] of which I

10

stand here as the humble representative and advocate. There is none other which prepares so many agreeable surprises for its followers, more wonderful than the transformation scene of a pantomime, or, like this, seems to raise them, by successive steps of initiation to higher and higher states of conscious intellectual being.—SYLVESTER, J. J.

> *A Plea for the Mathematician, Nature, Vol. 1, p. 261.*

203. Thought-economy is most highly developed in mathematics, that science which has reached the highest formal development, and on which natural science so frequently calls for assistance. Strange as it may seem, the strength of mathematics lies in the avoidance of all unnecessary thoughts, in the utmost economy of thought-operations. The symbols of order, which we call numbers, form already a system of wonderful simplicity and economy. When in the multiplication of a number with several digits we employ the multiplication table and thus make use of previously accomplished results rather than to repeat them each time, when by the use of tables of logarithms we avoid new numerical calculations by replacing them by others long since performed, when we employ determinants instead of carrying through from the beginning the solution of a system of equations, when we decompose new integral expressions into others that are familiar,—we see in all this but a faint reflection of the intellectual activity of a *Lagrange* or *Cauchy*, who with the keen discernment of a military commander marshalls a whole troop of completed operations in the execution of a new one.—MACH, E.

> *Populär-wissenschafliche Vorlesungen (1903), pp. 224–225.*

204. Pure mathematics proves itself a royal science both through its content and form, which contains within itself the cause of its being and its methods of proof. For in complete independence mathematics creates for itself the object of which it treats, its magnitudes and laws, its formulas and symbols.

DILLMANN, E.

> *Die Mathematik die Fackelträgerin einer neuen Zeit (Stuttgart, 1889), p. 94.*

205. The essence of mathematics lies in its freedom.

CANTOR, GEORGE.
Mathematische Annalen, Bd. 21, p. 564.

206. Mathematics pursues its own course unrestrained, not indeed with an unbridled licence which submits to no laws, but rather with the freedom which is determined by its own nature and in conformity with its own being.—HANKEL, HERMANN.
Die Entwickelung der Mathematik in den letzten Jahrhunderten (Tübingen, 1884), p. 16.

207. Mathematics is perfectly free in its development and is subject only to the obvious consideration, that its concepts must be free from contradictions in themselves, as well as definitely and orderly related by means of definitions to the previously existing and established concepts.

CANTOR, GEORGE.
Grundlagen einer allgemeinen Manigfaltigkeits-lehre (Leipzig, 1883), Sect. 8.

208. Mathematicians assume the right to choose, within the limits of logical contradiction, what path they please in reaching their results.—ADAMS, HENRY.
A Letter to American Teachers of History (Washington, 1910), Introduction, p. v.

209. Mathematics is the predominant science of our time; its conquests grow daily, though without noise; he who does not employ it *for* himself, will some day find it employed *against* himself.—HERBART, J. F.
Werke [Kehrbach] (Langensalza, 1890), Bd. 5, p. 105.

210. Mathematics is not the discoverer of laws, for it is not induction; neither is it the framer of theories, for it is not hypothesis; but it is the judge over both, and it is the arbiter to which each must refer its claims; and neither law can rule nor theory explain without the sanction of mathematics.

PEIRCE, BENJAMIN.
Linear Associative Algebra, American Journal of Mathematics, Vol. 4 (1881), p. 97.

211. Mathematics is a science continually expanding; and its growth, unlike some political and industrial events, is attended by universal acclamation.—WHITE, H. S.

> *Congress of Arts and Sciences (Boston and New York, 1905), Vol. 1, p. 455.*

212. Mathematics accomplishes really nothing outside of the realm of magnitude; marvellous, however, is the skill with which it masters magnitude wherever it finds it. We recall at once the network of lines which it has spun about heavens and earth; the system of lines to which azimuth and altitude, declination and right ascension, longitude and latitude are referred; those abscissas and ordinates, tangents and normals, circles of curvature and evolutes; those trigonometric and logarithmic functions which have been prepared in advance and await application. A look at this apparatus is sufficient to show that mathematicians are not magicians, but that everything is accomplished by natural means; one is rather impressed by the multitude of skilful machines, numerous witnesses of a manifold and intensely active industry, admirably fitted for the acquisition of true and lasting treasures.—HERBART, J. F.

> *Werke [Kehrbach] (Langensalza, 1890), Bd. 5, p. 101.*

213. They [mathematicians] only take those things into consideration, of which they have clear and distinct ideas, designating them by proper, adequate, and invariable names, and premising only a few axioms which are most noted and certain to investigate their affections and draw conclusions from them, and agreeably laying down a very few hypotheses, such as are in the highest degree consonant with reason and not to be denied by anyone in his right mind. In like manner they assign generations or causes easy to be understood and readily admitted by all, they preserve a most accurate order, every proposition immediately following from what is supposed and proved before, and reject all things howsoever specious and probable which can not be inferred and deduced after the same manner.—BARROW, ISAAC.

> *Mathematical Lectures (London, 1734), p. 66.*

214. The dexterous management of terms and being able to *fend* and *prove* with them, I know has and does pass in the world for a great part of learning; but it is learning distinct from knowledge, for knowledge consists only in perceiving the habitudes and relations of ideas one to another, which is done without words; the intervention of sounds helps nothing to it. And hence we see that there is least use of distinction where there is most knowledge: I mean in mathematics, where men have determined ideas with known names to them; and so, there being no room for equivocations, there is no need of distinctions.—LOCKE, JOHN.
Conduct of the Understanding, Sect. 31.

215. In mathematics it [sophistry] had no place from the beginning: Mathematicians having had the wisdom to define accurately the terms they use, and to lay down, as axioms, the first principles on which their reasoning is grounded. Accordingly we find no parties among mathematicians, and hardly any disputes.—REID, THOMAS.
Essays on the Intellectual Powers of Man,
Essay 1, chap. 1.

216. In most sciences one generation tears down what another has built and what one has established another undoes. In Mathematics alone each generation builds a new story to the old structure.—HANKEL, HERMANN.
Die Entwickelung der Mathematik in den
letzten Jahrhunderten (Tübingen, 1884), p. 25.

217. Mathematics, the priestess of definiteness and clearness.—HERBART, J. F.
Werke [Kehrbach] (Langensalza, 1890), Bd. 1,
p. 171.

218. . . . mathematical analysis is co-extensive with nature itself, it defines all perceivable relations, measures times, spaces, forces, temperatures; it is a difficult science which forms but slowly, but preserves carefully every principle once acquired; it increases and becomes stronger incessantly amidst all the changes and errors of the human mind.

Its chief attribute is clearness; it has no means for expressing confused ideas. It compares the most diverse phenomena and discovers the secret analogies which unite them. If matter escapes us, as that of air and light because of its extreme tenuity, if bodies are placed far from us in the immensity of space, if man wishes to know the aspect of the heavens at successive periods separated by many centuries, if gravity and heat act in the interior of the solid earth at depths which will forever be inaccessible, mathematical analysis is still able to trace the laws of these phenomena. It renders them present and measurable, and appears to be the faculty of the human mind destined to supplement the brevity of life and the imperfection of the senses, and what is even more remarkable, it follows the same course in the study of all phenomena; it explains them in the same language, as if in witness to the unity and simplicity of the plan of the universe, and to make more manifest the unchangeable order which presides over all natural causes.— FOURIER, J.

*Théorie Analytique de la Chaleur, Discours
Préliminaire.*

219. Let us now declare the means whereby our understanding can rise to knowledge without fear of error. There are two such means: intuition and deduction. By intuition I mean not the varying testimony of the senses, nor the deductive judgment of imagination naturally extravagant, but the conception of an attentive mind so distinct and so clear that no doubt remains to it with regard to that which it comprehends; or, what amounts to the same thing, the self-evidencing conception of a sound and attentive mind, a conception which springs from the light of reason alone, and is more certain, because more simple, than deduction itself. . . .

It may perhaps be asked why to intuition we add this other mode of knowing, by deduction, that is to say, the process which, from something of which we have certain knowledge, draws consequences which necessarily follow therefrom. But we are obliged to admit this second step; for there are a great many things which, without being evident of themselves, nevertheless bear the marks of certainty if only they are deduced from true and incontestable principles by a continuous and uninterrupted movement of thought, with distinct intuition of each thing; just as we know that the last link of a long chain holds to the first, although we can not take in with one glance of the eye the intermediate links, provided that, after having run over them in succession, we can recall them all, each as being joined to its fellows, from the first up to the last. Thus we distinguish intuition from deduction, inasmuch as in the latter case there is conceived a certain progress or succession, while it is not so in the former; . . . whence it follows that primary propositions, derived immediately from principles, may be said to be known, according to the way we view them, now by intuition, now by deduction; although the principles themselves can be known only by intuition, the remote consequences only by deduction.

DESCARTES.

Rules for the Direction of the Mind, Philosophy of D. [Torrey] (New York, 1892), pp. 64, 65.

220. Analysis and natural philosophy owe their most important discoveries to this fruitful means, which is called *induction*. Newton was indebted to it for his theorem of the binomial and the principle of universal gravity.—LAPLACE.

A Philosophical Essay on Probabilities [Truscott and Emory] (New York 1902), p. 176.

221. There is in every step of an arithmetical or algebraical calculation a real induction, a real inference from facts to facts, and what disguises the induction is simply its comprehensive nature, and the consequent extreme generality of its language.

MILL, J. S.

System of Logic, Bk. 2, chap. 6, 2.

222. It would appear that Deductive and Demonstrative Sciences are all, without exception, Inductive Sciences: that their evidence is that of experience, but that they are also, in virtue of the peculiar character of one indispensable portion of the general formulae according to which their inductions are made, Hypothetical Sciences. Their conclusions are true only upon certain suppositions, which are, or ought to be, approximations to the truth, but are seldom, if ever, exactly true; and to this hypothetical character is to be ascribed the peculiar certainty, which is supposed to be inherent in demonstration.

MILL, J. S.
System of Logic, Bk. 2, chap. 6, 1.

223. The peculiar character of mathematical truth is, that it is necessarily and inevitably true; and one of the most important lessons which we learn from our mathematical studies is a knowledge that there are such truths, and a familiarity with their form and character.

This lesson is not only lost, but read backward, if the student is taught that there is no such difference, and that mathematical truths themselves are learned by experience.—WHEWELL, W.
Thoughts on the Study of Mathematics. Principles of English University Education (London, 1838).

224. These sciences, Geometry, Theoretical Arithmetic and Algebra, have no principles besides definitions and axioms, and no process of proof but *deduction;* this process, however, assuming a most remarkable character; and exhibiting a combination of simplicity and complexity, of rigour and generality, quite unparalleled in other subjects.—WHEWELL, W.
The Philosophy of the Inductive Sciences, Part 1, Bk. 2, chap. 1, sect. 2 (London, 1858).

225. The apodictic quality of mathematical thought, the certainty and correctness of its conclusions, are due, not to a special mode of ratiocination, but to the character of the concepts with which it deals. What is that distinctive characteristic? I answer: *precision, sharpness, completeness,** of definition. But how comes your mathematician by such completeness? There is no mysterious trick involved; some ideas admit of such precision, others do not; and the mathematician is one who deals with those that do.—KEYSER, C. J.
The Universe and Beyond; Hibbert Journal, Vol. 3 (1904–1905), p. 309.

226. The reasoning of mathematicians is founded on certain and infallible principles. Every word they use conveys a deter-

* i. e., in terms of the absolutely clear and *in*definable.

minate idea, and by accurate definitions they excite the same ideas in the mind of the reader that were in the mind of the writer. When they have defined the terms they intend to make use of, they premise a few axioms, or self-evident principles, that every one must assent to as soon as proposed. They then take for granted certain postulates, that no one can deny them, such as, that a right line may be drawn from any given point to another, and from these plain, simple principles they have raised most astonishing speculations, and proved the extent of the human 'mind to be more spacious and capacious than any other science.—ADAMS, JOHN.

Diary, Works (Boston, 1850), Vol. 2, p. 21.

227. It may be observed of mathematicians that they only meddle with such things as are certain, passing by those that are doubtful and unknown. They profess not to know all things, neither do they affect to speak of all things. What they know to be true, and can make good by invincible arguments, that they publish and insert among their theorems. Of other things they are silent and pass no judgment at all, choosing rather to acknowledge their ignorance, than affirm anything rashly. They affirm nothing among their arguments or assertions which is not most manifestly known and examined with utmost rigour, rejecting all probable conjectures and little witticisms. They submit nothing to authority, indulge no affection, detest subterfuges of words, and declare their sentiments, as in a court of justice, *without passion, without apology;* knowing that their reasons, as Seneca testifies of them, are not brought to *persuade,* but to compel.—BARROW, ISAAC.

Mathematical Lectures (London, 1734), p. 64.

228. What is exact about mathematics but exactness? And is not this a consequence of the inner sense of truth?—GOETHE.

Sprüche in Prosa, Natur, 6, 948.

229. . . . the three positive characteristics that distinguish mathematical knowledge from other knowledge . . . may be briefly expressed as follows: first, mathematical knowledge bears more distinctly the imprint of truth on all its results than any other kind of knowledge; secondly, it is always a sure preliminary step to the attainment of other correct knowledge; thirdly, it has no need of other knowledge.—SCHUBERT, H.

Mathematical Essays and Recreations (Chicago, 1898), p. 35.

230. It is now necessary to indicate more definitely the reason why mathematics not only carries conviction in itself, but also transmits conviction to the objects to which it is applied. The reason is found, first of all, in the perfect precision with which the elementary mathematical concepts are determined; in this respect each science must look to its own salvation . . . . But this is not all. As soon as human thought attempts long chains of conclusions, or difficult matters generally, there arises not only the danger of error but also the suspicion of error, because since all details cannot be surveyed with clearness at the same instant one must in the end be satisfied with a *belief* that nothing has been overlooked from the beginning. Every one knows how much this is the case even in arithmetic, the most elmenetary use of mathematics. No one would imagine that the higher parts of mathematics fare better in this respect; on the contrary, in more complicated conclusions the uncertainty and suspicion of hidden errors increases in rapid progression. How does mathematics manage to rid itself of this inconvenience which attaches to it in the highest degree? By making proofs more rigorous? By giving new rules according to which the old rules shall be applied? Not in the least. A very great uncertainty continues to attach to the result of each single computation. But there are checks. In the realm of mathematics each point may be reached by a hundred different ways; and if each of a hundred ways leads to the same point, one may be sure that the right point has been reached. A calculation without a check is as good as none. Just so it is with every isolated proof in any speculative science whatever; the proof may be ever so ingenious, and ever so perfectly true and correct, it will still fail to convince permanently. He will therefore be much deceived, who, in metaphysics, or in psychology which depends on metaphysics, hopes to see his greatest care in the precise determination of the concepts and in the logical conclusions rewarded by conviction, much less by success in transmitting conviction to

others. Not only must the conclusions support each other, without coercion or suspicion of subreption, but in all matters originating in experience, or judging concerning experience, the results of speculation must be verified by experience, not only superficially, but in countless special cases.—HERBART, J. F.
Werke [Kehrbach] (Langensalza, 1890), Bd. 5, p. 105.

231. [In mathematics] we behold the conscious logical activity of the human mind in its purest and most perfect form. Here we learn to realize the laborious nature of the process, the great care with which it must proceed, the accuracy which is necessary to determine the exact extent of the general propositions arrived at, the difficulty of forming and comprehending abstract concepts; but here we learn also to place confidence in the certainty, scope and fruitfulness of such intellectual activity.
HELMHOLTZ, H.
Ueber das Verhältniss der Naturwissenschaften zur Gesammtheit der Wissenschaft, Vorträge und Reden, Bd. 1 (1896), p. 176.

232. It is true that mathematics, owing to the fact that its whole content is built up by means of purely logical deduction from a small number of universally comprehended principles, has not unfittingly been designated as the science of the *self-evident* [Selbstverständlichen]. Experience however, shows that for the majority of the cultured, even of scientists, mathematics remains the science of the *incomprehensible* [Unverständlichen].
PRINGSHEIM, ALFRED.
Ueber Wert und angeblichen Unwert der Mathematik, Jahresbericht der Deutschen Mathematiker Vereinigung (1904), p. 357.

233. Mathematical reasoning is deductive in the sense that it is based upon definitions which, as far as the validity of the reasoning is concerned (apart from any existential import), needs only the test of self-consistency. Thus no external verification of definitions is required in mathematics, as long as it is considered merely as mathematics.—WHITEHEAD, A. N.
Universal Algebra (Cambridge, 1898), Preface, p. vi.

234. The mathematician pays not the least regard either to testimony or conjecture, but deduces everything by demonstrative reasoning, from his definitions and axioms. Indeed, whatever is built upon conjecture, is improperly called science; for conjecture may beget opinion, but cannot produce knowledge.—REID, THOMAS.

Essays on the Intellectual Powers of Man,
Essay 1, chap. 3.

235. . . . for the saving the long progression of the thoughts to remote and first principles in every case, the mind should provide itself several stages; that is to say, intermediate principles, which it might have recourse to in the examining those positions that come in its way. These, though they are not self-evident principles, yet, if they have been made out from them by a wary and unquestionable deduction, may be depended on as certain and infallible truths, and serve as unquestionable truths to prove other points depending upon them, by a nearer and shorter view than remote and general maxims. . . . And thus mathematicians do, who do not in every new problem run it back to the first axioms through all the whole train of intermediate propositions. Certain theorems that they have settled to themselves upon sure demonstration, serve to resolve to them multitudes of propositions which depend on them, and are as firmly made out from thence as if the mind went afresh over every link of the whole chain that tie them to first self-evident principles.—LOCKE, JOHN.

The Conduct of the Understanding, Sect. 21.

236. Those intervening ideas, which serve to show the agreement of any two others, are called *proofs;* and where the agreement or disagreement is by this means plainly and clearly perceived, it is called *demonstration;* it being *shown* to the understanding, and the mind made to see that it is so. A quickness in the mind to find out these intermediate ideas, (that shall discover the agreement or disagreement of any other) and to apply them right, is, I suppose, that which is called *sagacity.*

LOCKE, JOHN.
An Essay concerning Human Understanding,
Bk. 6, chaps. 2, 3.

237. . . . the speculative propositions of mathematics do not relate to *facts;* . . . all that we are convinced of by any demonstration in the science, is of a necessary connection subsisting between certain suppositions and certain conclusions. When we find these suppositions actually take place in a particular instance, the demonstration forces us to apply the conclusion. Thus, if I could form a triangle, the three sides of which were accurately mathematical lines, I might affirm of this individual figure, that its three angles are equal to two right angles; but,.as the imperfection of my senses puts it out of my power to be, in any case, *certain* of the exact correspondence of the diagram which I delineate, with the definitions given in the elements of geometry, I never can apply with confidence to a particular figure, a mathematical theorem. On the other hand, it appears from the daily testimony of our senses that the speculative truths of geometry may be applied to material objects with a degree of accuracy sufficient for the purposes of life; and from such applications of them, advantages of the most important kind have been gained to society.—STEWART, DUGALD.

> *Elements of the Philosophy of the Human Mind, Part 3, chap. 1, sect. 3.*

238. No process of sound reasoning can establish a result not contained in the premises.—MELLOR, J. W.

> *Higher Mathematics for Students of Chemistry and Physics (New York, 1902), p. 2.*

239. . . . we cannot get more out of the mathematical mill than we put into it, though we may get it in a form infinitely more useful for our purpose.—HOPKINSON, JOHN.

> *James Forrest Lecture, 1894.*

240. The iron labor of conscious logical reasoning demands great perseverance and great caution; it moves on but slowly, and is rarely illuminated by brilliant flashes of genius. It knows little of that facility with which the most varied instances come thronging into the memory of the philologist or historian. Rather is it an essential condition of the methodical progress of mathematical reasoning that the mind should remain concentrated on a single point, undisturbed alike by collateral ideas on the one hand, and by wishes and hopes on the other, and moving on steadily in the direction it has deliberately chosen.

HELMHOLTZ, H.
Ueber das Verhältniss der Naturwissenschaften zur Gesammtheit der Wissenschaft, Vorträge und Reden, Bd. 1 (1896), p. 178.

241. If it were always necessary to reduce everything to intuitive knowledge, demonstration would often be insufferably prolix. This is why mathematicians have had the cleverness to divide the difficulties and to demonstrate separately the intervening propositions. And there is art also in this; for as the mediate truths (which are called *lemmas*, since they appear to be a digression) may be assigned in many ways, it is well, in order to aid the understanding and memory, to choose of them those which greatly shorten the process, and appear memorable and worthy in themselves of being demonstrated. But there is another obstacle, viz.: that it is not easy to demonstrate all the axioms, and to reduce demonstrations wholly to intuitive knowledge. And if we had chosen to wait for that, perhaps we should not yet have the science of geometry.—LEIBNITZ, G. W.
New Essay on Human Understanding [Langley], Bk. 4, chaps. 2, 8.

242. In Pure Mathematics, where all the various truths are necessarily connected with each other, (being all necessarily connected with those *hypotheses* which are the principles of the science), an arrangement is beautiful in proportion as the principles are few; and what we admire perhaps chiefly in the science, is the astonishing variety of consequences which may be demonstrably deduced from so small a number of premises.

STEWART, DUGALD.
The Elements of the Philosophy of the Human Mind, Part 3, chap. 1, sect. 3.

243. Whenever . . . a controversy arises in mathematics, the issue is not whether a thing is true or not, but whether the proof might not be conducted more simply in some other way, or whether the proposition demonstrated is sufficiently important for the advancement of the science as to deserve especial enunciation and emphasis, or finally, whether the proposition is not a special case of some other and more general truth which is as easily discovered.—SCHUBERT, H.

> Mathematical Essays and Recreations (Chicago, 1898), p. 28.

244. . . . just as the astronomer, the physicist, the geologist, or other student of objective science looks about in the world of sense, so, not metaphorically speaking but literally, the mind of the mathematician goes forth in the universe of logic in quest of the things that are there; exploring the heights and depths for facts—ideas, classes, relationships, implications, and the rest; observing the minute and elusive with the powerful microscope of his Infinitesimal Analysis; observing the elusive and vast with the limitless telescope of his Calculus of the Infinite; making guesses regarding the order and internal harmony of the data observed and collocated; testing the hypotheses, not merely by the complete induction peculiar to mathematics, but, like his colleagues of the outer world, resorting also to experimental tests and incomplete induction; frequently finding it necessary, in view of unforeseen disclosures, to abandon one hopeful hypothesis or to transform it by retrenchment or by enlargement:—thus, in his own domain, matching, point for point, the processes, methods and experience familiar to the devotee of natural science.—KEYSER, CASSIUS, J.

> Lectures on Science, Philosophy and Art (New York, 1908), p. 26.

245. That mathematics "do not cultivate the power of generalization," . . . will be admitted by no person of competent knowledge, except in a very qualified sense. The generalizations of mathematics, are, no doubt, a different thing from the generalizations of physical science; but in the difficulty of seizing them, and the mental tension they require, they are no contemptible preparation for the most arduous efforts of the scientific mind. Even the fundamental notions of the higher mathematics, from those of the differential calculus upwards are products of a very high abstraction. . . . To perceive the mathematical laws common to the results of many mathematical operations, even in so simple a case as that of the binomial theorem, involves a vigorous exercise of the same faculty which gave us Kepler's laws, and rose through those laws to the theory of universal gravitation. Every process of what has been called Universal Geometry—the great creation of Descartes and his successors, in which a single train of reasoning solves whole classes of problems at once, and others common to large groups of them—is a practical lesson in the management of wide generalizations, and abstraction of the points of agreement from those of difference among objects of great and confusing diversity, to which the purely inductive sciences cannot furnish many superior. Even so elementary an operation as that of abstracting from the particular configuration of the triangles or other figures, and the relative situation of the particular lines or points, in the diagram which aids the apprehension of a common geometrical demonstration, is a very useful, and far from being always an easy, exercise of the faculty of generalization so strangely imagined to have no place or part in the processes of mathematics.—MILL, JOHN STUART.

An Examination of Sir William Hamilton's Philosophy (London, 1878), pp. 612, 613.

246. When the greatest of American logicians, speaking of the powers that constitute the born geometrician, had named Conception, Imagination, and Generalization, he paused. Thereupon from one of the audience there came the challenge, "What of reason?" The instant response, not less just than brilliant, was: "Ratiocination—that is but the smooth pavement on which the chariot rolls."—KEYSER, C. J.

Lectures on Science, Philosophy and Art (New York, 1908), p. 31.

247. . . . the reasoning process [employed in mathematics] is not different from that of any other branch of knowledge, . . . but there is required, and in a great degree, that attention of mind which is in some part necessary for the acquisition of all knowledge, and in this branch is indispensably necessary. This must be given in its fullest intensity; . . . the other elements especially characteristic of a mathematical mind are quickness in perceiving logical sequence, love of order, methodical arrangement and harmony, distinctness of conception.—PRICE, B.

> Treatise on Infinitesimal Calculus (Oxford, 1868), Vol. 3, p. 6.

248. Histories make men wise; poets, witty; the mathematics, subtile; natural philosophy, deep; moral, grave; logic and rhetoric, able to contend.—BACON, FRANCIS.

> Essays, Of Studies.

249. The Mathematician deals with two properties of objects only, number and extension, and all the inductions he wants have been formed and finished ages ago. He is now occupied with nothing but deduction and verification.—HUXLEY, T. H.

> On the Educational Value of the Natural History Sciences; Lay Sermons, Addresses and Reviews; (New York, 1872), p. 87.

250. [Mathematics] is that [subject] which knows nothing of observation, nothing of experiment, nothing of induction, nothing of causation.—HUXLEY, T. H.

> The Scientific Aspects of Positivism, Fortnightly Review (1898); Lay Sermons, Addresses and Reviews, (New York, 1872), p. 169.

251. We are told that "Mathematics is that study which knows nothing of observation, nothing of experiment, nothing of induction, nothing of causation." I think no statement could have been made more opposite to the facts of the case; that mathematical analysis is constantly invoking the aid of new principles, new ideas, and new methods, not capable of being defined by any form of words, but springing direct from the inherent powers and activities of the human mind, and from continually renewed introspection of that inner world of thought of which the phenomena are as varied and require as close attention to discern as those of the outer physical world (to which the inner one in each individual man may, I think, be conceived to stand somewhat in the same relation of correspondence as a shadow to the object from which it is projected, or as the hollow palm of one hand to the closed fist which it grasps of the other), that it is unceasingly calling forth the faculties of observation and comparison, that one of its principal weapons is induction, that it has frequent recourse to experimental trial and verification, and that it affords a boundless scope for the exercise of the highest efforts of the imagination and invention.

SYLVESTER, J. J.
Presidential Address to British Association,
Exeter British Association Report (1869),
pp. 1–9.; Collected Mathematical Papers,
Vol. 2, p. 654.

252. The actual evolution of mathematical theories proceeds by a process of induction strictly analogous to the method of induction employed in building up the physical sciences; observation, comparison, classification, trial, and generalisation are essential in both cases. Not only are special results, obtained independently of one another, frequently seen to be really included in some generalisation, but branches of the subject which have been developed quite independently of one another are sometimes found to have connections which enable them to be synthesised in one single body of doctrine. The essential nature of mathematical thought manifests itself in the discernment of fundamental identity in the mathematical aspects of what are superficially very different domains. A striking example of this species of immanent identity of mathematical form was exhibited by the discovery of that distinguished mathematician . . . Major MacMahon, that all possible Latin squares are capable of enumeration by the consideration of certain differential operators. Here we have a case in which an enumeration, which appears to be not amenable to direct treatment, can actually be carried out in a simple manner when the underlying identity of the operation is recognised with that involved in certain operations due to differential operators, the calculus of which belongs superficially to a wholly different region of thought from that relating to Latin squares.

HOBSON, E. W.
Presidential Address British Association for
the Advancement of Science (1910); Nature,
Vol. 84, p. 290.

253. It has been asserted . . . that the power of observation is not developed by mathematical studies; while the truth is, that; from the most elementary mathematical notion that arises in the mind of a child to the farthest verge to which mathematical investigation has been pushed and applied, this power is in constant exercise. By observation, as here used, can only be meant the fixing of the attention upon objects (physical or mental) so as to note distinctive peculiarities—to recognize resemblances, differences, and other relations. Now the first mental act of the child recognizing the distinction between *one* and more than one, between *one* and *two, two* and *three,*-etc., is exactly this. So, again, the first geometrical notions are as pure an exercise of this power as can be given. To know a straight line, to distinguish it from a curve; to recognize a triangle and distinguish the several forms—what are these, and all perception of form, but a series of observations? Nor is it alone in securing these fundamental conceptions of number and form that observation plays so important a part. The very genius of the common geometry as a method of reasoning—a system of investigation—is, that it is but a series of observations. The figure being before the eye in actual representation, or before the mind in conception, is so closely scrutinized, that all its distinctive features are perceived; auxiliary lines are drawn (the imagination leading in this), and a new series of inspections is made; and thus, by means of direct, simple observations, the investigation proceeds. So characteristic of common geometry is this method of investigation, that Comte, perhaps the ablest of all writers upon the philosophy of mathematics, is disposed to class geometry, as to its method, with the natural sciences, being based upon observation. Moreover, when we consider applied mathematics, we need only to notice that the exercise of this faculty is so essential, that the basis of all such reasoning, the very material with which we build, have received the name *observations.* Thus we might proceed to consider the whole range of the human faculties, and find for the most of them ample scope for exercise in mathematical studies. Certainly, the *memory* will not be found to be neglected. The very first steps in number—counting, the multiplication table, etc., make heavy demands on this power; while the higher branches require the memorizing of formulas which are simply appalling to the uninitiated. So the *imagination,* the creative faculty of the mind, has constant exercise in all original mathematical investigations, from the solution of the simplest problems to the discovery of the most recondite principle; for it is not by sure, consecutive steps, as many suppose, that we advance from the known to the unknown. The imagination, not the logical faculty, leads in this advance. In fact, practical observation is often in advance of logical exposition. Thus, in the discovery of truth, the imagination habitually presents hypotheses, and observation supplies facts, which it may require ages for the tardy reason to connect logically with the known. Of this truth, mathematics, as well as all other sciences, affords abundant illustrations. So remarkably true is this, that today it is seriously questioned by the majority of thinkers, whether the sublimest branch of mathematics,—the *infinitesimal calculus*— has anything more than an empirical foundation, mathematicians themselves not being agreed as to its logical basis. That the imagination, and not the logical faculty, leads in all original investigation, no one who has ever succeeded in producing an original demonstration of one of the simpler propositions of geometry, can have any doubt. Nor are *induction, analogy,* the *scrutinization* of *premises* or the *search* for them, or the *balancing* of *probabilities,* spheres of mental operations foreign to mathematics. No one, indeed, can claim pre-eminence for mathematical studies in all these departments of intellectual culture, but it may, perhaps, be claimed that scarcely any department of science affords discipline to so great a number of faculties, and that none presents so complete a gradation in the exercise of these faculties, from the first principles of the science to the farthest extent of its applications, as mathematics.

OLNEY, EDWARD.
Kiddle and Schem's Encyclopedia of Education,
(New York, 1877), Article "Mathematics."

254. The opinion appears to be gaining ground that this very general conception of functionality, born on mathematical ground, is destined to supersede the narrower notion of causation, traditional in connection with the natural sciences. As an abstract formulation of the idea of determination in its most general sense, the notion of functionality includes and transcends the more special notion of causation as a one-sided determination of future phenomena by means of present conditions; it can be used to express the fact of the subsumption under a general law of past, present, and future alike, in a sequence of phenomena. From this point of view the remark of Huxley that Mathematics "knows nothing of causation" could only be taken to express the whole truth, if by the term "causation" is understood "efficient causation." The latter notion has, however, in recent times been to an increasing extent regarded as just as irrelevant in the natural sciences as it is in Mathematics; the idea of thorough-going determinancy, in accordance with formal law, being thought to be alone significant in either domain.—HOBSON, E. W.

Presidential Address British Association for the Advancement of Science (1910); Nature, Vol. 84, p. 290.

255. Most, if not all, of the great ideas of modern mathematics have had their origin in observation. Take, for instance, the arithmetical theory of forms, of which the foundation was laid in the diophantine theorems of Fermat, left without proof by their author, which resisted all efforts of the myriad-minded Euler to reduce to demonstration, and only yielded up their cause of being when turned over in the blow-pipe flame of Gauss's transcendent genius; or the doctrine of double periodicity, which resulted from the observation of Jacobi of a purely analytical fact of transformation; or Legendre's law of reciprocity; or Sturm's theorem about the roots of equations, which, as he informed me with his own lips, stared him in the face in the midst of some mechanical investigations connected (if my memory serves me right) with the motion of compound pendulums; or Huyghen's method of continued fractions, characterized by Lagrange as one of the principal discoveries of that great mathematician, and to which he appears to have been led by the construction of his Planetary Automaton; or the new algebra, speaking of which one of my predecessors (Mr. Spottiswoode) has said, not without just reason and authority, from this chair, "that it reaches out and indissolubly connects itself each year with fresh branches of mathematics, that the theory of equations has become almost new through it, algebraic geometry transfigured in its light, that the calculus of variations, molecular physics, and mechanics" (he might, if speaking at the present moment, go on to add the theory of elasticity and the development of the integral calculus) "have all felt its influence."—SYLVESTER, J. J.

> *A Plea for the Mathematician, Nature, Vol. 1, p. 238; Collected Mathematical Papers, Vol. 2, pp. 655, 656.*

256. The ability to imagine relations is one of the most indispensable conditions of all precise thinking. No subject can be named, in the investigation of which it is not imperatively needed; but it can be nowhere else so thoroughly acquired as in the study of mathematics.—FISKE, JOHN.

> *Darwinism and other Essays (Boston, 1893), p. 296.*

257. The great science [mathematics] occupies itself at least just as much with the power of imagination as with the power of logical conclusion.—HERBART, F. J.

> *Pestalozzi's Idee eines ABC der Anschauung. Werke [Kehrbach] (Langensaltza, 1890), Bd. 1, p. 174.*

258. The moving power of mathematical invention is not reasoning but imagination.—DE MORGAN, A.

> *Quoted in Graves' Life of Sir W. R. Hamilton, Vol. 3 (1889), p. 219.*

259. There is an astonishing imagination, even in the science of mathematics. . . . We repeat, there was far more imagination in the head of Archimedes than in that of Homer.

> VOLTAIRE.
> *A Philosophical Dictionary (Boston, 1881), Vol. 3, p. 40. Article "Imagination."*

260. As the prerogative of Natural Science is to cultivate a taste for observation, so that of Mathematics is, almost from the starting point, to stimulate the faculty of invention.

> SYLVESTER, J. J.
> *A Plea for the Mathematician, Nature, Vol. 1, p. 261; Collected Mathematical Papers, Vol. 2 (Cambridge, 1908), p. 717.*

261. A marveilous newtrality have these things mathe-maticall, and also a strange participation between things supernaturall, immortall, intellectuall, simple and indivisible, and things naturall, mortall, sensible, componded and divisible.

DEE, JOHN.
Euclid (1570), Preface.

262. Mathematics stands forth as that which unites, mediates between Man and Nature, inner and outer world, thought and perception, as no other subject does.—FROEBEL.

*[Herford translation] (London, 1893), Vol. 1,
p. 84.*

263. The intrinsic character of mathematical research and knowledge is based essentially on three properties: first, on its conservative attitude towards the old truths and discoveries of mathematics; secondly, on its progressive mode of development, due to the incessant acquisition of new knowledge on the basis of the old; and thirdly, on its self-sufficiency and its consequent absolute independence.—SCHUBERT, H.

*Mathematical Essays and Recreations (Chicago,
1898), p. 27.*

264. Our science, in contrast with others, is not founded on a single period of human history, but has accompanied the devel-opment of culture through all its stages. Mathematics is as much interwoven with Greek culture as with the most modern problems in Engineering. She not only lends a hand to the progressive natural sciences but participates at the same time in the abstract investigations of logicians and philosophers.

KLEIN, F.
Klein und Riecke: Ueber angewandte Mathe-matik und Physik (1900), p. 228.

265. There is probably no other science which presents such different appearances to one who cultivates it and to one who does not, as mathematics. To this person it is ancient, venera-ble, and complete; a body of dry, irrefutable, unambiguous reasoning. To the mathematician, on the other hand, his science is yet in the purple bloom of vigorous youth, everywhere stretching out after the "attainable but unattained" and full of the excitement of nascent thoughts; its logic is beset with ambiguities, and its analytic processes, like Bunyan's road, have a quagmire on one side and a deep ditch on the other and branch off into innumerable by-paths that end in a wilderness.

CHAPMAN, C. H.
*Bulletin American Mathematical Society, Vol.
2 (First series), p. 61.*

266. Mathematical science is in my opinion an indivisible whole, an organism whose vitality is conditioned upon the connection of its parts. For with all the variety of mathematical knowledge, we are still clearly conscious of the similarity of the logical devices, the *relationship* of the *ideas* in mathematics as a whole and the numerous analogies in its different departments. We also notice that, the farther a mathematical theory is developed, the more harmoniously and uniformly does its construction proceed, and unsuspected relations are disclosed between hitherto separated branches of the science. So it happens that, with the extension of mathematics, its organic character is not lost but manifests itself the more clearly.—HILBERT, D.
*Mathematical Problems, Bulletin American
Mathematical Society, Vol. 8, p. 478.*

267. The mathematics have always been the implacable enemies of scientific romances.—ARAGO.
Oeuvres (1855), t. 3, p. 498.

268. Those skilled in mathematical analysis know that its object is not simply to calculate numbers, but that it is also employed to find the relations between magnitudes which cannot be expressed in numbers and between functions whose law is not capable of algebraic expression.—COURNOT, AUGUSTIN.
*Mathematical Theory of the Principles of
Wealth [Bacon, N. T.], (New York, 1897), p. 3.*

269. Coterminous with space and coeval with time is the Kingdom of Mathematics; within this range her dominion is supreme; otherwise than according to her order nothing can exist; in contradiction to her laws nothing takes place. On her

mysterious scroll is to be found written for those who can read it that which has been, that which is, and that which is to come. Everything material which is the subject of knowledge has number, order, or position; and these are her first outlines for a sketch of the universe. If our feeble hands cannot follow out the details, still her part has been drawn with an unerring pen, and her work cannot be gainsaid. So wide is the range of mathematical sciences, so indefinitely may it extend beyond our actual powers of manipulation that at some moments we are inclined tò fall down with even more than reverence before her majestic presence. But so strictly limited are her promises and powers, about so much that we might wish to know does she offer no information whatever, that at other moments we are fain to call her results but a vain thing, and to reject them as a stone where we had asked for bread. If one aspect of the subject encourages our hopes, so does the other tend to chasten our desires, and he is perhaps the wisest, and in the long run the happiest, among his fellows, who has learned not only this science, but also the larger lesson which it directly teaches, namely, to temper our aspirations to that which is possible, to moderate our desires to that which is attainable, to restrict our hopes to that of which accomplishment, if not immediately practicable, is at least distinctly within the range of conception.

SPOTTISWOODE, W.

Quoted in Sonnenschein's Encyclopedia of Education (London, 1906), p. 208.

270. But it is precisely mathematics, and the pure science generally, from which the general educated public and independent students have been debarred, and into which they have only rarely attained more than a very meagre insight. The reason of this is twofold. In the first place, the ascendant and consecutive character of mathematical knowledge renders its results absolutely insusceptible of presentation to persons who are unacquainted with what has gone before, and so necessitates on the part of its devotees a thorough and patient exploration of the field from the very beginning, as distinguished from those sciences which may, so to speak, be begun at the end, and which are consequently cultivated with the greatest zeal. The second reason is that, partly through the exigencies of academic instruction, but mainly through the martinet traditions of antiquity and the influence of mediæval logic-mongers, the great bulk of the elementary text-books of mathematics have unconsciously assumed a very repellant form,—something similar to what is termed in the theory of protective mimicry in biology "the terrifying form." And it is mainly to this formidableness and touch-me-not character of exterior, concealing withal a harmless body, that the undue neglect of typical mathematical studies is to be attributed.—McCORMACK, T. J.

> Preface to De Morgan's Elementary Illustrations of the Differential and Integral Calculus (Chicago, 1899).

271. Mathematics in gross, it is plain, are a grievance in natural philosophy, and with reason: for mathematical proofs, like diamonds, are hard as well as clear, and will be touched with nothing but strict reasoning. Mathematical proofs are out of the reach of topical arguments; and are not to be attacked by the equivocal use of words or declaration, that make so great a part of other discourses,—nay, even of controversies.

> LOCKE, JOHN.
> Second Reply to the Bishop of Worcester.

272. The belief that mathematics, because it is abstract, because it is static and cold and gray, is detached from life, is a mistaken belief. Mathematics, even in its purest and most abstract estate, is not detached from life. It is just the ideal handling of the problems of life, as sculpture may idealize a human figure or as poetry or painting may idealize a figure or a scene. Mathematics is precisely the ideal handling of the problems of life, and the central ideas of the science, the great concepts about which its stately doctrines have been built up, are precisely the chief ideas with which life must always deal and which, as it tumbles and rolls about them through time and space, give it its interests and problems, and its order and rationality. That such is the case a few indications will suffice to show. The mathematical concepts of constant and variable are represented familiarly in life by the notions of fixedness and change. The concept of equation or that of an equational system, imposing restriction upon variability, is matched in life by the concept of natural and spiritual law, giving order to what were else chaotic change and providing partial freedom in lieu of none at all. What is known in mathematics under the name of limit is everywhere present in life in the guise of some ideal, some excellence high-dwelling among the rocks, an "ever flying perfect" as Emerson calls it, unto which we may approximate nearer and nearer, but which we can never quite attain, save in aspiration. The supreme concept of functionality finds its correlate in life in the all-pervasive sense of interdependence and mutual determination among the elements of the world. What is known in mathematics as transformation—that is, lawful transfer of attention, serving to match in orderly fashion the things of one system with those of another—is conceived in life as a process of transmutation by which, in the flux of the world, the content of the present has come out of the past and in its turn, in ceasing to be, gives birth to its successor, as the boy is father to the man and as things, in general, become what they are not. The mathematical concept of invariance and that of infinitude, especially the imposing doctrines that explain their meanings and bear their names—What are they but mathematicizations of that which has ever been the chief of life's hopes and dreams, of that which has ever been the object of its deepest passion and of its dominant enterprise, I mean the finding of the worth that abides, the finding of permanence in the midst of change, and the discovery of a presence, in what has seemed to be a finite world, of being that is infinite? It is needless further to multiply examples of a correlation that is so abounding and complete as indeed to suggest a doubt whether it be juster to view mathematics as the abstract idealization of life than to regard life as the concrete realization of mathematics.

KEYSER, C. J.
The Humanization of the Teaching of Mathematics; Science, New Series, Vol. 35, pp. 645–646.

273. Mathematics, like dialectics, is an organ of the inner higher sense; in its execution it is an art like eloquence. Both alike care nothing for the content, to both nothing is of value but the form. It is immaterial to mathematics whether it

computes pennies or guineas, to rhetoric whether it defends truth or error.—GOETHE.

Wilhelm Meisters Wanderjahre, Zweites Buch.

274. The genuine spirit of Mathesis is devout. No intellectual pursuit more truly leads to profound impressions of the existence and attributes of a Creator, and to a deep sense of our filial relations to him, than the study of these abstract sciences. Who can understand so well how feeble are our conceptions of Almighty Power, as he who has calculated the attraction of the sun and the planets, and weighed in his balance the irresistible force of the lightning? Who can so well understand how confused is our estimate of the Eternal Wisdom, as he who has traced out the secret laws which guide the hosts of heaven, and combine the atoms on earth? Who can so well understand that man is made in the image of his Creator, as he who has sought to frame new laws and conditions to govern imaginary worlds, and found his own thoughts similar to those on which his Creator has acted?—HILL, THOMAS.

The Imagination in Mathematics; North American Review, Vol. 85, p. 226.

275. . . . what is physical is subject to the laws of mathematics, and what is spiritual to the laws of God, and the laws of mathematics are but the expression of the thoughts of God.

HILL, THOMAS.
The Uses of Mathesis; Bibliotheca Sacra, Vol. 32, p. 523.

276. It is in the inner world of pure thought, where all *entia* dwell, where is every type of order and manner of correlation and variety of relationship, it is in this infinite ensemble of eternal verities whence, if there be one cosmos or many of them, each derives its character and mode of being,—it is there that the spirit of mathesis has its home and its life.

Is it a restricted home, a narrow life, static and cold and grey with logic, without artistic interest, devoid of emotion and mood and sentiment? That world, it is true, is not a world of *solar* light, not clad in the colours that liven and glorify the things of sense, but it is an illuminated world, and over it all and everywhere throughout are hues and tints transcending *sense*, painted there by radiant pencils of *psychic* light, the light in which it lies. It is a silent world, and, nevertheless, in respect to the highest principle of art—the interpenetration of content and form, the perfect fusion of mode and meaning—it even surpasses music. In a sense, it is a static world, but so, too, are the worlds of the sculptor and the architect. The figures, however, which reason constructs and the mathematic vision beholds, transcend the temple and the statue, alike in simplicity and in intricacy, in delicacy and in grace, in symmetry and in poise. Not only are this home and this life thus rich in æsthetic interests, really controlled and sustained by motives of a sublimed and supersensuous art, but the religious aspiration, too, finds there, especially in the beautiful doctrine of invariants, the most perfect symbols of what it seeks—the changeless in the midst of change, abiding things in a world of flux, configurations that remain the same despite the swirl and stress of countless hosts of curious transformations. The domain of mathematics is the sole domain of certainty. There and there alone prevail the standards by which every hypothesis respecting the external universe and all observation and all experiment must be finally judged. It is the realm to which all speculation and all thought must repair for chastening and sanitation—the court of last resort, I say it reverently, for all intellection whatsoever, whether of demon or man or deity. It is there that mind as mind attains its highest estate, and the condition of knowledge there is the ultimate object, the tantalising goal of the aspiration, the *Anders-Streben*, of all other knowledge of every kind.—KEYSER, C. J.

The Universe and Beyond; Hibbert Journal,
Vol. 3 (1904–1905), pp. 313–314.

CHAPTER III

301. The world of ideas which it [mathematics] discloses or illuminates, the contemplation of divine beauty and order which it induces, the harmonious connection of its parts, the infinite hierarchy and absolute evidence of the truths with which mathematical science is concerned, these, and such like, are the surest grounds of its title of human regard, and would remain unimpaired were the plan of the universe unrolled like a map at our feet, and the mind of man qualified to take in the whole scheme of creation at a glance.—SYLVESTER, J. J.

> *A Plea for the Mathematician, Nature, 1, p. 262; Collected Mathematical Papers (Cambridge, 1908), 2, p. 659.*

302. It may well be doubted whether, in all the range of Science, there is any field so fascinating to the explorer—so rich in hidden treasures—so fruitful in delightful surprises—as that of Pure Mathematics. The charm lies chiefly . . . in the absolute *certainty* of its results: for that is what, beyond all mental treasures, the human intellect craves for. Let us only be sure of *something!* More light, more light! Ἐν δὲ φάει καὶ ὀλέσσον "And if our fate be death, give light and let us die!" This is the cry that, through all the ages, is going up from perplexed Humanity, and Science has little else to offer, that will really meet the demands of its votaries, than the conclusions of Pure Mathematics.—DODGSON, C. L.

> *A New Theory of Parallels (London, 1895), Introduction.*

303. In every case the awakening touch has been the mathematical spirit, the attempt to count, to measure, or to calculate. What to thè poet or the seer may appear to be the very death of all his poetry and all his visions—the cold touch of the calculating mind,—this has proved to be the spell by which knowledge has been born, by which new sciences have been created, and hundreds of definite problems put before the minds and into the hands of diligent students. It is the geometrical figure, the dry algebraical formula, which transforms the vague reasoning of the philosopher into a tangible and manageable conception; which represents, though it does not fully describe, which corresponds to, though it does not explain, the things and processes of nature: this clothes the fruitful, but otherwise indefinite, ideas in such a form that the strict logical methods of thought can be applied, that the human mind can in its inner chamber evolve a train of reasoning the result of which corresponds to the phenomena of the outer world.—MERZ, J. T.

> *A History of European Thought in the Nineteenth Century (Edinburgh and London, 1904), Vol. 1, p. 314.*

304. Mathematics . . . the ideal and norm of all careful thinking.—HALL, G. STANLEY.

> *Educational Problems (New York, 1911), p. 393.*

305. Mathematics is the only true metaphysics.

> THOMSON, W. (LORD KELVIN).
> *Thompson, S. P.: Life of Lord Kelvin (London, 1910), p. 10.*

306. He who knows not mathematics and the results of recent scientific investigation dies without knowing *truth*.

> SCHELLBACH, C. H.
> *Quoted in Young's Teaching of Mathematics (London, 1907), p. 44.*

307. The reasoning of mathematics is a type of perfect reasoning.—BARNETT, P. A.

> *Common Sense in Education and Teaching (New York, 1905), p. 222.*

308. Mathematics, once fairly established on the foundation of a few axioms and definitions, as upon a rock, has grown from age to age, so as to become the most solid fabric that human reason can boast.—REID, THOMAS.

> *Essays on the Intellectual Powers of Man, 4th. Ed., p. 461.*

309. The analytical geometry of Descartes and the calculus of Newton and Leibniz have expanded into the marvelous mathematical method—more daring than anything that the history of philosophy records—of Lobachevsky and Riemann, Gauss and Sylvester. Indeed, mathematics, the indispensable tool of the sciences, defying the senses to follow its splendid flights, is demonstrating today, as it never has been demonstrated before, the supremacy of the pure reason.

— BUTLER, NICHOLAS MURRAY.
The Meaning of Education and other Essays and Addresses (New York, 1905), p. 45.

310. Mathematics is the gate and key of the sciences. . . . Neglect of mathematics works injury to all knowledge, since he who is ignorant of it cannot know the other sciences or the things of this world. And what is worse, men who are thus ignorant are unable to perceive their own ignorance and so do not seek a remedy.—BACON, ROGER.
Opus Majus, Part 4, Distinctia Prima, cap. 1.

311. Just as it will never be successfully challenged that the French language, progressively developing and growing more perfect day by day, has the better claim to serve as a developed court and world language, so no one will venture to estimate lightly the debt which the world owes to mathematicians, in that they treat in their own language matters of the utmost importance, and govern, determine and decide whatever is subject, using the word in the highest sense, to number and measurement.—GOETHE.
Sprüche in Prosa, Natur, III, 868.

312. Do not imagine that mathematics is hard and crabbed, and repulsive to common sense. It is merely the etherealization of common sense.—THOMSON, W. (LORD KELVIN).
Thompson, S. P.: Life of Lord Kelvin (London, 1910), p. 1139.

313. The advancement and perfection of mathematics are intimately connected with the prosperity of the State.

NAPOLEON I.
Correspondance de Napoléon, t. 24 (1868), p. 112.

314. The love of mathematics is daily on the increase, not only with us but in the army. The result of this was unmistakably apparent in our last campaigns. Bonaparte himself has a mathematical head, and though all who study this science may not become geometricians like Laplace or Lagrange, or heroes like Bonaparte, there is yet left an influence upon the mind which enables them to accomplish more than they could possibly have achieved without this training.—LALANDE.
Quoted in Bruhns' Alexander von Humboldt (1872), Bd. 1, p. 232.

315. In Pure Mathematics, where all the various truths are necessarily connected with each other, (being all necessarily connected with those hypotheses which are the principles of the science), an arrangement is beautiful in proportion as the principles are few; and what we admire perhaps chiefly in the science, is the astonishing variety of consequences which may be demonstrably deduced from so small a number of premises.

STEWART, DUGALD.
Philosophy of the Human Mind, Part 3, chap. 1, sect. 3; Collected Works [Hamilton] (Edinburgh, 1854), Vol. 4.

316. It is curious to observe how differently these great men [Plato and Bacon] estimated the value of every kind of knowledge. Take Arithmetic for example. Plato, after speaking slightly of the convenience of being able to reckon and compute in the ordinary transactions of life, passes to what he considers as a far more important advantage. The study of the properties of numbers, he tells us, habituates the mind to the contemplation of pure truth, and raises us above the material universe. He would have his disciples apply themselves to this study, not that they may be able to buy or sell, not that they may qualify themselves to be shop-keepers or travelling merchants, but that they may learn to withdraw their minds from the ever-shifting spectacle of this visible and tangible world, and to fix them on the immutable essences of things.

Bacon, on the other hand, valued this branch of knowledge only on account of its uses with reference to that visible and tangible world which Plato so much despised. He speaks with scorn of the mystical arithmetic of the later Platonists, and laments the propensity of mankind to employ, on mere matters of curiosity, powers the whole exertion of which is required for purposes of solid advantage. He advises arithmeticians to leave these trifles, and employ themselves in framing convenient expressions which may be of use in physical researches.

MACAULAY.

Lord Bacon: Edinburgh Review, July, 1837.
Critical and Miscellaneous Essays (New York,
1879), Vol. 1, p. 397.

317. *Ath.* There still remain three studies suitable for freemen. Calculation in arithmetic is one of them; the measurement of length, surface, and depth is the second; and the third has to do with the revolutions of the stars in reference to one another . . . there is in them something that is necessary and cannot be set aside, . . . if I am not mistaken, [something of] divine necessity; for as to the human necessities of which men often speak when they talk in this manner, nothing can be more ridiculous than such an application of the words.

Cle. And what necessities of knowledge are there, Stranger, which are divine and not human?

Ath. I conceive them to be those of which he who has no use nor any knowledge at all cannot be a god, or demi-god, or hero to mankind, or able to take any serious thought or charge of them.—PLATO.

Republic, Bk. 7. Jowett's Dialogues of Plato
(New York, 1897), Vol. 4, p. 334.

318. Those who assert that the mathematical sciences make no affirmation about what is fair or good make a false assertion; for they do speak of these and frame demonstrations of them in the most eminent sense of the word. For if they do not actually employ these names, they do not exhibit even the results and the reasons of these, and therefore can be hardly said to make any assertion about them. Of what is fair, however, the most important species are order and symmetry, and that which is definite, which the mathematical sciences make manifest in a most eminent degree. And since, at least, these appear to be the causes of many things—now, I mean, for example, order, and that which is a definite thing, it is evident that they would assert, also, the existence of a cause of this description, and its subsistence after the same manner as that which is fair subsists in.—ARISTOTLE.

> *Metaphysics* [*MacMahon*] *Bk. 12, chap. 3.*

319. Many arts there are which beautify the mind of man; of all other none do more garnish and beautify it than those arts which are called mathematical.—BILLINGSLEY, H.

> *The Elements of Geometrie of the most ancient Philosopher Euclide of Megara (London, 1570), Note to the Reader.*

320. As the sun eclipses the stars by his brilliancy, so the man of knowledge will eclipse the fame of others in assemblies of the people if he proposes algebraic problems, and still more if he solves them.—BRAHMAGUPTA.

> *Quoted in Cajori's History of Mathematics (New York, 1897). p. 92.*

321. So highly did the ancients esteem the power of figures and numbers, that Democritus ascribed to the figures of atoms the first principles of the variety of things; and Pythagoras asserted that the nature of things consisted of numbers.

> BACON, LORD.
>
> *De Augmentis, Bk. 3; Advancement of Learning, Bk. 2.*

322. There has not been any science so much esteemed and honored as this of mathematics, nor with so much industry and vigilance become the care of great men, and labored in by the potentates of the world, viz. emperors, kings, princes, etc.

> FRANKLIN, BENJAMIN.
>
> *On the Usefulness of Mathematics, Works (Boston, 1840), Vol. 2, p. 28.*

323. Whatever may have been imputed to some other studies under the notion of insignificancy and loss of time, yet these [mathematics], I believe, never caused repentance in any, except it was for their remissness in the prosecution of them.

FRANKLIN, BENJAMIN.
On the Usefulness of Mathematics, Works
(Boston, 1840), Vol. 2, p. 69.

324. What science can there be more noble, more excellent, more useful for men, more admirably high and demonstrative, than this of the mathematics?—FRANKLIN, BENJAMIN.
On the Usefulness of Mathematics, Works
(Boston, 1840), Vol. 2, p. 69.

325. The great truths with which it [mathematics] deals, are clothed with austere grandeur, far above all purposes of immediate convenience or profit. It is in them that our limited understandings approach nearest to the conception of that absolute and infinite, towards which in most other things they aspire in vain. In the pure mathematics we contemplate absolute truths, which existed in the divine mind before the morning stars sang together, and which will continue to exist there, when the last of their radiant host shall have fallen from heaven. They existed not merely in metaphysical possibility, but in the actual contemplation of the supreme reason. The pen of inspiration, ranging all nature and life for imagery to set forth the Creator's power and wisdom, finds them best symbolized in the skill of the surveyor. "He meted out heaven as with a span;" and an ancient sage, neither falsely nor irreverently, ventured to say, that "God is a geometer."—EVERETT, EDWARD.
Orations and Speeches (Boston, 1870), Vol. 3,
p. 514.

326. There is no science which teaches the harmonies of nature more clearly than mathematics, . . .—CARUS, PAUL.
Andrews: Magic Squares and Cubes (Chicago,
1908), Introduction.

327. For it being the nature of the mind of man (to the extreme prejudice of knowledge) to delight in the spacious liberty of generalities, as in a champion region, and not in the enclosures of particularity; the Mathematics were the goodliest fields to satisfy that appetite.—BACON, LORD.

De Augmentis, Bk. 3; Advancement of Learning, Bk. 2.

328. I would have my son mind and understand business, read little history, study the mathematics and cosmography; these are good, with subordination to the things of God. . . . These fit for public services for which man is born.

CROMWELL, OLIVER.

Letters and Speeches of Oliver Cromwell (New York, 1899), Vol. 1, p. 371.

329. Mathematics is the life supreme. The life of the gods is mathematics. All divine messengers are mathematicians. Pure mathematics is religion. Its attainment requires a theophany.—NOVALIS.

Schriften (Berlin, 1901), Bd. 2, p. 223.

330. The Mathematics which effectually exercises, not vainly deludes or vexatiously torments studious Minds with obscure Subtilties, perplexed Difficulties, or contentious Disquisitions; which overcomes without Opposition, triumphs without Pomp, compels without Force, and rules absolutely without Loss of Liberty; which does not privately overreach a weak Faith, but openly assaults an armed Reason, obtains a total Victory, and puts on inevitable Chains; whose Words are so many Oracles, and Works as many Miracles; which blabs out nothing rashly, nor designs anything from the Purpose, but plainly demonstrates and readily performs all Things within its Verge; which obtrudes no false Shadow of Science, but the very Science itself, the Mind firmly adheres to it, as soon as possessed of it, and can never after desert it of its own Accord, or be deprived of it by any Force of others: Lastly the Mathematics, which depend upon Principles clear to the Mind, and agreeable to Experience; which draws certain Conclusions, instructs by profitable Rules, unfolds pleasant Questions; and produces wonderful Effects; which is the fruitful Parent of, I had almost said all, Arts, the

unshaken Foundation of Sciences, and the plentiful Fountain of Advantage to human Affairs.—BARROW, ISAAC.
Oration before the University of Cambridge on being elected Lucasian Professor of Mathematics, Mathematical Lectures (London, 1734), p. 28.

331. Doubtless the reasoning faculty, the mind, is the leading and characteristic attribute of the human race. By the exercise of this, man arrives at the properties of the natural bodies. This is science, properly and emphatically so called. It is the science of pure mathematics; and in the high branches of this science lies the truly sublime of human acquisition. If any attainment deserves that epithet, it is the knowledge, which, from the mensuration of the minutest dust of the balance, proceeds on the rising scale of material bodies, everywhere weighing, everywhere measuring, everywhere detecting and explaining the laws of force and motion, penetrating into the secret principles which hold the universe of God together, and balancing worlds against worlds, and system against system. When we seek to accompany those who pursue studies at once so high, so vast, and so exact; when we arrive at the discoveries of Newton, which pour in day on the works of God, as if a second *fiat* had gone forth from his own mouth; when, further, we attempt to follow those who set out where Newton paused, making his goal their starting-place, and, proceeding with demonstration upon demonstration, and discovery upon discovery, bring new worlds and new systems of worlds within the limits of the known universe, failing to learn all only because all is infinite; however we may say of man, in admiration of his physical structure, that "in form and moving he is express and admirable," it is here, and here without irreverence, we may exclaim, "In apprehension how like a god!" The study of the pure mathematics will of course not be extensively pursued in an institution, which, like this [Boston Mechanics' Institute], has a direct practical tendency and aim. But it is still to be remembered, that pure mathematics lie at the foundation of mechanical philosophy, and that it is ignorance only which can speak or think of that sublime science as useless research or barren speculation.—WEBSTER, DANIEL.
Works (Boston, 1872), Vol. 1, p. 180.

332. The school of Plato has advanced the interests of the race as much through geometry as through philosophy. The modern engineer, the navigator, the astronomer, built on the truths which those early Greeks discovered in their purely speculative investigations. And if the poetry, statesmanship, oratory, and philosophy of our day owe much to Plato's divine Dialogues, our commerce, our manufactures, and our science are equally indebted to his Conic Sections. Later instances may be abundantly quoted, to show that the labors of the mathematician have outlasted those of the statesman, and wrought mightier changes in the condition of the world. Not that we would rank the geometer above the patriot, but we claim that he is worthy of equal honor.—HILL, THOMAS.

Imagination in Mathematics; North American Review, Vol. 85, p. 228.

333. The discoveries of Newton have done more for England and for the race, than has been done by whole dynasties of British monarchs; and we doubt not that in the great mathematical birth of 1853, the Quaternions of Hamilton, there is as much real promise of benefit to mankind as in any event of Victoria's reign.—HILL, THOMAS.

Imagination in Mathematics; North American Review, Vol. 85, p. 228.

334. Geometrical and Mechanical phenomena are the most general, the most simple, the most abstract of all,—the most irreducible to others. It follows that the study of them is an indispensable preliminary to that of all others. Therefore must Mathematics hold the first place in the hierarchy of the sciences, and be the point of departure of all Education, whether general or special.—COMTE, A.

Positive Philosophy [Martineau] Introduction, chap. 2.

CHAPTER IV

401. Mathematics because of its nature and structure is peculiarly fitted for high school instruction [Gymnasiallehrfach]. Especially the higher mathematics, even if presented only in its elements, combines within itself all those qualities which are demanded of a secondary subject. It engages, it fructifies, it quickens, compels attention, is as circumspect as inventive, induces courage and self-confidence as well as modesty and submission to truth. It yields the essence and kernel of all things, is brief in form and overflows with its wealth of content. It discloses the depth and breadth of the law and spiritual element behind the surface of phenomena; it impels from point to point and carries within itself the incentive toward progress; it stimulates the artistic perception, good taste in judgment and execution, as well as the scientific comprehension of things. Mathematics, therefore, above all other subjects, makes the student lust after knowledge, fills him, as it were, with a longing to fathom the cause of things and to employ his own powers independently; it collects his mental forces and concentrates them on a single point and thus awakens the spirit of individual inquiry, self-confidence and the joy of doing; it fascinates because of the view-points which it offers and creates certainty and assurance, owing to the universal validity of its methods. Thus, both what he receives and what he himself contributes toward the proper conception and solution of a problem, combine to mature the student and to make him skillful, to lead him away from the surface of things and to exercise him in the perception of their essence. A student thus prepared thirsts after knowledge and is ready for the university and its sciences. Thus it appears, that higher mathematics is the best guide to philosophy and to the philosophic conception of the world (considered as a self-contained whole) and of one's own being.—DILLMANN, E.
*Die Mathematik die Fackelträgerin einer neuen
Zeit (Stuttgart, 1889), p. 40.*

402. These Disciplines [mathematics] serve to inure and corroborate the Mind to a constant Diligence in Study; to undergo the Trouble of an attentive Meditation, and cheerfully contend with such Difficulties as lie in the Way. They wholly deliver us from a credulous Simplicity, most strongly fortify us against the Vanity of Scepticism, effectually restrain from a rash Presumption, most easily incline us to a due Assent, perfectly subject us to the Government of right Reason, and inspire us with Resolution to wrestle against the unjust Tyranny of false Prèjudices. If the Fancy be unstable and fluctuating, it is to be poised by this Ballast, and steadied by this Anchor, if the Wit be blunt it is sharpened upon this Whetstone; if luxuriant it is pared by this Knife; if headstrong it is restrained by this Bridle; and if dull it is roused by this Spur. The Steps are guided by no Lamp more clearly through the dark Mazes of Nature, by no Thread more surely through the intricate Labyrinths of Philosophy, nor lastly is the Bottom of Truth sounded more happily by any other Line. I will not mention how plentiful a Stock of Knowledge the Mind is furnished from these, with what wholesome Food it is nourished, and what sincere Pleasure It enjoys. But if I speak farther, I shall neither be the only Person, nor the first, who affirms it; that while the Mind is abstracted and elevated from sensible Matter, distinctly views pure Forms, conceives the Beauty of Ideas, and investigates the Harmony of Proportions; the Manners themselves are sensibly corrected and improved, the Affections composed and rectified, the Fancy calmed and settled, and the Understanding raised and excited to more divine Contemplation. All which I might defend by Authority, and confirm by the Suffrages of the greatest Philosophers.—BARROW, ISAAC.

Prefatory Oration: Mathematical Lectures (London, 1734), p. 31.

403. No school subject so readily furnishes tasks whose purpose can be made so clear, so immediate and so appealing to the sober second-thought of the immature learner as the right sort of elementary school mathematics.—MYERS, GEORGE.

Arithmetic in Public School Education (Chicago, 1911), p. 8.

404. Mathematics is a type of thought which seems ingrained in the human mind, which manifests itself to some extent with even the primitive races, and which is developed to a high degree with the growth of civilization. . . . A type of thought, a body of results, so essentially characteristic of the human mind, so little influenced by environment, so uniformly present in every civilization, is one of which no well-informed mind today can be ignorant.—YOUNG, J. W. A.

> *The Teaching of Mathematics (London, 1907),*
> *p. 14.*

405. Probably among all the pursuits of the University, mathematics pre-eminently demand self-denial, patience, and perseverance from youth, precisely at that period when they have liberty to act for themselves, and when on account of obvious temptations, habits of restraint and application are peculiarly valuable.—TODHUNTER, ISAAC.

> *The Conflict of Studies and other Essays*
> *(London, 1873), p. 12.*

406. Mathematics renders its best service through the immediate furthering of rigorous thought and the spirit of invention.—HERBART, J. F.

> *Mathematischer Lehrplan für Realschulen:*
> *Werke [Kehrbach] (Langensalza, 1890), Bd. 5,*
> *p. 170.*

407. It seems to me that the older subjects, classics and mathematics, are strongly to be recommended on the ground of the accuracy with which we can compare the relative performance of the students. In fact the definiteness of these subjects is obvious, and is commonly admitted. There is however another advantage, which I think belongs in general to these subjects, that the examinations can be brought to bear on what is really most valuable in these subjects.—TODHUNTER, ISAAC.

> *Conflict of Studies and other Essays (London,*
> *1873), pp. 6, 7.*

408. It is better to teach the child arithmetic and Latin grammar than rhetoric and moral philosophy, because they require exactitude of performance it is made certain that the lesson is mastered, and that power of performance is worth more than knowledge.—EMERSON, R. W.

Lecture on Education.

409. Besides accustoming the student to demand complete proof, and to know when he has not obtained it, mathematical studies are of immense benefit to his education by habituating him to precision. It is one of the peculiar excellencies of mathematical discipline, that the mathematician is never satisfied with *à peu près*. He requires the exact truth. Hardly any of the non-mathematical sciences, except chemistry, has this advantage. One of the commonest modes of loose thought, and scources of error both in opinion and in practice, is to overlook the importance of quantities. Mathematicians and chemists are taught by the whole course of their studies, that the most fundamental difference of quality depends on some very slight difference in proportional quantity; and that from the qualities of the influencing elements, without careful attention to their quantities, false expectation would constantly be formed as to the very nature and essential character of the result produced.

MILL, J. S.

An Examination of Sir William Hamilton's Philosophy (London, 1878), p. 611.

410. In mathematics I can report no deficience, except it be that men do not sufficiently understand the excellent use of the Pure Mathematics, in that they do remedy and cure many defects in the wit and faculties intellectual. For if the wit be too dull, they sharpen it; if too wandering, they fix it; if too inherent in the senses, they abstract it. So that as tennis is a game of no use in itself, but of great use in respect it maketh a quick eye and a body ready to put itself into all positions; so in the Mathematics, that use which is collateral and intervenient is no less worthy than that which is principal and intended.

BACON, LORD.

De Augmentis, Bk. 3; Advancement of Learning, Bk. 2.

411. If a man's wit be wandering, let him study mathematics; for in demonstrations, if his wit be called away never so little, he must begin again.—BACON, LORD.

Essays: On Studies.

412. If one be bird-witted, that is easily distracted and unable to keep his attention as long as he should, mathematics provides a remedy; for in them if the mind be caught away but a moment, the demonstration has to be commenced anew.—BACON, LORD.

De Augmentis, Bk. 6; Advancement of Learning, Bk. 2.

413. The metaphysical philosopher from his point of view recognizes mathematics as an instrument of education, which strengthens the power of attention, develops the sense of order and the faculty of construction, and enables the mind to grasp under the simple formulae the quantitative differences of physical phenomena.—JOWETT, B.

Dialogues of Plato (New York, 1897), Vol. 2, p. 78.

414. Nor do I know any study which can compete with mathematics in general in furnishing matter for severe and continued thought. Metaphysical problems may be even more difficult; but then they are far less definite, and, as they rarely lead to any precise conclusion, we miss the power of checking our own operations, and of discovering whether we are thinking and reasoning or merely fancying and dreaming.

TODHUNTER, ISAAC.
Conflict of Studies (London, 1873), p. 13.

415. Another great and special excellence of mathematics is that it demands earnest voluntary exertion. It is simply impossible for a person to become a good mathematician by the happy accident of having been sent to a good school; this may give him a preparation and a start, but by his own individual efforts alone can he reach an eminent position.

TODHUNTER, ISAAC.
Conflict of Studies (London, 1873), p. 2.

416. The faculty of resolution is possibly much invigorated by mathematical study, and especially by that highest branch of it which, unjustly, merely on account of its retrograde operations, has been called, as if par excellence, analysis.—POE, E. A.
The Murders in Rue Morgue.

417. He who gives a portion of his time and talent to the investigation of mathematical truth will come to all other questions with a decided advantage over his opponents. He will be in argument what the ancient Romans were in the field: to them the day of battle was a day of comparative recreation, because they were ever accustomed to exercise with arms much heavier than they fought; and reviews differed from a real battle in two respects: they encountered more fatigue, but the victory was bloodless.—COLTON, C. C.
Lacon (New York, 1866).

418. Mathematics is the study which forms the foundation of the course [West Point Military Academy]. This is necessary, both to impart to the mind that combined strength and versatility, the peculiar vigor and rapidity of comparison necessary for military action, and to pave the way for progress in the higher military sciences.
Congressional Committee on Military Affairs, 1834; U. S. Bureau of Education, Bulletin 1912, No. 2, p. 10.

419. Mathematics, among all school subjects, is especially adapted to further clearness, definite brevity and precision in expression, although it offers no exercise in flights of rhetoric. This is due in the first place to the logical rigour with which it develops thought, avoiding every departure from the shortest, most direct way, never allowing empty phrases to enter. Other subjects excel in the development of expression in other respects: translation from foreign languages into the mother tongue gives exercise in finding the proper word for the given foreign word and gives knowledge of laws of syntax, the study of poetry and prose furnish fit patterns for connected presentation and elegant form of expression, composition is to exercise the pupil in a like presentation of his own or borrowed thoughts and their development, the natural sciences teach description of natural objects, apparatus and processes, as well as the statement of laws on the grounds of immediate sense-perception. But all these aids for exercise in the use of the mother tongue, each in its way valuable and indispensable, do not guarantee, in the same manner as mathematical training, the exclusion of words whose concepts, if not entirely wanting, are not sufficiently clear. They do not furnish in the same measure that which the mathematician demands particularly as regards precision of expression.—REIDT, F.

Anleitung zum mathematischen Unterricht in höheren Schulen (Berlin, 1906), p. 17.

420. One rarely hears of the mathematical recitation as a preparation for public speaking. Yet mathematics shares with these studies [foreign languages, drawing and natural science] their advantages, and has another in a higher degree than either of them.

Most readers will agree that a prime requisite for healthful experience in public speaking is that the attention of the speaker and hearers alike be drawn wholly away from the speaker and concentrated upon the thought. In perhaps no other classroom is this so easy as in the mathematical, where the close reasoning, the rigorous demonstration, the tracing of necessary conclusions from given hypotheses, commands and secures the entire mental power of the student who is explaining, and of his classmates. In what other circumstances do students feel so instinctively that manner counts for so little and mind for so much? In what other circumstances, therefore, is a simple, unaffected, easy, graceful manner so naturally and so healthfully cultivated? Mannerisms that are mere affectation or the result of bad literary habit recede to the background and finally disappear, while those peculiarities that are the expression of personality and are inseparable from its activity continually develop, where the student frequently presents, to an audience of his intellectual peers, a connected train of reasoning. . . .

One would almost wish that our institutions of the science and art of public speaking would put over their doors the motto

that Plato had over the entrance to his school of philosophy:
"Let no one who is unacquainted with geometry enter here."

WHITE, W. F.
A Scrap-book of Elementary Mathematics
(Chicago, 1908), p. 210.

421. The training which mathematics gives in working with
symbols is an excellent preparation for other sciences; . . . the
world's work requires constant mastery of symbols.

YOUNG, J. W. A.
The Teaching of Mathematics (New York,
1907), p. 42.

422. One striking peculiarity of mathematics is its unlimited
power of evolving examples and problems. A student may read
a book of Euclid, or a few chapters of Algebra, and within that
limited range of knowledge it is possible to set him exercises as
real and as interesting as the propositions themselves which he
has studied; deductions which might have pleased the Greek
geometers, and algebraic propositions which Pascal and Fermat
would not have disdained to investigate.—TODHUNTER, ISAAC.
Private Study of Mathematics: Conflict of
Studies and other Essays (London, 1873), p. 82.

423. Would you have a man reason well, you must use him
to it betimes; exercise his mind in observing the connection
between ideas, and following them in train. Nothing does this
better than mathematics, which therefore, I think should be
taught to all who have the time and opportunity, not so much
to make them mathematicians, as to make them reasonable
creatures; for though we all call ourselves so, because we are
born to it if we please, yet we may truly say that nature gives
us but the seeds of it, and we are carried no farther than industry and application have carried us.—LOCKE, JOHN.
Conduct of the Understanding, Sect. 6.

424. Secondly, the study of mathematics would show them
the necessity there is in reasoning, to separate all the distinct
ideas, and to see the habitudes that all those concerned in the
present inquiry have to one another, and to lay by those which
relate not to the proposition in hand, and wholly to leave them

out of the reckoning. This is that which, in other respects besides quantity is absolutely requisite to just reasoning, though in them it is not so easily observed and so carefully practised. In those parts of knowledge where it is thought demonstration has nothing to do, men reason as it were in a lump; and if upon a summary and confused view, or upon a partial consideration, they can raise the appearance of a probability, they usually rest content; especially if it be in a dispute where every little straw is laid hold on, and everything that can but be drawn in any way to give color to the argument is advanced with ostentation. But that mind is not in a posture to find truth that does not distinctly take all the parts asunder, and, omitting what is not at all to the point, draws a conclusion from the result of all the particulars which in any way influence it.—LOCKE, JOHN.
Conduct of the Understanding, Sect. 7.

425. I have before mentioned mathematics, wherein algebra gives new helps and views to the understanding. If I propose these it is not to make every man a thorough mathematician or deep algebraist; but yet I think the study of them is of infinite use even to grown men; first by experimentally convincing them, that to make anyone reason well, it is not enough to have parts wherewith he is satisfied, and that serve him well enough in his ordinary course. A man in those studies will see, that however good he may think his understanding, yet in many things, and those very visible, it may fail him. This would take off that presumption that most men have of themselves in this part; and they would not be so apt to think their minds wanted no helps to enlarge them, that there could be nothing added to the acuteness and penetration of their understanding.

LOCKE, JOHN.
The Conduct of the Understanding, Sect. 7.

426. I have mentioned mathematics as a way to settle in the mind a habit of reasoning closely and in train; not that I think it necessary that all men should be deep mathematicians, but that, having got the way of reasoning which that study necessarily brings the mind to, they might be able to transfer it to other parts of knowledge, as they shall have occasion. For in all sorts of reasoning, every single argument should be managed as a mathematical demonstration; the connection and dependence of ideas should be followed till the mind is brought to the source on which it bottoms, and observes the coherence all along; . . . .—Locke, John.

The Conduct of the Understanding, Sect. 7.

427. As an exercise of the reasoning faculty, pure mathematics is an admirable exercise, because it consists of *reasoning* alone, and does not encumber the student with an exercise of *judgment:* and it is well to begin with learning one thing at a time, and to defer a combination of mental exercises to a later period.—Whately, R.

Annotations to Bacon's Essays (Boston, 1873), Essay 1, p. 493.

428. It hath been an old remark, that Geometry is an excellent Logic. And it must be owned that when the definitions are clear; when the postulata cannot be refused, nor the axioms denied; when from the distinct contemplation and comparison of figures, their properties are derived, by a perpetual well-connected chain of consequences, the objects being still kept in view, and the attention ever fixed upon them; there is acquired a habit of reasoning, close and exact and methodical; which habit strengthens and sharpens the mind, and being transferred to other subjects is of general use in the inquiry after truth.

Berkely, George.
The Analyst, 2; Works (London, 1898), Vol. 3, p. 10.

429. Suppose then I want to give myself a little training in the art of reasoning; suppose I want to get out of the region of conjecture and probability, free myself from the difficult task of weighing evidence, and putting instances together to arrive at general propositions, and simply desire to know how to deal with my general propositions when I get them, and how to deduce right inferences from them; it is clear that I shall obtain this sort of discipline best in those departments of thought in which the first principles are unquestionably true. For in all our thinking, if we come to erroneous conclusions, we come to them either by accepting false premises to start with—in which case our reasoning, however good, will not save us from error; or by reasoning badly, in which case the data we start from may be perfectly sound, and yet our conclusions may be false. But in the mathematical or pure sciences,—geometry, arithmetic, algebra, trigonometry, the calculus of variations or of curves,— we know at least that there is not, and cannot be, error in our first principles, and we may therefore fasten our whole attention upon the processes. As mere exercises in logic, therefore, these sciences, based as they all are on primary truths relating to space and number, have always been supposed to furnish the most exact discipline. When Plato wrote over the portal of his school. "Let no one ignorant of geometry enter here," he did not mean that questions relating to lines and surfaces would be discussed by his disciples. On the contrary, the topics to which he directed their attention were some of the deepest problems,— social, political, moral,—on which the mind could exercise itself. Plato and his followers tried to think out together conclusions respecting the being, the duty, and the destiny of man, and the relation in which he stood to the gods and to the unseen world. What had geometry to do with these things? Simply this: That a man whose mind has not undergone a rigorous training in systematic thinking, and in the art of drawing legitimate inferences from premises, was unfitted to enter on the discussion of these high topics; and that the sort of logical discipline which he needed was most likely to be obtained from geometry—the only mathematical science which in Plato's time had been formulated and reduced to a system. And we in this country [England] have long acted on the same principle. Our future lawyers, clergy, and statesmen are expected at the University to learn a good deal about curves, and angles, and numbers and proportions; not because these subjects have the smallest relation to the needs of their lives, but because in the very act of learning them they are likely to acquire that habit of steadfast and accurate thinking, which is indispensable to success in all the pursuits of life.—FITCH, J. C.

Lectures on Teaching (New York, 1906), pp. 291–292.

430. It is admitted by all that a finishèd or even a competent reasoner is not the work of nature alone; the experience of every day makes it evident that education develops faculties which would otherwise never have manifested their existence. It is, therefore, as necessary to *learn to reason* before we can expect to be able to reason, as it is to learn to swim or fence, in order to attain either of those arts. Now, something must be reasoned upon, it matters not much what it is, provided it can be reasoned upon with certainty. The properties of mind or matter, or the study of languages, mathematics, or natural history, may be chosen for this purpose. Now of all these, it is desirable to choose the one which admits of the reasoning being verified, that is, in which we can find out by other means, such as measurement and ocular demonstration of all sorts, whether the results are true or not. When the guiding property of the loadstone was first ascertained, and it was necessary to learn how to use this new discovery, and to find out how far it might be relied on, it would have been thought advisable to make many passages between ports that were well known before attempting a voyage of discovery. So it is with our reasoning faculties: it is desirable that their powers should be exerted upon objects of such a nature, that we can tell by other means whether the results which we obtain are true or false, and this before it is safe to trust entirely to reason. Now the mathematics are peculiarly well adapted for this purpose, on the following grounds:

1. Every term is distinctly explained, and has but one meaning, and it is rarely that two words are employed to mean the same thing.

2. The first principles are self-evident, and, though derived from observation, do not require more of it than has been made by children in general.

3. The demonstration is strictly logical, taking nothing for granted except self-evident first principles, resting nothing upon probability, and entirely independent of authority and opinion.

4. When the conclusion is obtained by reasoning, its truth or falsehood can be ascertained, in geometry by actual measurement, in algebra by common arithmetical calculation. This gives confidence, and is absolutely necessary, if, as was said before, reason is not to be the instructor, but the pupil.

5. There are no words whose meanings are so much alike that the ideas which they stand for may be confounded. Between the meaning of terms there is no distinction, except a total distinction, and all adjectives and adverbs expressing difference of degrees are avoided.—DE MORGAN, AUGUSTUS.

> *On the Study and Difficulties of Mathematics*
> *(Chicago, 1898), chap. 1.*

431. The instruction of children should aim gradually to combine knowing and doing [Wissen und Können]. Among all sciences mathematics seems to be the only one of a kind to satisfy this aim most completely.—KANT, IMMANUEL.

> *Werke [Rosenkranz und Schubert], Bd. 9*
> *(Leipzig, 1838), p. 409.*

432. Every discipline must be honored for reason other than its utility, otherwise it yields no enthusiasm for industry.

For both reasons, I consider mathematics the chief subject for the common school. No more highly honored exercise for the mind can be found; the buoyancy [Spannkraft] which it produces is even greater than that produced by the ancient languages, while its utility is unquestioned.

> HERBART, J. F.
>
> *Mathematischer Lehrplan für Realgymnasien,*
> *Werke [Kehrbach], (Langensalza, 1890), Bd. 5,*
> *p. 167.*

433. The motive for the study of mathematics is insight into the nature of the universe. Stars and strata, heat and electricity, the laws and processes of becoming and being, incorporate mathematical truths. If language imitates the voice of the Creator, revealing His heart, mathematics discloses His intellect, repeating the story of how things came into being. And the value of mathematics, appealing as it does to our energy and to our honor, to our desire to know the truth and thereby to live as of right in the household of God, is that it establishes us in larger and larger certainties. As literature develops emotion, understanding, and sympathy, so mathematics develops observation, imagination, and reason.

CHANCELLOR, W. E.
A Theory of Motives, Ideals and Values in Education (Boston and New York, 1907), p. 406.

434. Mathematics in its pure form, as arithmetic, algebra, geometry, and the applications of the analytic method, as well as mathematics applied to matter and force, or statics and dynamics, furnishes the peculiar study that gives to us, whether as children or as men, the command of nature in this its quantitative aspect; mathematics furnishes the instrument, the tool of thought, which we wield in this realm.—HARRIS, W. T.
Psychologic Foundations of Education (New York, 1898), p. 325.

435. Little can be understood of even the simplest phenomena of nature without some knowledge of mathematics, and the attempt to penetrate deeper into the mysteries of nature compels simultaneous development of the mathematical processes.

YOUNG, J. W. A.
The Teaching of Mathematics (New York, 1907), p. 16.

436. For many parts of nature can neither be invented with sufficient subtility nor demonstrated with sufficient perspicuity nor accommodated unto use with sufficient dexterity, without the aid and intervening of mathematics.—BACON, LORD.
De Augmentis, Bk. 2; Advancement of Learning, Bk. 3.

437. I confess, that after I began . . . to discern how useful mathematicks may be made to physicks, I have often wished that I had employed about the speculative part of geometry, and the cultivation of the specious Algebra I had been taught very young, a good part of that time and industry, that I had spent about surveying and fortification (of which I remember I once wrote an entire treatise) and other parts of practick mathematicks.—BOYLE, ROBERT.
The Usefulness of Mathematiks to Natural Philosophy; Works (London, 1772), Vol. 3, p. 426.

438. Mathematics gives the young man a clear idea of demonstration and habituates him to form long trains of thought and reasoning methodically connected and sustained by the final certainty of the result; and it has the further advantage, from a purely moral point of view, of inspiring an absolute and fanatical respect for truth. In addition to all this, mathematics, and chiefly algebra and infinitesimal calculus, excite to a high degree the conception of the signs and symbols—necessary instruments to extend the power and reach of the human mind by summarizing an aggregate of relations in a condensed form and in a kind of mechanical way. These auxiliaries are of special value in mathematics because they are there adequate to their definitions, a characteristic which they do not possess to the same degree in the physical and mathematical [natural?] sciences.

There are, in fact, a mass of mental and moral faculties that can be put in full play only by instruction in mathematics; and they would be made still more available if the teaching was directed so as to leave free play to the personal work of the student.—BERTHELOT, M. P. E. M.

Science as an Instrument of Education; Popular Science Monthly (1897), p. 253.

439. Mathematical knowledge, therefore, appears to us of value not only in so far as it serves as means to other ends, but for its own sake as well, and we behold, both in its systematic external and internal development, the most complete and purest logical mind-activity, the embodiment of the highest intellect-esthetics.—PRINGSHEIM, ALFRED.

Ueber Wert und angeblichen Unwert der Mathematik; Jahresbericht der Deutschen Mathematiker Vereinigung, Bd. 13, p. 381.

440. The advantages which mathematics derives from the peculiar nature of those relations about which it is conversant, from its simple and definite phraseology, and from the severe logic so admirably displayed in the concatenation of its innumerable theorems, are indeed immense, and well entitled to separate and ample illustration.—STEWART, DUGALD.

Philosophy of the Human Mind, Part 2, chap. 2, sect. 3.

441. I do not intend to go deeply into the question how far mathematical studies, as the representatives of conscious logical reasoning, should take a more important place in school education. But it is, in reality, one of the questions of the day. In proportion as the range of science extends, its system and organization must be improved, and it must inevitably come about that individual students will find themselves compelled to go through a stricter course of training than grammar is in a position to supply. What strikes me in my own experience with students who pass from our classical schools to scientific and medical studies, is first, a certain laxity in the application of strictly universal laws. The grammatical rules, in which they have been exercised, are for the most part followed by long lists of exceptions; accordingly they are not in the habit of relying implicitly on the certainty of a legitimate deduction from a strictly universal law. Secondly, I find them for the most part too much inclined to trust to authority, even in cases where they might form an independent judgment. In fact, in philological studies, inasmuch as it is seldom possible to take in the whole of the premises at a glance, and inasmuch as the decision of disputed questions often depends on an æsthetic feeling for beauty of expression, or for the genius of the language, attainable only by long training, it must often happen that the student is referred to authorities even by the best teachers. Both faults are traceable to certain indolence and vagueness of thought, the sad effects of which are not confined to subsequent scientific studies. But certainly the best remedy for both is to be found in mathematics, where there is absolute certainty in the reasoning, and no authority is recognized but that of one's own intelligence.—HELMHOLTZ, H.

> On the Relation of Natural Science to Science in
> general; Popular Lectures on Scientific Sub-
> jects; Atkinson (New York, 1900), pp. 25–26.

442. What renders a problem definite, and what leaves it indefinite, may best be understood from mathematics. The very important idea of solving a problem within limits of error is an element of rational culture, coming from the same source. The art of totalizing fluctuations by curves is capable of being carried, in conception, far beyond the mathematical domain,

where it is first learned. The distinction between laws and coefficients applies in every department of causation. The theory of Probable Evidence is the mathematical contribution to Logic, and is of paramount importance.—BAIN, ALEXANDER.
Education as a Science (New York, 1898),
pp. 151–152.

443. We receive it as a fact, that some minds are so constituted as absolutely to require for their nurture the severe logic of the abstract sciences; that rigorous sequence of ideas which leads from the premises to the conclusion, by a path, arduous and narrow, it may be, and which the youthful reason may find it hard to mount, but where it cannot stray; and on which, if it move at all, it must move onward and upward. . . . Even for intellects of a different character, whose natural aptitude is for moral evidence and those relations of ideas which are perceived and appreciated by taste, the study of the exact sciences may be recommended as the best protection against the errors into which they are most likely to fall. Although the study of language is in many respects no mean exercise in logic, yet it must be admitted that an eminently practical mind is hardly to be formed without mathematical training.—EVERETT, EDWARD.
Orations and Speeches (Boston, 1870), Vol. 2,
p. 510.

444. The value of mathematical instruction as a preparation for those more difficult investigations, consists in the applicability not of its doctrines but of its methods. Mathematics will ever remain the past perfect type of the deductive method in general; and the applications of mathematics to the simpler branches of physics furnish the only school in which philosophers can effectually learn the most difficult and important of their art, the employment of the laws of simpler phenomena for explaining and predicting those of the more complex. These grounds are quite sufficient for deeming mathematical training an indispensable basis of real scientific education, and regarding with Plato, one who is ἀγεωμέτρητος, as wanting in one of the most essential qualifications for the successful cultivation of the higher branches of philosophy.—MILL, J. S.
System of Logic, Bk. 3, chap. 24, sect. 9.

445. This science, Geometry, is one of indispensable use and constant reference, for every student of the laws of nature; for the relations of space and number are the *alphabet* in which those laws are written. But besides the interest and importance of this kind which geometry possesses, it has a great and peculiar value for all who wish to understand the foundations of human knowledge, and the methods by which it is acquired. For the student of geometry acquires, with a degree of insight and clearness which the unmathematical reader can but feebly imagine, a conviction that there are necessary truths, many of them of a very complex and striking character; and that a few of the most simple and self-evident truths which it is possible for the mind of man to apprehend, may, by systematic deduction, lead to the most remote and unexpected results.

WHEWELL, WILLIAM.
The Philosophy of the Inductive Sciences,
Part 1, Bk. 2, chap. 4, sect. 8 (London, 1858).

446. Mathematics, while giving no quick remuneration, like the art of stenography or the craft of bricklaying, does furnish the power for deliberate thought and accurate statement, and to speak the truth is one of the most social qualities a person can possess. Gossip, flattery, slander, deceit, all spring from a slovenly mind that has not been trained in the power of truthful statement, which is one of the highest utilities.—DUTTON, S. T.
Social Phases of Education in the School and
the Home (London, 1900), p. 30.

447. It is from this absolute indifference and tranquility of the mind, that mathematical speculations derive some of their most considerable advantages; because there is nothing to interest the imagination; because the judgment sits free and unbiased to examine the point. All proportions, every arrangement of quantity, is alike to the understanding, because the same truths result to it from all; from greater from lesser, from equality and inequality.—BURKE, EDMUND.
On the Sublime and Beautiful, Part 3, sect. 2.

448. Out of the interaction of form and content in mathematics grows an acquaintance with methods which enable the student to produce independently within certain though moderate limits, and to extend his knowledge through his own reflection. The deepening of the consciousness of the intellectual powers connected with this kind of activity, and the gradual awakening of the feeling of intellectual self-reliance may well be considered as the most beautiful and highest result of mathematical training.—PRINGSHEIM, ALFRED.

Ueber Wert und angeblichen Unwert der Mathematik; Jahresbericht der Deutschen Mathematiker Vereinigung (1904), p. 374.

449. He who would know what geometry is, must venture boldly into its depths and learn to think and feel as a geometer. I believe that it is impossible to do this, and to study geometry as it admits of being studied and am conscious it can be taught, without finding the reason invigorated, the invention quickened, the sentiment of the orderly and beautiful awakened and enhanced, and reverence for truth, the foundation of all integrity of character, converted into a fixed principle of the mental and moral constitution, according to the old and expressive adage " abeunt studia in mores."—SYLVESTER, J. J.

A probationary Lecture on Geometry; Collected Mathematical Papers (Cambridge, 1908), Vol. 2, p. 9.

450. Mathematical knowledge adds vigour to the mind, frees it from prejudice, credulity, and superstition.

ARBUTHNOT, JOHN.
Usefulness of Mathematical Learning.

451. When the boy begins to understand that the visible point is preceded by an invisible point, that the shortest distance between two points is conceived as a straight line before it is ever drawn with the pencil on paper, he experiences a feeling of pride, of satisfaction. And justly so, for the fountain of all thought has been opened to him, the difference between the ideal and the real, *potentia et actu,* has become clear to him; henceforth the philosopher can reveal him nothing new, as a geometrician he has discovered the basis of all thought.

GOETHE.
Sprüche in Prosa, Ethisches, VI, 455.

452. In mathematics, . . . and in natural philosophy since mathematics was applied to it, we see the noblest instance of the force of the human mind, and of the sublime heights to which it may rise by cultivation. An acquaintance with such sciences naturally leads us to think well of our faculties, and to indulge sanguine expectations concerning the improvement of other parts of knowledge. To this I may add, that, as mathematical and physical truths are perfectly uninteresting in their consequences, the understanding readily yields its assent to the evidence which is presented to it; and in this way may be expected to acquire the habit of trusting to its own conclusions, which will contribute to fortify it against the weaknesses of scepticism, in the more interesting inquiries after moral truth in which it may afterwards engage.—STEWART, DUGALD.
> *Philosophy of the Human Mind, Part 3,*
> *chap. 1, sect. 3.*

453. Those that can readily master the difficulties of Mathematics find a considerable charm in the study, sometimes amounting to fascination. This is far from universal; but the subject contains elements of strong interest of a kind that constitutes the pleasures of knowledge. The marvellous devices for solving problems elate the mind with the feeling of intellectual power; and the innumerable constructions of the science leave us lost in wonder.—BAIN, ALEXANDER.
> *Education as a Science (New York, 1898),*
> *p. 153.*

454. Thinking is merely the comparing of ideas, discerning relations of likeness and of difference between ideas, and drawing inferences. It is seizing general truths on the basis of clearly apprehended particulars. It is but generalizing and particularizing. Who will deny that a child can deal profitably with sequences of ideas like: How many marbles are 2 marbles and 3 marbles? 2 pencils and 3 pencils? 2 balls and 3 balls? 2 children and 3 children? 2 inches and 3 inches? 2 feet and 3 feet? 2 and 3? Who has not seen the countenance of some little learner light up at the end of such a series of questions with the exclamation, "Why it's always that way. Isn't it?" This is the glow of pleasure that the generalizing step always affords him who takes the step himself. This is the genuine life-giving joy which comes from feeling that one can successfully take this step. The reality of such a discovery is as great, and the lasting effect upon the mind of him that makes it is as sure as was that by which the great Newton hit upon the generalization of the law of gravitation. It is through these thrills of discovery that love to learn and intellectual pleasure are begotten and fostered. Good arithmetic teaching abounds in such opportunities.

MYERS, GEORGE.
Arithmetic in Public Education (Chicago), p. 13.

455. A *general course* in mathematics should be required of all officers for its practical value, but no less for its educational value in training the mind to logical forms of thought, in developing the sense of absolute truthfulness, together with a confidence in the accomplishment of definite results by definite means.—ECHOLS, C. P.

Mathematics at West Point and Annapolis; U. S. Bureau of Education, Bulletin 1912, No. 2, p. 11.

456. Exercise in the most rigorous thinking that is possible will of its own accord strengthen the sense of truth and right, for each advance in the ability to distinguish between correct and false thoughts, each habit making for rigour in thought development will increase in the sound pupil the ability and the wish to ascertain what is right in life and to defend it.

REIDT, F.
Anleitung zum mathematischen Unterricht in den höheren Schulen (Berlin, 1906), p. 28.

457. I do not maintain that the *chief value* of the study of arithmetic consists in the lessons of morality that arise from this study. I claim only that, to be impressed from day to day, that there is something *that is right* as an answer to the questions with which one is *able* to grapple, and that there is a wrong answer—that there are ways in which the right answer can be established as right, that these ways automatically reject error and slovenliness, and that the learner is able himself to manipulate these ways and to arrive at the establishment of the true as opposed to the untrue, this relentless hewing *to* the line and stopping *at* the line, must color distinctly the thought life of the pupil with more than a tinge of morality. . . . To be neighborly with truth, to feel one's self somewhat facile in ways of recognizing and establishing what is right, what is correct, to find the wrong persistently and unfailingly rejected as of no value, to feel that one can apply these ways for himself, that one can think and work independently, have a real, a positive, and a purifying effect upon moral character. They are the -quiet, steady undertones of the work that always appeal to the learner for the sanction of his best judgment, and these are the really significant matters in school work. It is not the noise and bluster, not even the dramatics or the polemics from the teacher's desk, that abide longest and leave the deepest and stablest imprint upon character. It is these still, small voices that speak unmistakably for the right and against the wrong and the erroneous that really form human character. When the school subjects are arranged on the basis of the degree to which they contribute to the moral upbuilding of human character good arithmetic will be well up the list.—MYERS, GEORGE.

Arithmetic in Public Education (Chicago), p. 18.

458. In destroying the predisposition to anger, science of all kind is useful; but the mathematics possess this property in the most eminent degree.—DR. RUSH.

Quoted in Day's Collacon (London, no date).

459. The mathematics are the friends to religion, inasmuch as they charm the passions, restrain the impetuosity of the imagination, and purge the mind from error and prejudice. Vice is error, confusion and false reasoning; and all truth is more or less opposite to it. Besides, mathematical truth may serve for a pleasant entertainment for those hours which young men are apt to throw away upon their vices; the delightfulness of them being such as to make solitude not only easy but desirable.

ARBUTHNOT, JOHN.
Usefulness of Mathematical Learning.

460. There is no prophet which preaches the superpersonal God more plainly than mathematics.—CARUS, PAUL.

> *Reflections on Magic Squares; Monist (1906), p. 147.*

461. Mathematics must subdue the flights of our reason; they are the staff of the blind; no one can take a step without them; and to them and experience is due all that is certain in physics.

VOLTAIRE.

> *Oeuvres Complètes (Paris, 1880), t. 35, p. 219.*

CHAPTER V

501. In mathematics two ends are constantly kept in view: First, stimulation of the inventive faculty, exercise of judgment, development of logical reasoning, and the habit of concise statement; second, the association of the branches of pure mathematics with each other and with applied science, that the pupil may see clearly the true relations of principles and things.

> *International Commission on the Teaching of Mathematics, American Report; U. S. Bureau of Education, Bulletin 1912, No. 4, p. 7.*

502. The ends to be attained [in the teaching of mathematics in the secondary schools] are the knowledge of a body of geometrical truths, the power to draw correct inferences from given premises, the power to use algebraic processes as a means of finding results in practical problems, and the awakening of interest in the science of mathematics.

> *International Commission on the Teaching of Mathematics, American Report; U. S. Bureau of Education, Bulletin 1912, No. 4, p. 7.*

503. General preparatory instruction must continue to be the aim in the instruction at the higher institutions of learning. Exclusive selection and treatment of subject matter with reference to specific avocations is disadvantageous.

> *Resolution adopted by the German Association for the Advancement of Scientific and Mathematical Instruction; Jahresbericht der Deutschen Mathematiker Vereinigung (1896), p. 41.*

504. In the secondary schools mathematics should be a part of general culture and not contributory to technical training of any kind; it should cultivate space intuition, logical thinking, the power to rephrase in clear language thoughts recognized as correct, and ethical and esthetic effects; so treated, mathematics is a quite indispensable factor of general education in so far as the latter shows its traces in the comprehension of the development of civilization and the ability to participate in the further tasks of civilization.

Unterrichtsblätter für Mathematik und Naturwissenschaft (1904), p. 128.

505. Indeed, the aim of teaching [mathematics] should be rather to strengthen his [the pupil's] faculties, and to supply a method of reasoning applicable to other subjects, than to furnish him with an instrument for solving practical problems.

MAGNUS, PHILIP.
Perry's Teaching of Mathematics (London, 1902), p. 84.

506. The participation in the *general development of the mental powers* without special reference to his future vocation must be recognized as the essential aim of mathematical instruction.

REIDT, F.
Anleitung zum Mathematischen Unterricht an höheren Schulen (Berlin, 1906), p. 12.

507. I am of the decided opinion, that mathematical instruction must have for its first aim a deep penetration and complete command of abstract mathematical theory together with a clear insight into the structure of the system, and doubt not that the instruction which accomplishes this is valuable and interesting even if it neglects practical applications. If the instruction sharpens the understanding, if it arouses the scientific interest, whether mathematical or philosophical, if finally it calls into life an esthetic feeling for the beauty of a scientific edifice, the instruction will take on an ethical value as well, provided that with the interest it awakens also the impulse toward scientific activity. I contend, therefore, that even without reference to its applications mathematics in the high schools has a value equal to that of the other subjects of instruction.

GOETTING, E.
Ueber das Lehrziel im mathematischen Unterricht der höheren Realanstalten; Jahresbericht der Deutschen Mathematiker Vereinigung, Bd. 2, p. 192.

508. Mathematics will not be properly esteemed in wider circles until more than the *a b c* of it is taught in the schools, and until the unfortunate impression is gotten rid of that mathematics serves no other purpose in instruction than the *formal* training of the mind. The aim of mathematics is its *content*, its form is a secondary consideration and need not necessarily be that historic form which is due to the circumstance that mathematics took permanent shape under the influence of Greek logic.—HANKEL, H.

> *Die Entwickelung der Mathematik in den letzten Jahrhunderten (Tübingen, 1884), p. 6.*

509. The idea that aptitude for mathematics is rarer than aptitude for other subjects is merely an illusion which is caused by belated or neglected beginners.—HERBART, J. F.

> *Umriss pädagogischer Vorlesungen; Werke [Kehrbach] (Langensalza, 1902), Bd. 10, p. 101.*

510. I believe that the useful methods of mathematics are easily to be learned by quite young persons, just as languages are easily learned in youth. What a wondrous philosophy and history underlie the use of almost every word in every language—yet the child learns to use the word unconsciously. No doubt when such a word was first invented it was studied over and lectured upon, just as one might lecture now upon the idea of a rate, or the use of Cartesian co-ordinates, and we may depend upon it that children of the future will use the idea of the calculus, and use squared paper as readily as they now cipher. . . . When Egyptian and Chaldean philosophers spent years in difficult calculations, which would now be thought easy by young children, doubtless they had the same notions of the depth of their knowledge that Sir William Thomson might now have of his. How is it, then, that Thomson gained his immense knowledge in the time taken by a Chaldean philosopher to acquire a simple knowledge of arithmetic? The reason is plain. Thomson, when a child, was taught in a few years more than all that was known three thousand years ago of the properties of numbers. When it is found essential to a boy's future that machinery should be given to his brain, it is given to him; he is taught to use it, and his bright memory makes the use of it a second nature to him; but it is not till after-life that he makes a close investigation of what there actually is in his brain which has enabled him to do so much. It is taken because the child has much faith. In after years he will accept nothing without careful consideration. The machinery given to the brain of children is getting more and more complicated as time goes on; but there is really no reason why it should not be taken in as early, and used as readily, as were the axioms of childish education in ancient Chaldea.—PERRY, JOHN.

The Teaching of Mathematics (London, 1902), p. 14.

517. The ancients devoted a lifetime to the study of arithmetic; it required days to extract a square root or to multiply two numbers together. Is there any harm in skipping all that, in letting the school boy learn multiplication sums, and in starting his more abstract reasoning at a more advanced point? Where would be the harm in letting the boy assume the truth of many propositions of the first four books of Euclid, letting him assume their truth partly by faith, partly by trial? Giving him the whole fifth book of Euclid by simple algebra? Letting him assume the sixth as axiomatic? Letting him, in fact, begin his severer studies where he is now in the habit of leaving off? We do much less orthodox things. Every here and there in one's mathematical studies one makes exceedingly large assumptions, because the methodical study would be ridiculous even in the eyes of the most pedantic of teachers. I can imagine a whole year devoted to the philosophical study of many things that a student now takes in his stride without trouble. The present method of training the mind of a mathematical teacher causes it to strain at gnats and to swallow camels. Such gnats are most of the propositions of the sixth book of Euclid; propositions generally about incommensurables; the use of arithmetic in geometry; the parallelogram of forces, etc., decimals.—PERRY, JOHN.

The Teaching of Mathematics (London, 1904), p. 12.

512. The teaching of elementary mathematics should be conducted so that the way should be prepared for the building upon them of the higher mathematics. The teacher should always bear in mind and look forward to what is to come after. The pupil should not be taught what may be sufficient for the time, but will lead to difficulties in the future. . . . I think the fault in teaching arithmetic is that of not attending to general principles and teaching instead of particular rules. . . . I am inclined to attack the teaching of mathematics on the grounds that it does not dwell sufficiently on a few general axiomatic principles.—HUDSON, W. H. H.

> *Perry's Teaching of Mathematics (London, 1904), p. 33.*

513. "Mathematics in Prussia! Ah, sir, they teach mathematics in Prussia as you teach your boys rowing in England: they are trained by men who have been trained by men who have themselves been trained for generations back."

> LANGLEY, E. M.
> *Perry's Teaching of Mathematics (London, 1904), p. 43.*

514. A superficial knowledge of mathematics may lead to the belief that this subject can be taught incidentally, and that exercises akin to counting the petals of flowers or the legs of a grasshopper are mathematical. Such work ignores the fundamental idea out of which quantitative reasoning grows—the equality of magnitudes. It leaves the pupil unaware of that relativity which is the essence of mathematical science. Numerical statements are frequently required in the study of natural history, but to repeat these as a drill upon numbers will scarcely lend charm to these studies, and certainly will not result in mathematical knowledge.—SPEER, W. W.

> *Primary Arithmetic (Boston, 1897), pp. 26–27.*

515. Mathematics is no more the art of reckoning and computation than architecture is the art of making bricks or hewing wood, no more than painting is the art of mixing colors on a palette, no more than the science of geology is the art of breaking rocks, or the science of anatomy the art of butchering.

> KEYSER, C. J.
> *Lectures on Science, Philosophy and Art (New York, 1908), p. 29.*

516. The study of mathematics—from ordinary reckoning up to the higher processes—must be connected with knowledge of nature, and at the same time with experience, that it may enter the pupil's circle of thought.—HERBART, J. F.

Letters and Lectures on Education [*Felkin*] (*London, 1908*), *p. 117.*

517. First, as concerns the *success* of teaching mathematics. No instruction in the high schools is as difficult as that of mathematics, since the large majority of students are at first decidedly disinclined to be harnessed into the rigid framework of logical conclusions. The interest of young people is won much more easily, if sense-objects are made the starting point and the transition to abstract formulation is brought about gradually. For this reason it is psychologically quite correct to follow this course.

Not less to be recommended is this course if we inquire into the essential purpose of mathematical instruction. Formerly it was too exclusively held that this purpose is to sharpen the understanding. Surely another important end is to implant in the student the conviction that *correct thinking based on true premises secures mastery over the outer world.* To accomplish this the outer world must receive its share of attention from the very beginning.

Doubtless this is true but there is a danger which needs pointing out. It is as in the case of language teaching where the modern tendency is to secure in addition to grammar also an understanding of the authors. The danger lies in grammar being completely set aside leaving the subject without its indispensable solid basis. Just so in the teaching of mathematics it is possible to accumulate interesting applications to such an extent as to stunt the essential logical development. This should in no wise be permitted, for thus the kernel of the whole matter is lost. Therefore: We do want throughout a quickening of mathematical instruction by the introduction of applications, but we do not want that the pendulum, which in former decades may have inclined too much toward the abstract side, should now swing to the other extreme; we would rather pursue the proper middle course.—KLEIN, FELIX.

Ueber den Mathematischen Unterricht an den hoheren Schulen; Jahresbericht der Deutschen Mathematiker Vereinigung, Bd. 11, p. 131.

518. It is above all the duty of the methodical text-book to adapt itself to the pupil's power of comprehension, only challenging his higher efforts with the increasing development of his imagination, his logical power and the ability of abstraction. This indeed constitutes a test of the art of teaching, it is here where pedagogic tact becomes manifest. In reference to the axioms, caution is necessary. It should be pointed out comparatively early, in how far the mathematical body differs from the material body. Furthermore, since mathematical bodies are really portions of space, this space is to be conceived as mathematical space and to be clearly distinguished from real or physical space. Gradually the student will become conscious that the portion of the real space which lies beyond the visible stellar universe is not cognizable through the senses, that we know nothing of its properties and consequently have no basis for judgments concerning it. Mathematical space, on the other hand, may be subjected to conditions, for instance, we may condition its properties at infinity, and these conditions constitute the axioms, say the Euclidean axioms. But every student will require years before the conviction of the truth of this last statement will force itself upon him.—HOLZMÜLLER, GUSTAV.
Methodisches Lehrbuch der Elementar-Mathematik (Leipzig, 1904), Teil I, Vorwort, pp. 4–5.

519. Like almost every subject of human interest, this one [mathematics] is just as easy or as difficult as we choose to make it. A lifetime may be spent by a philosopher in discussing the truth of the simplest axiom. The simplest fact as to our existence may fill us with such wonder that our minds will remain overwhelmed with wonder all the time. A Scotch ploughman makes a working religion out of a system which appalls a mental philosopher. Some boys of ten years of age study the methods of the differential calculus; other much cleverer boys working at mathematics to the age of nineteen have a difficulty in comprehending the fundamental ideas of the calculus.—PERRY, JOHN.
The Teaching of Mathematics (London, 1902), pp. 19–20.

520. Poor teaching leads to the inevitable idea that the subject [mathematics] is only adapted to peculiar minds, when it is the one universal science and the one whose four ground-rules are taught us almost in infancy and reappear in the motions of the universe.—SAFFORD, T. H.

> *Mathematical Teaching* (*Boston, 1907*), *p. 19.*

521. The number of mathematical students . . . would be much augmented if those who hold the highest rank in science would condescend to give more effective assistance in clearing the elements of the difficulties which they present.

> DE MORGAN, A.
> *Study and Difficulties of Mathematics* (*Chicago, 1902*), *Preface.*

522. He that could teach mathematics well, would not be a bad teacher in any of the rest [physics, chemistry, biology, psychology] unless by the accident of total inaptitude for experimental illustration; while the mere experimentalist is likely to fall into the error of missing the essential condition of science as reasoned truth; not to speak of the danger of making the instruction an affair of sensation, glitter, or pyrotechnic show.

> BAIN, ALEXANDER.
> *Education as a Science* (*New York, 1898*), *p. 298.*

523. I should like to draw attention to the inexhaustible variety of the problems and exercises which it [mathematics] furnishes; these may be graduated to precisely the amount of attainment which may be possessed, while yet retaining an interest and value. It seems to me that no other branch of study at all compares with mathematics in this. When we propose a deduction to a beginner we give him an exercise in many cases that would have been admired in the vigorous days of Greek geometry. Although grammatical exercises are well suited to insure the great benefits connected with the study of languages, yet these exercises seem to me stiff and artificial in comparison with the problems of mathematics. It is not absurd to maintain that Euclid and Apollonius would have regarded with interest many of the elegant deductions which are invented for the use of our students in geometry; but it seems scarcely conceivable

that the great masters in any other line of study could condescend to give a moment's attention to the elementary books of
the beginner.—TODHUNTER, ISAAC.

> *Conflict of Studies (London, 1873), pp. 10–11.*

524. The visible figures by which principles are illustrated
should, so far as possible, have no accessories. They should be
magnitudes pure and simple, so that the thought of the pupil
may not be distracted, and that he may know what features of
the thing represented he is to pay attention to.

> *Report of the Committee of Ten on Secondary
> School Subjects, (New York, 1894), p. 109.*

525. Geometrical reasoning, and arithmetical process, have
each its own office: to mix the two in elementary instruction,
is injurious to the proper acquisition of both.

> DE MORGAN, A.
> *Trigonometry and Double Algebra (London,
> 1849), p. 92.*

526. Equations are Expressions of Arithmetical Computation, and properly have no place in Geometry, except as far as
Quantities truly Geometrical (that is, Lines, Surfaces, Solids,
and Proportions) may be said to be some equal to others. Multiplications, Divisions, and such sort of Computations, are
newly received into Geometry, and that unwarily, and contrary
to the first Design of this Science. For whosoever considers the
Construction of a Problem by a right Line and a Circle, found
out by the first Geometricians, will easily perceive that Geometry was invented that we might expeditiously avoid, by drawing
Lines, the Tediousness of Computation. Therefore these two
Sciences ought not to be confounded. The Ancients did so in-
dustriously distinguish them from one another, that they never
introduced Arithmetical Terms into Geometry. And the Moderns, by confounding both, have lost the Simplicity in which all
the Elegance of Geometry consists. Wherefore that is *Arithmetically* more simple which is determined by the more simple
Equation, but that is *Geometrically* more simple which is determined by the more simple drawing of Lines; and in Geometry,

that ought to be reckoned best which is geometrically most simple.—NEWTON.

> *On the Linear Construction of Equations;*
> *Universal Arithmetic (London, 1769), Vol. 2,*
> *p. 470.*

527. As long as algebra and geometry proceeded along separate paths, their advance was slow and their applications limited.

But when these sciences joined company, they drew from each other fresh vitality and thenceforward marched on at a rapid pace toward perfection.—LAGRANGE.

> *Leçons Élémentaires sur les Mathematiques,*
> *Leçon cinquiéme. [McCormack].*

528. The greatest enemy to true arithmetic work is found in so-called practical or illustrative problems, which are freely given to our pupils, of a degree of difficulty and complexity altogether unsuited to their age and mental development. . . . I am, myself, no bad mathematician, and all the reasoning powers with which nature endowed me have long been as fully developed as they are ever likely to be; but I have, not infrequently, been puzzled, and at times foiled, by the subtle logical difficulty running through one of these problems, given to my own children. The head-master of one of our Boston high schools confessed to me that he had sometimes been unable to unravel one of these tangled skeins, in trying to help his own daughter through her evening's work. During this summer, Dr. Fairbairn, the distinguished head of one of the colleges of Oxford, England, told me that not only had he himself encountered a similar difficulty, in the case of his own children, but that, on one occasion, having as his guest one of the first mathematicians of England, the two together had been completely puzzled by one of these arithmetical conundrums.—WALKER, F. A.

> *Discussions in Education (New York, 1899),*
> *pp. 253-254.*

529. It is often assumed that because the young child is not competent to study geometry systematically he need be taught nothing geometrical; that because it would be foolish to present to him physics and mechanics as sciences it is useless to present to him any physical or mechanical principles.

An error of like origin, which has wrought incalculable mischief, denies to the scholar the use of the symbols and methods of algebra in connection with his early essays in numbers because, forsooth, he is not as yet capable of mastering quadratics! . . . The whole infant generation, wrestling with arithmetic, seek for a sign and groan and travail together in pain for the want of it; but no sign is given them save the sign of the prophet Jonah, *the withered gourd*, fruitless endeavor, wasted strength.—WALKER, F. A.

> *Industrial Education; Discussions in Education (New York, 1899), p. 132.*

530. Particular and contingent inventions in the solution of problems, which, though many times more concise than a general method would allow, yet, in my judgment, are less proper to instruct a learner, as acrostics, and such kind of artificial poetry, though never so excellent, would be but improper examples to instruct one that aims at Ovidean poetry.—NEWTON, ISAAC.

> *Letter to Collins, 1670; Macclesfield, Correspondence of Scientific Men (Oxford, 1841), Vol. 2, p. 307.*

531. The logic of the subject [algebra], which, both educationally and scientifically speaking, is the most important part of it, is wholly neglected. The whole training consists in example grinding. What should have been merely the help to attain the end has become the end itself. The result is that algebra, as we teach it, is neither an art nor a science, but an ill-digested farrago of rules, whose object is the solution of examination problems. . . . The result, so far as problems worked in examinations go, is, after all, very miserable, as the reiterated complaints of examiners show; the effect on the examinee is a well-known enervation of mind, an almost incurable superficiality, which might be called Problematic Paralysis—a disease which unfits a man to follow an argument extending beyond the length of a printed octavo page.—CHRYSTAL, GEORGE.

> *Presidential Address British Association for the Advancement of Science, 1885; Nature, Vol. 32, pp. 447–448.*

532. It is a serious question whether America, following England's lead, has not gone into problem-solving too extensively. Certain it is that we are producing no text-books in which the theory is presented in the delightful style which characterizes many of the French works . . . , or those of the recent Italian school, or, indeed, those of the continental writers in general.

SMITH, D. E.
The Teaching of Elementary Mathematics (New York, 1902), p. 219.

533. The problem for a writer of a text-book has come now, in fact, to be this—to write a book so neatly trimmed and compacted that no coach, on looking through it, can mark a single passage which the candidate for a minimum pass can safely omit. Some of these text-books I have seen, where the scientific matter has been, like the lady's waist in the nursery song, compressed "so gent and sma'," that the thickness barely, if at all, surpasses what is devoted to the publisher's advertisements. We shall return, I verily believe, to the Compendium of Martianus Capella. The result of all this is that science, in the hands of specialists, soars higher and higher into the light of day, while educators and the educated are left more and more to wander in primeval darkness.—CHRYSTAL, GEORGE.

Presidential Address British Association for the Advancement of Science, 1885; Nature, Vol. 32, p. 448.

534. Some persons have contended that mathematics ought to be taught by making the illustrations obvious to the senses. Nothing can be more absurd or injurious: it ought to be our never-ceasing effort to make people think, not feel.

COLERIDGE, S. T.
Lectures on Shakespere (Bohn Library), p. 52.

535. I have come to the conclusion that the exertion, without which a knowledge of mathematics cannot be acquired, is not materially increased by logical rigor in the method of instruction.—PRINGSHEIM, ALFRED.

Jahresbericht der Deutschen Mathematiker Vereinigung (1898), p. 143.

536. The only way in which to treat the elements of an exact and rigorous science is to apply to them all the rigor and exactness possible.—D'ALEMBERT.

> Quoted by De Morgan: Trigonometry and Double Algebra (London, 1849), Title page.

537. It is an error to believe that rigor in proof is an enemy of simplicity. On the contrary we find it confirmed by numerous examples that the rigorous method is at the same time the simpler and the more easily comprehended. The very effort for rigor forces us to find out simpler methods of proof.

> HILBERT, D.
> Mathematical Problems; Bulletin American Mathematical Society, Vol. 8, p. 441.

538. Few will deny that even in the first scientific instruction in mathematics the most rigorous method is to be given preference over all others. Especially will every teacher prefer a consistent proof to one which is based on fallacies or proceeds in a vicious circle, indeed it will be morally impossible for the teacher to present a proof of the latter kind consciously and thus in a sense deceive his pupils. Notwithstanding these objectionable so-called proofs, so far as the foundation and the development of the system is concerned, predominate in our textbooks to the present time. Perhaps it will be answered, that rigorous proof is found too difficult for the pupil's power of comprehension. Should this be anywhere the case,—which would only indicate some defect in the plan or treatment of the whole,—the only remedy would be to merely state the theorem in a historic way, and forego a proof with the frank confession that no proof has been found which could be comprehended by the pupil; a remedy which is ever doubtful and should only be applied in the case of extreme necessity. But this remedy is to be preferred to a proof which is no proof, and is therefore either wholly unintelligible to the pupil, or deceives him with an appearance of knowledge which opens the door to all superficiality and lack of scientific method.—GRASSMANN, HERMANN.

> Stücke aus dem Lehrbuche der Arithmetik; Werke, Bd. 2 (Leipsig, 1904), p. 296.

539. The average English author [of mathematical texts] leaves one under the impression that he has made a bargain with his reader to put before him the truth, the greater part of the truth, and nothing but the truth; and that if he has put the facts of his subject into his book, however difficult it may be to unearth them, he has fulfilled his contract with his reader. This is a very much mistaken view, because *effective teaching* requires a great deal more than a bare recitation of facts, even if these are duly set forth in logical order—as in English books they often are not. The probable difficulties which will occur to the student, the objections which the intelligent student will naturally and necessarily raise to some statement of fact or theory—these things our authors seldom or never notice, and yet a recognition and anticipation of them by the author would be often of priceless value to the student. Again, a touch of *humour* (strange as the contention may seem) in mathematical works is not only possible with perfect propriety, but very helpful; and I could give instances of this even from the pure mathematics of Salmon and the physics of Clerk Maxwell.—MINCHIN, G. M.

> *Perry's Teaching of Mathematics (London, 1902), pp. 59–61.*

540. Remember this, the rule for giving an extempore lecture is—let the the mind rest from the subject entirely for an interval preceding the lecture, after the notes are prepared; the thoughts will ferment without your knowing it, and enter into new combinations; but if you keep the mind active upon the subject up to the moment, the subject will not ferment but stupefy.

> DE MORGAN, A.
> *Letter to Hamilton; Graves: Life of W. R. Hamilton (New York, 1882–1889), Vol. 3, . p. 487.*

CHAPTER VI

601. The first thing to be attended to in reading any algebraic treatise is the gaining a perfect understanding of the different processes there exhibited, and of their connection with one another. This cannot be attained by the mere reading of the book, however great the attention which may be given. It is impossible in a mathematical work to fill up every process in the manner in which it must be filled up in the mind of the student before he can be said to have completely mastered it. Many results must be given of which the details are suppressed, such are the additions, multiplications, extractions of square roots, etc., with which the investigations abound. These must not be taken on trust by the student, but must be worked out by his own pen, which must never be out of his own hand while engaged in any mathematical process.—DE MORGAN, A.

> *Study and Difficulties of Mathematics (Chicago, 1902), chap. 12.*

602. The student should not lose any opportunity of exercising himself in numerical calculation and particularly in the use of logarithmic tables. His power of applying mathematics to questions of practical utility is in direct proportion to the facility which he possesses in computation.—DE MORGAN, A.

> *Study and Difficulties of Mathematics (Chicago, 1902), chap. 12.*

603. The examples which a beginner should choose for practice should be simple and should not contain very large numbers. The powers of the mind cannot be directed to two things at once; if the complexity of the numbers used requires all the student's attention, he cannot observe the principle of the rule which he is following.—DE MORGAN, A.

> *Study and Difficulties of Mathematics (Chicago, 1902), chap. 3.*

604. Euclid and Archimedes are allowed to be knowing, and to have demonstrated what they say: and yet whosoever shall read over their writings without perceiving the connection of their proofs, and seeing what they show, though he may understand all their words, yet he is not the more knowing. He may believe, indeed, but does not know what they say, and so is not advanced one jot in mathematical knowledge by all his reading of those approved mathematicians.—LOCKE, JOHN.
Conduct of the Understanding, sect. 24.

605. The student should read his author with the most sustained attention, in order to discover the meaning of every sentence. If the book is well written, it will endure and repay his close attention: the text ought to be fairly intelligible, even without illustrative examples. Often, far too often, a reader hurries over the text without any sincere and vigorous effort to understand it; and rushes to some example to clear up what ought not to have been obscure, if it had been adequately considered. The habit of scrupulously investigating the text seems to me important on several grounds. The close scrutiny of language is a very valuable exercise both for studious and practical life. In the higher departments of mathematics the habit is indispensable: in the long investigations which occur there it would be impossible to interpose illustrative examples at every stage, the student must therefore encounter and master, sentence by sentence, an extensive and complicated argument.
TODHUNTER, ISAAC.
Private Study of Mathematics; Conflict of Studies and other Essays (London, 1873), p. 67.

606. It must happen that in some cases the author is not understood, or is very imperfectly understood; and the question is what is to be done. After giving a reasonable amount of attention to the passage, let the student pass on, reserving the obscurity for future efforts. . . . The natural tendency of solitary students, I believe, is not to hurry away prematurely from a hard passage, but to hang far too long over it; the just pride that does not like to acknowledge defeat, and the strong will that cannot endure to be thwarted, both urge to a continuance of effort even when success seems hopeless. It is only by experience we gain the conviction that when the mind is thoroughly fatigued it has neither the power to continue with advantage its course in an assigned direction, nor elasticity to strike out a new path; but that, on the other hand, after being withdrawn for a time from the pursuit, it may return and gain the desired end.

TODHUNTER, ISAAC.
Private Study of Mathematics; Conflict of Studies and other Essays (London, 1873), p. 68.

607. Every mathematical book that is worth reading must be read "backwards and forwards," if I may use the expression. I would modify Lagrange's advice a little and say, "Go on, but often return to strengthen your faith." When you come on a hard or dreary passage, pass it over; and come back to it after you have seen its importance or found the need for it further on.

CHRYSTAL, GEORGE.
Algebra, Part 2 (Edinburgh, 1889), Preface, p. 8.

608. The large collection of problems which our modern Cambridge books supply will be found to be almost an exclusive peculiarity of these books; such collections scarcely exist in foreign treatises on mathematics, nor even in English treatises of an earlier date. This fact shows, I think, that a knowledge of mathematics may be gained without the perpetual working of examples. . . . Do not trouble yourselves with the examples, make it your main business, I might almost say your exclusive business, to understand the text of your author.

TODHUNTER, ISAAC.
Private Study of Mathematics; Conflict of Studies and other Essays (London, 1873), p. 74.

609. In my opinion the English excel in the art of writing text-books for mathematical teaching; as regards the clear exposition of theories and the abundance of excellent examples, carefully selected, very few books exist in other countries which can compete with those of Salmon and many other distinguished English authors that could be named.—CREMONA, L.
Projective Geometry [Leudesdorf] (Oxford, 1885), Preface.

610. The solution of fallacies, which give rise to absurdities, should be to him who is not a first beginner in mathematics an excellent means of testing for a proper intelligible insight into mathematical truth, of sharpening the wit, and of confining the judgment and reason within strictly orderly limits.—VIOLA, J.

> *Mathematische Sophismen (Wien, 1864), Vorwort.*

611. Success in the solution of a problem generally depends in a great measure on the selection of the most appropriate method of approaching it; many properties of conic sections (for instance) being demonstrable by a few steps of pure geometry which would involve the most laborious operations with trilinear co-ordinates, while other properties are almost self-evident under the method of trilinear co-ordinates, which it would perhaps be actually impossible to prove by the old geometry.—WHITWORTH, W. A.

> *Modern Analytic Geometry (Cambridge, 1866), p. 154.*

612. The deep study of nature is the most fruitful source of mathematical discoveries. By offering to research a definite end, this study has the advantage of excluding vague questions and useless calculations; besides it is a sure means of forming analysis itself and of discovering the elements which it most concerns us to know, and which natural science ought always to conserve.—FOURIER, J.

> *Théorie Analytique de la Chaleur, Discours Préliminaire.*

613. It is certainly true that all physical phenomena are subject to strictly mathematical conditions, and mathematical processes are unassailable in themselves. The trouble arises from the data employed. Most phenomena are so highly complex that one can never be quite sure that he is dealing with all the factors until the experiment proves it. So that experiment is rather the criterion of mathematical conclusions and must lead the way.—DOLBEAR, A. E.

> *Matter, Ether, Motion (Boston, 1894), p. 89.*

614. Students should learn to study at an early stage the great works of the great masters instead of making their minds sterile through the everlasting exercises of college, which are of no use whatever, except to produce a new Arcadia where indolence is veiled under the form of useless activity. . . . Hard study on the great models has ever brought out the strong; and of such must be our new scientific generation if it is to be worthy of the era to which it is born and of the struggles to which it is destined.—BELTRAMI.

> *Giornale di matematiche, Vol. 11, p. 153.*
> [*Young, J. W.*]

615. The history of mathematics may be instructive as well as agreeable; it may not only remind us of what we have, but may also teach us to increase our store. Says De Morgan, "The early history of the mind of men with regards to mathematics leads us to point out our own errors; and in this respect it is well to pay attention to the history of mathematics." It warns us against hasty conclusions; it points out the importance of a good notation upon the progress of the science; it discourages excessive specialization on the part of the investigator, by showing how apparently distinct branches have been found to possess unexpected connecting links; it saves the student from wasting time and energy upon problems which were, perhaps, solved long since; it discourages him from attacking an unsolved problem by the same method which has led other mathematicians to failure; it teaches that fortifications can be taken by other ways than by direct attack, that when repulsed from a direct assault it is well to reconnoitre and occupy the surrounding ground and to discover the secret paths by which the apparently unconquerable position can be taken.—CAJORI, F.

> *History of Mathematics (New York, 1897),*
> *pp. 1–2.*

616. The history of mathematics is important also as a valuable contribution to the history of civilization. Human progress is closely identified with scientific thought. Mathematical and physical researches are a reliable record of intellectual progress.—CAJORI, F.

> *History of Mathematics (New York, 1897),*
> *p. 4.*

617. It would be rash to say that nothing remains for discovery or improvement even in elementary mathematics, but it may be safely asserted that the ground has been so long and so thoroughly explored as to hold out little hope of profitable return for a casual adventurer.—TODHUNTER, ISAAC.

Private Study of Mathematics; Conflict of Studies and other Essays (London, 1873), p. 73.

618. We do not live in a time when knowledge can be extended along a pathway smooth and free from obstacles, as at the time of the discovery of the infinitesimal calculus, and in a measure also when in the development of projective geometry obstacles were suddenly removed which, having hemmed progress for a long time, permitted a stream of investigators to pour in upon virgin soil. There is no longer any browsing along the beaten paths; and into the primeval forest only those may venture who are equipped with the sharpest tools.—BURKHARDT, H.

Mathematisches und wissenschaftliches Denken; Jahresbericht der Deutschen Mathematiker Vereinigung, Bd. 11, p. 55.

619. Though we must not without further consideration condemn a body of reasoning merely because it is easy, nevertheless we must not allow ourselves to be lured on merely by easiness; and we should take care that every problem which we choose for attack, whether it be easy or difficult, shall have a useful purpose, that it shall contribute in some measure to the up-building of the great edifice.—SEGRE, CORRADI.

Some Recent Tendencies in Geometric Investigation; Rivista di Matematica (1891), p. 63. Bulletin American Mathematical Society, 1904, p. 465. [Young, J. W.].

620. No mathematician now-a-days sets any store on the discovery of isolated theorems, except as affording hints of an unsuspected new sphere of thought, like meteorites detached from some undiscovered planetary orb of speculation.

SYLVESTER, J. J.

Notes to the Exeter Association Address; Collected Mathematical Papers (Cambridge, 1908), Vol. 2, p. 715.

621. Isolated, so-called "pretty theorems" have even less value in the eyes of a modern mathematician than the discovery of a new "pretty flower" has to the scientific botanist, though the layman finds in these the chief charm of the respective sciences.—HANKEL, HERMANN.

> *Die Entwickelung der Mathematik in den letzten Jahrhunderten (Tübingen, 1884), p. 15.*

622. It is, so to speak, a scientific tact, which must guide mathematicians in their investigations, and guard them from spending their forces on scientifically worthless problems and abstruse realms, a tact which is closely related to *esthetic tact* and which is the only thing in our science which cannot be taught or acquired, and is yet the indispensable endowment of every mathematician.—HANKEL, HERMANN.

> *Die Entwickelung der Mathematik in den letzten Jahrhunderten (Tübingen, 1884), p. 21.*

623. The mathematician requires tact and good taste at every step of his work, and he has to learn to trust to his own instinct to distinguish between what is really worthy of his efforts and what is not; he must take care not to be the slave of his symbols, but always to have before his mind the realities which they merely serve to express. For these and other reasons it seems to me of the highest importance that a mathematician should be trained in no narrow school; a wide course of reading in the first few years of his mathematical study cannot fail to influence for good the character of the whole of his subsequent work.

> GLAISHER, J. W. L.
>
> *Presidential Address British Association for the Advancement of Science, Section A, (1890); Nature, Vol. 42, p. 467.*

624. As long as a branch of science offers an abundance of problems, so long it is alive; a lack of problems foreshadows extinction or the cessation of independent development.

> HILBERT, D.
>
> *Mathematical Problems; Bulletin American Mathematical Society, Vol. 8, p. 438.*

625. In mathematics as in other fields, to find one self lost in wonder at some manifestation is frequently the half of a new discovery.—DIRICHLET, P. G. L.
Werke, Bd. 2 (Berlin, 1897), p. 233.

626. The student of mathematics often finds it hard to throw off the uncomfortable feeling that his science, in the person of his pencil, surpasses him in intelligence,—an impression which the great Euler confessed he often could not get rid of. This feeling finds a sort of justification when we reflect that the majority of the ideas we deal with were conceived by others, often centuries ago. In a great measure it is really the intelligence of other people that confronts us in science.—MACH, ERNST.
Popular Scientific Lectures (Chicago, 1910), p. 196.

627. It is probably this fact [referring to the circumstance that the problems of the parallel axiom, the squaring of the circle, the solution of the equation of the fifth degree, have finally found fully satisfactory and rigorous solutions] along with other philosophical reasons that gives rise to the conviction (which every mathematician shares, but which no one has yet supported by proof) that every definite mathematical problem must necessarily be susceptible of an exact settlement, either in the form of an actual answer to the question asked, or by the proof of the impossibility of its solution and therewith the necessary failure of all attempts. . . . This conviction of the solvability of every mathematical problem is a powerful incentive to the worker. We hear within us the perpetual call: There is the problem. Seek its solution. You can find it by pure reason, for in mathematics there is no *ignorabimus*.—HILBERT, D.
Mathematical Problems; Bulletin American Mathematical Society, Vol. 8, pp. 444-445.

628. He who seeks for methods without having a definite problem in mind seeks for the most part in vain.—HILBERT, D.
Mathematical Problems; Bulletin American Mathematical Society, Vol. 8, p. 444.

629. A mathematical problem should be difficult in order to entice us, yet not completely inaccessible, lest it mock at our efforts. It should be to us a guide post on the mazy paths to hidden truths, and ultimately a reminder of our pleasure in the successful solution.—HILBERT, D.

> *Mathematical Problems; Bulletin American Mathematical Society, Vol. 8, p. 438.*

630. The great mathematicians have acted on the principle "*Divinez avant de demontrer*," and it is certainly true that almost all important discoveries are made in this fashion.

> KASNER, EDWARD.
> *The Present Problems in Geometry; Bulletin American Mathematical Society, Vol. 11, p. 285.*

631. "Divide *et impera*" is as true in algebra as in statecraft; but no less true and even more fertile is the maxim "auge *et impera*." The more to do or to prove, the easier the doing or the proof.—SYLVESTER, J. J.

> *Proof of the Fundamental Theorem of Invariants; Philosophic Magazine (1878), p. 186; Collected Mathematical Papers, Vol. 3, p. 126.*

632. As in the domains of practical life so likewise in science there has come about a division of labor. The individual can no longer control the whole field of mathematics: it is only possible for him to master separate parts of it in such a manner as to enable him to extend the boundaries of knowledge by creative research.—LAMPE, E.

> *Die reine Mathematik in den Jahren 1884–1899, p. 10.*

633. With the extension of mathematical knowledge will it not finally become impossible for the single investigator to embrace all departments of this knowledge? In answer let me point out how thoroughly it is ingrained in mathematical science that every real advance goes hand in hand with the invention of sharper tools and simpler methods which at the same time assist in understanding earlier theories and to cast aside some more complicated developments. It is therefore possible for the individual investigator, when he makes these sharper tools and simpler methods his own, to find his way more easily in the various branches of mathematics than is possible in any other science.—HILBERT, D.

Mathematical Problems; Bulletin American Mathematical Society, Vol. 8, p. 479.

634. It would seem at first sight as if the rapid expansion of the region of mathematics must be a source of danger to its future progress. Not only does the area widen but the subjects of study increase rapidly in number, and the work of the mathematician tends to become more and more specialized. It is, of course, merely a brilliant exaggeration to say that no mathematician is able to understand the work of any other mathematician, but it is certainly true that it is daily becoming more and more difficult for a mathematician to keep himself acquainted, even in a general way, with the progress of any of the branches of mathematics except those which form the field of his own labours. I believe, however, that the increasing extent of the territory of mathematics will always be counteracted by increased facilities in the means of communication. Additional knowledge opens to us new principles and methods which may conduct us with the greatest ease to results which previously were most difficult of access; and improvements in notation may exercise the most powerful effects both in the simplification and accessibility of a subject. It rests with the worker in mathematics not only to explore new truths, but to devise the language by which they may be discovered and expressed; and the genius of a great mathematician displays itself no less in the notation he invents for deciphering his subject than in the results attained. . . . I have great faith in the power of well-chosen notation to simplify complicated theories and to bring remote ones near and I think it is safe to predict that the increased knowledge of principles and the resulting improvements in the symbolic language of mathematics will always enable us to grapple satisfactorily with the difficulties arising from the mere extent of the subject.—GLAISHER, J. W. L.

Presidential Address British Association for the Advancement of Science, Section A., (1890), Nature, Vol. 42, p. 466.

635. Quite distinct from the theoretical question of the manner in which mathematics will rescue itself from the perils to which it is exposed by its own prolific nature is the practical problem of finding means of rendering available for the student the results which have been already accumulated, and making it possible for the learner to obtain some idea of the present state of the various departments of mathematics. . . . The great mass of mathematical literature will be always contained in Journals and Transactions, but there is no reason why it should not be rehdered far more useful and accessible than at present by means of treatises or higher text-books. The whole science suffers from want of avenues of approach, and many beautiful branches of mathematics are regarded as difficult and technical merely because they are not easily accessible. . . . I feel very strongly that any introduction to a new subject written by a competent person confers a real benefit on the whole science. The number of excellent text-books of an elementary kind that are published in this country makes it all the more to be regretted that we have so few that are intended for the advanced student. As an example of the higher kind of text-book, the want of which is so badly felt in many subjects, I may mention the second part of Prof. Chrystal's "Algebra" published last year, which in a small compass gives a great mass of valuable and fundamental knowledge that has hitherto been beyond the reach of an ordinary student, though in reality lying so close at hand. I may add that in any treatise or higher text-book it is always desirable that references to the original memoirs should be given, and, if possible, short historic notices also. I am sure that no subject loses more than mathematics by any attempt to dissociate it from its history.—GLAISHER, J. W. L.

Presidential Address British Association for
the Advancement of Science, Section A (1890);
Nature, Vol. 42, p. 466.

636. The more a science advances, the more will it be possible to understand immediately results which formerly could be demonstrated only by means of lengthy intermediate considerations: a mathematical subject cannot be considered as finally completed until this end has been attained.— GORDAN, PAUL.

Formensystem binärer Formen (Leipzig, 1875),
p. 2.

637. An old French geometer used to say that a mathematical theory was never to be considered complete till you had made it so clear that you could explain it to the first man you met in the street.—SMITH, H. J. S.

Nature, Vol. 8 (1873), p. 452.

638. In order to comprehend and fully control arithmetical concepts and methods of proof, a high degree of abstraction is necessary, and this condition has at times been charged against arithmetic as a fault. I am of the opinion that all other fields of knowledge require at least an equally high degree of abstraction as mathematics,—provided, that in these fields the foundations are also everywhere examined with the rigour and completeness which is actually necessary.—HILBERT, D.

Die Theorie der algebraischen Zahlkorper, Vorwort; Jahresbericht der Deutschen Mathematiker Vereinigung, Bd. 4.

639. The anxious precision of modern mathematics is necessary for accuracy, . . . it is necessary for research. It makes for clearness of thought and for fertility in trying new combinations of ideas. When the initial statements are vague and slipshod, at every subsequent stage of thought, common sense has to step in to limit applications and to explain meanings. Now in creative thought common sense is a bad master. Its sole criterion for judgment is that the new ideas shall look like the old ones, in other words it can only act by suppressing originality.—WHITEHEAD, A. N.

Introduction to Mathematics (New York, 1911), p. 157.

640. Mathematicians attach great importance to the elegance of their methods and their results. This is not pure dilettantism. What is it indeed that gives us the feeling of elegance in a solution, in a demonstration? It is the harmony of the diverse parts, their symmetry, their happy balance; in a word it is all that introduces order, all that gives unity, that permits us to see clearly and to comprehend at once both the *ensemble* and the details. But this is exactly what yields great results, in fact the more we see this aggregate clearly and at a single glance, the better we perceive its analogies with other neighboring objects, consequently the more chances we have of divining the possible generalizations. Elegance may produce the feeling of the unforeseen by the unexpected meeting of objects we are not accustomed to bring together; there again it is fruitful, since it thus unveils for us kinships before unrecognized. It is fruitful even when it results only from the contrast between the simplicity of the means and the complexity of the problem set; it makes us then think of the reason for this contrast and very often makes us see that chance is not the reason; that it is to be found in sòme unexpected law. In a word, the feeling of mathematical elegance is only the satisfaction due to any adaptation of the solution to the needs of our mind, and it is because of this very adaptation that this solution can be for us an instrument. Consequently this esthetic satisfaction is bound up with the economy of thought.—POINCARÉ, H.

> *The Future of Mathematics; Monist, Vol. 20, p. 80. [Halsted].*

641. The importance of a result is largely relative, is judged differently by different men, and changes with the times and circumstances. It has often happened that great importance has been attached to a problem merely on account of the difficulties which it presented; and indeed if for its solution it has been necessary to invent new methods, noteworthy artifices, etc., the science has gained more perhaps through these than through the final result. In general we may call important all investigations relating to things which in themselves are important; all those which have a large degree of generality, or which unite under a single point of view subjects apparently distinct, simplifying and elucidating them; all those which lead to results that promise to be the source of numerous consequences; etc.—SEGRE, CORRADI.

> *Some Recent Tendencies in Geometric Investigations. Rivista di Matematica, Vol. 1, p. 44. Bulletin American Mathematical Society, 1904, p. 444. [Young, J. W.].*

642. Geometric writings are not rare in which one would seek in vain for an idea at all novel, for a result which sooner or later might be of service, for anything in fact which might be destined to survive in the science; and one finds instead treatises on trivial problems or investigations on special forms which have absolutely no use, no importance, which have their origin not in the science itself but in the caprice of the author; or one finds applications of known methods which have already been made thousands of times; or generalizations from known results which are so easily made that the knowledge of the latter suffices to give at once the former. Now such work is not merely useless; it is actually harmful because it produces a real incumbrance in the science and an embarrassment for the more serious investigators; and because often it crowds out certain lines of thought which might well have deserved to be studied.

SEGRE, CORRADI.
On some Recent Tendencies in Geometric Investigations; Rivista di Matematica, 1891, p. 43. Bulletin American Mathematical Society, 1904, p. 443 [Young, J. W.].

643. A student who wishes now-a-days to study geometry by dividing it sharply from analysis, without taking account of the progress which the latter has made and is making, that student no matter how great his genius, will never be a whole geometer. He will not possess those powerful instruments of research which modern analysis puts into the hands of modern geometry. He will remain ignorant of many geometrical results which are to be found, perhaps implicitly, in the writings of the analyst. And not only will he be unable to use them in his own researches, but he will probably toil to discover them himself, and, as happens very often, he will publish them as new, when really he has only rediscovered them.—SEGRE, CORRADI.
On some recent Tendencies in Geometrical Investigations; Rivista di Matematica, 1891, p. 43. Bulletin American Mathematical Society, 1904, p. 443 [Young, J. W.].

644. Research may start from definite problems whose importance it recognizes and whose solution is sought more or less directly by all forces. But equally legitimate is the other method of research which only selects the field of its activity and, contrary to the first method, freely reconnoitres in the search for problems which are capable of solution. Different individuals will hold different views as to the relative value of these two methods. If the first method leads to greater penetration it is also easily exposed to the danger of unproductivity. To the second method we owe the acquisition of large and new fields, in which the details of many things remain to be determined and explored by the first method.—CLEBSCH, A.

> Zum Gedächtniss an Julius Plücker; Göttinger Abhandlungen, 16, 1871, Mathematische Classe, p. 6.

645. During a conversation with the writer in the last weeks of his life, *Sylvester* remarked as curious that notwithstanding he had always considered the bent of his mind to be rather analytical than geometrical, he found in nearly every case that the solution of an analytical problem turned upon some quite simple geometrical notion, and that he was never satisfied until he could present the argument in geometrical language.

MACMAHON, P. A.

> Proceedings London Royal Society, Vol. 63, p. 17.

646. The origin of a science is usually to be sought for not in any systematic treatise, but in the investigation and solution of some particular problem. This is especially the case in the ordinary history of the great improvements in any department of mathematical science. Some problem, mathematical or physical, is proposed, which is found to be insoluble by known methods. This condition of insolubility may arise from one of two causes: Either there exists no machinery powerful enough to effect the required reduction, or the workmen are not sufficiently expert to employ their tools in the performance of an entirely new piece of work. The problem proposed is, however, finally solved, and in its solution some new principle, or new application of old principles, is necessarily introduced. If a principle is brought to light it is soon found that in its application it is not necessarily limited to the particular question which occasioned its discovery, and it is then stated in an abstract form and applied to problems of gradually increasing generality.

Other principles, similar in their nature, are added, and the original principle itself receives such modifications and extensions as are from time to time deemed necessary. The same is true of new applications of old principles; the application is first thought to be merely confined to a particular problem, but it is soon recognized that this problem is but one, and generally a very simple one, out of a large class, to which the same process of investigation and solution are applicable. The result in both of these cases is the same. A time comes when these several problems, solutions, and principles are grouped together and found to produce an entirely new and consistent method; a nomenclature and uniform system of notation is adopted, and the principles of the new method become entitled to rank as a distinct science.—CRAIG, THOMAS.

> A Treatise on Projection, Preface. U. S. Coast and Geodetic Survey, Treasury Department Document, No. 61.

647. The aim of research is the discovery of the equations which subsist between the elements of phenomena.

> MACH, ERNST.
> Popular Scientific Lectures (Chicago, 1910), p. 205.

648. Let him [the author] be permitted also in all humility to add . . . that in consequence of the large arrears of algebraical and arithmetical speculations waiting in his mind their turn to be called into outward existence, he is driven to the alternative of leaving the fruits of his meditations to perish (as has been the fate of too many foregone theories, the still-born progeny of his brain, now forever resolved back again into the primordial matter of thought), or venturing to produce from time to time such imperfect sketches as the present, calculated to evoke the mental co-operation of his readers, in whom the algebraical instinct has been to some extent developed, rather than to satisfy the strict demands of rigorously systematic exposition.

> SYLVESTER, J. J.
> Philosophic Magazine (1863), p. 460.

649. In other branches of science, where quick publication seems to be so much desired, there may possibly be some excuse for giving to the world slovenly or ill-digested work, but there is no such excuse in mathematics. The form ought to be as

perfect as the substance, and the demonstrations as rigorous as those of Euclid. The mathematician has to deal with the most exact facts of Nature, and he should spare no effort to render his interpretation worthy of his subject, and to give to his work its highest degree of perfection. *"Pauca sed matura"* was Gauss's motto.—GLAISHER, J. W. L.
> *Presidential Address British Association for the Advancement of Science, Section A, (1890); Nature, Vol. 42, p. 467.*

650. It is the man not the method that solves the problem.
MASCHKE, H.
> *Present Problems of Algebra and Analysis; Congress of Arts and Sciences (New York and Boston, 1905), Vol. 1, p. 530.*

651. Today it is no longer questioned that the principles of the analysts are the more far-reaching. Indeed, the synthesists lack two things in order to engage in a general theory of algebraic configurations: these are on the one hand a definition of imaginary elements, on the other an interpretation of general algebraic concepts. Both of these have subsequently been developed in synthetic form, but to do this the essential principle of synthetic geometry had to be set aside. This principle which manifests itself so brilliantly in the theory of linear forms and the forms of the second degree, is the possibility of immediate proof by means of visualized constructions.— KLEIN, FELIX.
> *Riemannsche Flächen (Leipzig, 1906), Bd. 1, p. 234.*

652. Abstruse mathematical researches . . . are . . . often abused for having no obvious physical application. The fact is that the most useful parts of science have been investigated for the sake of truth, and not for their usefulness. A new branch of mathematics, which has sprung up in the last twenty years, was denounced by the Astronomer Royal before the University of Cambridge as doomed to be forgotten, on account of its uselessness. Now it turns out that the reason why we cannot go further in our investigations of molecular action is that we do not know enough of this branch of mathematics.—CLIFFORD, W. K.
> *Conditions of Mental Development; Lectures and Essays (London, 1901), Vol. 1, p. 115.*

653. In geometry, as in most sciences, it is very rare that an isolated proposition is of immediate utility. But the theories most powerful in practice are formed of propositions which curiosity alone brought to light, and which long remained useless without its being able to divine in what way they should one day cease to be so. In this sense it may be said, that in real science, no theory, no research, is in effect useless.—VOLTAIRE.

A Philosophical Dictionary, Article "Geometry"; (Boston, 1881), Vol. 1, p. 374.

654. Scientific subjects do not progress necessarily on the lines of direct usefulness. Very many applications of the theories of pure mathematics have come many years, sometimes centuries, after the actual discoveries themselves. The weapons were at hand, but the men were not able to use them.

FORSYTH, A. R.

Perry's Teaching of Mathematics (London, 1902), p. 35.

655. It is no paradox to say that in our most theoretical moods we may be nearest to our most practical applications.

WHITEHEAD, A. N.

Introduction to Mathematics (New York), p. 100.

656. Although with the majority of those who study and practice in these capacities [engineers, builders, surveyors, geographers, navigators, hydrographers, astronomers], second-hand acquirements, trite formulas, and appropriate tables are sufficient for ordinary purposes, yet these trite formulas and familiar rules were originally or gradually deduced from the profound investigations of the most gifted minds, from the dawn of science to the present day. . . . The further developments of the science, with its possible applications to larger purposes of human utility and grander theoretical generalizations, is an achievement reserved for a few of the choicest spirits, touched from time to time by Heaven to these highest issues. The intellectual world is filled with latent and undiscovered truth as the material world is filled with latent electricity.

EVERETT, EDWARD.

Orations and Speeches, Vol. 3 (Boston, 1870), p. 513.

657. If we view mathematical speculations with reference to their use, it appears that they should be divided into two classes. To the first belong those which furnish some marked advantage either to common life or to some art, and the value of such is usually determined by the magnitude of this advantage. The other class embraces those speculations which, though offering no direct advantage, are nevertheless valuable in that they extend the boundaries of analysis and increase our resources and skill. Now since many investigations, from which great advantage may be expected, must be abandoned solely because of the imperfection of analysis, no small value should be assigned to those speculations which promise to enlarge the field of anaylsis.—EULER.

Novi Comm. Petr., Vol. 4, Preface.

658. The discovery of the conic sections, attributed to Plato, first threw open the higher species of form to the contemplation of geometers. But for this discovery, which was probably regarded in Plato's time and long after him, as the unprofitable amusement of a speculative brain, the whole course of practical philosophy of the present day, of the science of astronomy, of the theory of projectiles, of the art of navigation, might have run in a different channel; and the greatest discovery that has ever been made in the history of the world, the law of universal gravitation, with its innumerable direct and indirect consequences and applications to every department of human research and industry, might never to this hour have been elicited.

SYLVESTER, J. J.

A Probationary Lecture on Geometry; Collected Mathematical Papers, Vol. 2 (Cambridge, 1908), p. 7.

659. No more impressive warning can be given to those who would confine knowledge and research to what is apparently useful, than the reflection that conic sections were studied for eighteen hundred years merely as an abstract science, without regard to any utility other than to satisfy the craving for knowledge on the part of mathematicians, and that then at the end of this long period of abstract study, they were found to be the

necessary key with which to attain the knowledge of the most
important laws of nature.—WHITEHEAD, A. N.
Introduction to Mathematics (New York,
York, 1911), pp. 136-137.

660. The Greeks in the first vigour of their pursuit of mathematical truth, at the time of Plato and soon after, had by no
means confined themselves to those propositions which had a
visible bearing on the phenomena of nature; but had followed
out many beautiful trains of research concerning various kinds
of figures, for the sake of their beauty alone; as for instance in
their doctrine of Conic Sections, of which curves they had discovered all the principal properties. But it is curious to remark,
that these investigations, thus pursued at first as mere matters
of curiosity and intellectual gratification, were destined, two
thousand years later, to play a very important part in establishing that system of celestial motions which succeeded the
Platonic scheme of cycles and epicycles. If the properties of
conic sections had not been demonstrated by the Greeks and
thus rendered familiar to the mathematicians of succeeding
ages, Kepler would probably not have been able to discover
those laws respecting the orbits and motions of planets which
were the occasion of the greatest revolution that ever happened
in the history of science.—WHEWELL, W.
History of Scientific Ideas, Bk. 2, chap. 14,
sect. 3.

661. The greatest mathematicians, as Archimedes, Newton,
and Gauss, always united theory and applications in equal
measure.—KLEIN, FELIX.
Elementarmathematik vom höheren Stand-
punkte aus (Leipzig, 1909), Bd. 2, p. 392.

662. We may see how unexpectedly recondite parts of pure
mathematics may bear upon physical science, by calling to
mind the circumstance that Fresnel obtained one of the most
curious confirmations of the theory (the laws of Circular Polari-
zation by reflection) through an interpretation of an algebraical
expression, which, according to the original conventional meaning of the symbols, involved an impossible quantity.

WHEWELL, W.
History of Scientific Ideas, Bk. 2, chap. 14, sect. 8.

663. A great department of thought must have its own inner life, however transcendent may be the importance of its relations to the outside. No department of science, least of all one requiring so high a degree of mental concentration as Mathematics, can be developed entirely, or even mainly, with a view to applications outside its own range. The increased complexity and specialisation of all branches of knowledge makes it true in the present, however it may have been in former times, that important advances in such a department as Mathematics can be expected only from men who are interested in the subject for its own sake, and who, whilst keeping an open mind for suggestions from outside, allow their thought to range freely in those lines of advance which are indicated by the present state of their subject, untrammelled by any preoccupation as to applications to other departments of science. Even with a view to applications, if Mathematics is to be adequately equipped for the purpose of coping with the intricate problems which will be presented to it in the future by Physics, Chemistry and other branches of physical science, many of these problems probably of a character which we cannot at present forecast, it is essential that Mathematics should be allowed to develop freely on its own lines.—HOBSON, E. W.

*Presidential Address British Association for
the Advancement of Science, Section A, (1910);
Nature, Vol. 84, p. 286.*

664. To emphasize this opinion that mathematicians would be unwise to accept practical issues as the sole guide or the chief guide in the current of their investigations, . . . let me take one more instance, by choosing a subject in which the purely mathematical interest is deemed supreme, the theory of functions of a complex variable. That at least is a theory in pure mathematics, initiated in that region, and developed in that region; it is built up in scores of papers, and its plan certainly has not been, and is not now, dominated or guided by considerations of applicability to natural phenomena. Yet what has turned out to be its relation to practical issues? The investigations of Lagrange and others upon the construction of maps appear as a portion of the general property of conformal representation; which is merely the general geometrical method of regarding functional relations in that theory. Again, the interesting and important investigations upon discontinuous two-dimensional fluid motion in hydrodynamics, made in the last twenty years, can all be, and now are all, I believe, deduced from similar considerations by interpreting functional relations between complex variables. In the dynamics of a rotating heavy body, the only substantial extension of our knowledge since the time of Lagrange has accrued from associating the general properties of functions with the discussion of the equations of motion. Further, under the title of conjugate functions, the theory has been applied to various questions in electrostatics, particularly in connection with condensors and electrometers. And, lastly, in the domain of physical astronomy, some of the most conspicuous advances made in the last few years have been achieved by introducing into the discussion the ideas, the principles, the methods, and the results of the theory of functions. . . . the refined and extremely difficult work of Poincaré and others in physical astronomy has been possible only by the use of the most elaborate developments of some purely mathematical subjects, developments which were made without a thought of such applications.—FORSYTH, A. R.

Presidential Address British Association for
the Advancement of Science, Section A, (1897);
Nature, Vol. 56, p. 377.

CHAPTER VII

701. Surely this is the golden age of mathematics.

PIERPONT, JAMES.
History of Mathematics in the Nineteenth Century; Congress of Arts and Sciences (Boston and New York, 1905), Vol. 1, p. 493.

702. The golden age of mathematics—that was not the age of Euclid, it is ours. Ours is the age when no less than six international congresses have been held in the course of nine years. It is in our day that more than a dozen mathematical societies contain a growing membership of more than two thousand men representing the centers of scientific light throughout the great culture nations of the world. It is in our time that over five hundred scientific journals are each devoted in part, while more than two score others are devoted exclusively, to the publication of mathematics. It is in our time that the *Jahrbuch über die Fortschritte der Mathematik*, though admitting only condensed abstracts with titles, and not reporting on all the journals, has, nevertheless, grown to nearly forty huge volumes in as many years. It is in our time that as many as two thousand books and memoirs drop from the mathematical press of the world in a single year, the estimated number mounting up to fifty thousand in the last generation. Finally, to adduce yet another evidence of a similar kind, it requires not less than seven ponderous tomes of the forthcoming *Encyclopaedie der Mathematischen Wissenschaften* to contain, not expositions, not demonstrations, but merely compact reports and bibliographic notices sketching developments that have taken place since the beginning of the nineteenth century.—KEYSER, C. J.
Lectures on Science, Philosophy and Art (New York, 1908), p. 8.

703. I have said that mathematics is the oldest of the sciences; a glance at its more recent history will show that it has the energy of perpetual youth. The output of contributions to the advance of the science during the last century and more has been so enormous that it is difficult to say whether pride in the greatness of achievement in this subject, or despair at his inability to cope with the multiplicity of its detailed developments, should be the dominant feeling of the mathematician. Few people outside of the small circle of mathematical specialists have any idea of the vast growth of mathematical literature. The Royal Society Catalogue contains a list of nearly thirty-nine thousand papers on subjects of Pure Mathematics alone, which have appeared in seven hundred serials during the nineteenth century. This represents only a portion of the total output, the very large number of treatises, dissertations, and monographs published during the century being omitted.

HOBSON, E. W.
Presidential Address British Association for the Advancement of Science, Section A, (1910); Nature, Vol. 84, p. 285.

704. Mathematics is one of the oldest of the sciences; it is also one of the most active, for its strength is the vigour of perpetual youth.—FORSYTH, A. R.
Presidential Address British Association for the Advancement of Science, Section A, (1897); Nature, Vol. 56, p. 378.

705. The nineteenth century which prides itself upon the invention of steam and evolution, might have derived a more legitimate title to fame from the discovery of pure mathematics.—RUSSELL, BERTRAND.
International Monthly, Vol. 4 (1901), p. 83.

706. One of the chiefest triumphs of modern mathematics consists in having discovered what mathematics really is.

RUSSELL, BERTRAND.
International Monthly, Vol. 4 (1901), p. 84.

707. Modern mathematics, that most astounding of intellectual creations, has projected the mind's eye through infinite time and the mind's hand into boundless space.—BUTLER, N. M.
The Meaning of Education and other Essays and Addresses (New York, 1905), p. 44.

708. The extraordinary development of mathematics in the last century is quite unparalleled in the long history of this most ancient of sciences. Not only have those branches of mathematics which were taken over from the eighteenth century steadily grown, but entirely new ones have sprung up in almost bewildering profusion, and many of them have promptly assumed proportions of vast extent.—PIERPONT, J.

> The History of Mathematics in the Nineteenth Century; Congress of Arts and Sciences (Boston and New York, 1905), Vol. 1, p. 474.

709. The Modern Theory of Functions—that stateliest of all the pure creations of the human intellect.—KEYSER, C. J.

> Lectures on Science, Philosophy and Art (New York, 1908), p. 16.

710. If a mathematician of the past, an Archimedes or even a Descartes, could view the field of geometry in its present condition, the first feature to impress him would be its lack of concreteness. There are whole classes of geometric theories which proceed not only without models and diagrams, but without the slightest (apparent) use of spatial intuition. In the main this is due, to the power of the analytic instruments of investigations as compared with the purely geometric.

> KASNER, EDWARD.
> The Present Problems in Geometry; Bulletin American Mathematical Society, 1905, p. 285.

711. In Euclid each proposition stands by itself; its connection with others is never indicated; the leading ideas contained in its proof are not stated; general principles do not exist. In modern methods, on the other hand, the greatest importance is attached to the leading thoughts which pervade the whole; and general principles, which bring whole groups of theorems under one aspect, are given rather than separate propositions. The whole tendency is toward generalization. A straight line is considered as given in its entirety, extending both ways to infinity, while Euclid is very careful never to admit anything but finite quantities. The treatment of the infinite is in fact another

fundamental difference between the two methods. Euclid avoids it, in modern mathematics it is systematically introduced, for only thus is generality obtained.—CAYLEY, ARTHUR.
Encyclopedia Britannica (9th edition), Article "Geometry."

712. This is one of the greatest advantages of modern geometry over the ancient, to be able, through the consideration of positive and negative quantities, to include in a single enunciation the several cases which the same theorem may present by a change in the relative position of the different parts of a figure. Thus in our day the nine principal problems and the numerous particular cases, which form the object of eighty-three theorems in the two books *De sectione determinata* of Appolonius constitute only one problem which is resolved by a single equation.
CHASLES, M.
Histoire de la Géométrie, chap. 1, sect. 35.

713. Euclid always contemplates a straight line as drawn between two definite points, and is very careful to mention when it is to be produced beyond this segment. He never thinks of the line as an entity given once for all as a whole. This careful definition and limitation, so as to exclude an infinity not immediately apparent to the senses, was very characteristic of the Greeks in all their many activities. It is enshrined in the difference between Greek architecture and Gothic architecture, and between Greek religion and modern religion. The spire of a Gothic cathedral and the importance of the unbounded straight line in modern Geometry are both emblematic of the transformation of the modern world.—WHITEHEAD, A. N.
Introduction to Mathematics (New York, 1911), p. 119.

714. The geometrical problems and theorems of the Greeks always refer to definite, oftentimes to rather complicated figures. Now frequently the points and lines of such a figure may assume very many different relative positions; each of these possible cases is then considered separately. On the contrary, present day mathematicians generate their figures one from another, and are accustomed to consider them subject to variation; in this manner they unite the various cases and combine them as much as possible by employing negative and imaginary magnitudes. For example, the problems which Appolonius treats in his two books *De sectione rationis*, are solved today by means of a single, universally applicable construction; Apollonius, on the contrary, separates it into more than eighty different cases varying only in position. Thus, as Hermann Hankel has fittingly remarked, the ancient geometry sacrifices to a seeming simplicity the true simplicity which consists in the unity of principles; it attained a trivial sensual presentability at the cost of the recognition of the relations of geometric forms in all their changes and in all the variations of their sensually presentable positions.—REYE, THEODORE.

> *Die synthetische Geometrie im Altertum und in der Neuzeit; Jahresbericht der Deutschen Mathematiker Vereinigung, Bd. 2, pp. 346–347.*

715. It is known that the mathematics prescribed for the high school [Gymnasien] is essentially Euclidean, while it is modern mathematics, the theory of functions and the infinitesimal calculus, which has secured for us an insight into the mechanism and laws of nature. Euclidean mathematics is indeed, a prerequisite for the theory of functions, but just as one, though he has learned the inflections of Latin nouns and verbs, will not thereby be enabled to read a Latin author much less to appreciate the beauties of a Horace, so Euclidean mathematics, that is the mathematics of the high school, is unable to unlock nature and her laws. Euclidean mathematics assumes the completeness and invariability of mathematical forms; these forms it describes with appropriate accuracy and enumerates their inherent and related properties with perfect clearness, order, and completeness, that is, Euclidean mathematics operates on forms after the manner that anatomy operates on the dead body and its members.

On the other hand, the mathematics of variable magnitudes—function theory or analysis—considers mathematical forms in their genesis. By writing the equation of the parabola, we express its law of generation, the law according to which the variable point moves. The path, produced before the eyes of the student by a point moving in accordance to this law, is the parabola.

If, then, Euclidean mathematics treats space and number forms after the manner in which anatomy treats the dead body, modern mathematics deals, as it were, with the living body, with growing and changing forms, and thus furnishes an insight, not only into nature as she is and appears, but also into nature as she generates and creates,—reveals her transition steps and in so doing creates a mind for and understanding of the laws of becoming. Thus modern mathematics bears the same relation to Euclidean mathematics that physiology or biology . . . bears to anatomy. But it is exactly in this respect that our view of nature is so far above that of the ancients; that we no longer look on nature as a quiescent complete whole, which compels admiration by its sublimity and wealth of forms, but that we conceive of her as a vigorous growing organism, unfolding according to definite, as delicate as far-reaching, laws; that we are able to lay hold of the permanent amidst the transitory, of law amidst fleeting phenomena, and to be able to give these their simplest and truest expression through the mathematical formulas.—DILLMANN, E.

> Die Mathematik die Fackelträgerin einer
> neuen Zeit (Stuttgart, 1889), p. 37.

716. The Excellence of *Modern Geometry* is in nothing more evident, than in those full and adequate Solutions it gives to Problems; representing all possible Cases in one view, and in one general Theorem many times comprehending whole Sciences; which deduced at length into Propositions, and demonstrated after the manner of the *Ancients*, might well become the subjects of large Treatises: For whatsoever Theorem solves the most complicated Problem of the kind, does with a due Reduction reach all the subordinate Cases.—HALLEY, E.

> An Instance of the Excellence of Modern Al-
> gebra, etc.; Philosophical Transactions, 1694,
> p. 960.

717. One of the most conspicuous and distinctive features of mathematical thought in the nineteenth century is its critical spirit. Beginning with the calculus, it soon permeates all analysis, and toward the close of the century it overhauls and recasts the foundations of geometry and aspires to further conquests in mechanics and in the immense domains of mathematical physics. . . . A searching examination of the foundations of arithmetic and the calculus has brought to light the insufficiency of much of the reasoning formerly considered as conclusive.—PIERPONT, J.

> *History of Mathematics in the Nineteenth Century; Congress of Arts and Sciences (Boston and New York, 1905), Vol. 1, p. 482.*

718. If we compare a mathematical problem with an immense rock, whose interior we wish to penetrate, then the work of the Greek mathematicians appears to us like that of a robust stonecutter, who, with indefatigable perseverance, attempts to demolish the rock gradually from the outside by means of hammer and chisel; but the modern mathematician resembles an expert miner, who first constructs a few passages through the rock and then explodes it with a single blast, bringing to light its inner treasures.—HANKEL, HERMANN.

> *Die Entwickelung der Mathematik in den letzten Jahrhunderten (Tübingen, 1884), p. 9.*

719. All the modern higher mathematics is based on a calculus of operations, on laws of thought. All mathematics, from the first, was so in reality; but the evolvers of the modern higher calculus have known that it is so. Therefore elementary teachers who, at the present day, persist in thinking about algebra and arithmetic as dealing with laws of number, and about geometry as dealing with laws of surface and solid content, are doing the best that in them lies to put their pupils on the wrong track for reaching in the future any true understanding of the higher algebras. Algebras deal not with laws of number, but with such laws of the human thinking machinery as have been discovered in the course of investigations on numbers. Plane geometry deals with such laws of thought as were discovered by men intent on finding out how to measure surface; and solid geometry with such additional laws of thought as were dis-

covered when men began to extend geometry into three dimensions.—BOOLE, M. E.
> *Logic of Arithmetic (Oxford, 1903), Preface, pp. 18–19.*

720. It is not only a decided preference for synthesis and a complete denial of general methods which characterizes the ancient mathematics as against our newer science [modern mathematics]: besides this external formal difference there is another real, more deeply seated, contrast, which arises from the different attitudes which the two assumed relative to the use of the concept of *variability*. For while the ancients, on account of considerations which had been transmitted to them from the philosophic school of the Eleatics, never employed the concept of motion, the spatial expression for variability, in their rigorous system, and made incidental use of it only in the treatment of phonoromically generated curves, modern geometry dates from the instant that Descartes left the purely algebraic treatment of equations and proceeded to investigate the variations which an algebraic expression undergoes when one of its variables assumes a continuous succession of values.—HANKEL, HERMANN.
> *Untersuchungen über die unendlich oft oszillierenden und unstetigen Functionen; Ostwald's Klassiker der exacten Wissenschaften, No. 153, pp. 44–45.*

721. Without doubt one of the most characteristic features of mathematics in the last century is the systematic and universal use of the complex variable. Most of its great theories received invaluable aid from it, and many owe their very existence to it.
> PIERPONT, J.
> *History of Mathematics in the Nineteenth Century; Congress of Arts and Sciences (Boston and New York, 1905), Vol. 1, p. 474.*

722. The notion, which is really the fundamental one (and I cannot too strongly emphasise the assertion), underlying and pervading the whole of modern analysis and geometry, is that of maginary magnitude in analysis and of imaginary space in geometry.—CAYLEY, ARTHUR.
> *Presidential Address; Collected Works, Vol. 11, p. 434.*

723. The solution of the difficulties which formerly surrounded the mathematical infinite is probably the greatest achievement of which our age has to boast.—RUSSELL, BERTRAND.

> The Study of Mathematics; Philosophical Essays (London, 1910), p. 77.

724. Induction and analogy are the special characteristics of modern mathematics, in which theorems have given place to theories and no truth is regarded otherwise than as a link in an infinite chain. "Omne exit in infinitum" is their favorite motto and accepted axiom.—SYLVESTER, J. J.

> A Plea for the Mathematician; Nature, Vol. 1, p. 261.

725. The conception of correspondence plays a great part in modern mathematics. It is the fundamental notion in the science of order as distinguished from the science of magnitude. If the older mathematics were mostly dominated by the needs of mensuration, modern mathematics are dominated by the conception of order and arrangement. It may be that this tendency of thought or direction of reasoning goes hand in hand with the modern discovery in physics, that the changes in nature depend not only or not so much on the quantity of mass and energy as on their distribution or arrangement.—MERZ, J. T.

> History of European Thought in the Nineteenth Century (Edinburgh and London, 1903), p. 736.

726. Now this establishment of correspondence between two aggregates and investigation of the propositions that are carried over by the correspondence may be called the central idea of modern mathematics.—CLIFFORD, W. K.

> Philosophy of the Pure Sciences; Lectures and Essays (London, 1901), Vol. 1, p. 402.

727. In our century the conceptions substitution and substitution group, transformation and transformation group, operation and operation group, invariant, differential invariant and differential parameter, appear more and more clearly as the most important conceptions of mathematics.—LIE, SOPHUS.

> Leipziger Berichte, No. 47 (1895), p. 261.

728. Generality of points of view and of methods, precision and elegance in presentation, have become, since Lagrange, the common property of all who would lay claim to the rank of scientific mathematicians. And, even if this generality leads at times to abstruseness at the expense of intuition and applicability, so that general theorems are formulated which fail to apply to a single special case, if furthermore precision at times degenerates into a studied brevity which makes it more difficult to read an article than it was to write it; if, finally, elegance of form has well-nigh become in our day the criterion of the worth or worthlessness of a proposition,—yet are these conditions of the highest importance to a wholesome development, in that they keep the scientific material within the limits which are necessary both intrinsically and extrinsically if mathematics is not to spend itself in trivialities or smother in profusion.—HANKEL, HERMANN.

Die Entwickelung der Mathematik in den letzten Jahrhunderten (Tübingen, 1884), pp. 14–15.

729. The development of abstract methods during the past few years has given mathematics a new and vital principle which furnishes the most powerful instrument for exhibiting the essential unity of all its branches.—YOUNG, J. W.

Fundamental Concepts of Algebra and Geomtry (New York, 1911), p. 225.

730. Everybody praises the incomparable power of the mathematical method, but so is everybody aware of its incomparable unpopularity.—ROSANES, J.

Jahresbericht der Deutschen Mathematiker Vereinigung, Bd. 13, p. 17.

731. Indeed the modern developments of mathematics constitute not only one of the most impressive, but one of the most characteristic, phenomena of our age. It is a phenomenon, however, of which the boasted intelligence of a "universalized" daily press seems strangely unaware; and there is no other great human interest, whether of science or of art, regarding which the mind of the educated public is permitted to hold so many fallacious opinions and inferior estimates.—KEYSER, C. J.

Lectures on Science, Philosophy and Arts (New York, 1908), p. 8.

732. It may be asserted without exaggeration that the domain of mathematical knowledge is the only one of which our otherwise omniscient journalism has not yet possessed itself.

PRINGSHEIM, ALFRED.

Ueber Wert und angeblichen Unwert der Mathematik; Jahresbericht der Deutschen Mathematiker Vereinigung, (1904) p. 357.

733. [The] inaccessibility of special fields of mathematics, except by the regular way of logically antecedent acquirements, renders the study discouraging or hateful to weak or indolent minds.—LEFEVRE, ARTHUR.

Number and its Algebra (Boston, 1903), sect. 223.

734. The majority of mathematical truths now possessed by us presuppose the intellectual toil of many centuries. A mathematician, therefore, who wishes today to acquire a thorough understanding of modern research in this department, must think over again in quickened tempo the mathematical labors of several centuries. This constant dependence of new truths on old ones stamps mathematics as a science of uncommon exclusiveness and renders it generally impossible to lay open to uninitiated readers a speedy path to the apprehension of the higher mathematical truths. For this reason, too, the theories and results of mathematics are rarely adapted for popular presentation . . . This same inaccessibility of mathematics, although it secures for it a lofty and aristocratic place among the sciences, also renders it odious to those who have never learned it, and who dread the great labor involved in acquiring an understanding of the questions of modern mathematics. Neither in the languages nor in the natural sciences are the investigations and results so closely interdependent as to make it impossible to acquaint the uninitiated student with single branches or with particular results of these sciences, without causing him to go through a long course of preliminary study.

SCHUBERT, H.

Mathematical Essays and Recreations (Chicago, 1898), p. 32.

735. Such is the character of mathematics in its profounder depths and in its higher and remoter zones that it is well nigh impossible to convey to one who has not devoted years to its exploration a just impression of the scope and magnitude of the existing body of the science. An imagination formed by other disciplines and accustomed to the interests of another field may scarcely receive suddenly an apocalyptic vision of that infinite interior world. But how amazing and how edifying were such a revelation, if it only could be made.—KEYSER, C. J.

> *Lectures on Science, Philosophy and Art (New York, 1908), p. 6.*

736. It is not so long since, during one of the meetings of the Association, one of the leading English newspapers briefly described a sitting of this Section in the words, "Saturday morning was devoted to pure mathematics, and so there was nothing of any general interest:" still, such toleration is better than undisguised and ill-informed hostility.—FORSYTH, A. R.

> *Report of the 67th meeting of the British Association for the Advancement of Science.*

737. The science [of mathematics] has grown to such vast proportion that probably no living mathematician can claim to have achieved its mastery as a whole.—WHITEHEAD, A. N.

> *An Introduction to Mathematics (New York, 1911), p. 252.*

738. There is perhaps no science of which the development has been carried so far, which requires greater concentration and will power, and which by the abstract height of the qualities required tends more to separate one from daily life.

> *Provisional Report of the American Subcommittee of the International Commission on the Teaching of Mathematics; Bulletin American Society (1910), p. 97.*

739. Angling may be said to be so like the mathematics, that it can never be fully learnt.—WALTON, ISAAC.

> *The Complete Angler, Preface.*

740. The flights of the imagination which occur to the pure mathematician are in general so much better described in his formulæ than in words, that it is not remarkable to find the subject treated by outsiders as something essentially cold and uninteresting— . . . the only successful attempt to invest mathematical reasoning with a halo of glory—that made in this section by Prof. Sylvester—is known to a comparative few, . . .

TAIT, P. G.

Presidential Address British Association for the Advancement of Science (1871); Nature Vol. 4, p. 271.

CHAPTER VIII

801. The real mathematician is an enthusiast *per se.* Without enthusiasm no mathematics.—NOVALIS.
Schriften (Berlin, 1901), Zweiter Teil, p. 223.

802. It is true that a mathematician, who is not somewhat of a poet, will never be a perfect mathematician.—WEIERSTRASS.
Quoted by Mittag-Leffler; Compte rendu du deuxième congrès international des mathématiciens (Paris, 1902), p. 149.

803. The mathematician is perfect only in so far as he is a perfect being, in so far as he perceives the beauty of truth; only then will his work be thorough, transparent, comprehensive, pure, clear, attractive and even elegant. All this is necessary to resemble *Lagrange.*—GOETHE.
Wilhelm Meister's Wanderjahre, Zweites Buch; Sprüche in Prosa; Natur, VI, 950.

804. A thorough advocate in a just cause, a penetrating mathematician facing the starry heavens, both alike bear the semblance of divinity.—GOETHE.
Wilhelm Meister's Wanderjahre, Zweites Buch. Sprüche in Prosa; Natur, VI, 947.

805. Mathematicians practice absolute freedom.
ADAMS, HENRY.
A Letter to American Teachers of History (Washington, 1910), p. 169.

806. The mathematical method is the essence of mathematics. He who fully comprehends the method is a mathematician.
NOVALIS.
Schriften (Berlin, 1901), Zweiter Teil, p. 190.

807. He who is unfamiliar with mathematics [literally, he who is a layman in mathematics] remains more or less a stranger to our time.—DILLMANN, E.
> *Die Mathematik die Fackelträgerin einer neuen Zeit (Stuttgart, 1889), p. 39.*

808. Enlist a great mathematician and a distinguished Grecian; your problem will be solved. Such men can teach in a dwelling-house as well as in a palace. Part of the apparatus they will bring; part we will furnish. [Advice given to the Trustees of Johns Hopkins University on the choice of a professorial staff.]—GILMAN, D. C.
> *Report of the President of Johns Hopkins University (1888), p. 29.*

809. Persons, who have a decided mathematical talent, constitute, as it were, a favored class. They bear the same relation to the rest of mankind that those who are academically trained bear to those who are not.—MOEBIUS, P. J.
> *Ueber die Anlage zur Mathematik (Leipzig, 1900), p. 4.*

810. One may be a mathematician of the first rank without being able to compute. It is possible to be a great computer without having the slightest idea of mathematics.—NOVALIS.
> *Schriften, Zweiter Teil (Berlin, 1901), p. 223.*

811. It has long been a complaint against mathematicians that they are hard to convince: but it is a far greater disqualification both for philosophy, and for the affairs of life, to be too easily convinced; to have too low a standard of proof. The only sound intellects are those which, in the first instance, set their standards of proof high. Practice in concrete affairs soon teaches them to make the necessary abatement: but they retain the consciousness, without which there is no sound practical reasoning, that in accepting inferior evidence because there is no better to be had, they do not by that acceptance raise it to completeness.—MILL, J. S.
> *An Examination of Sir William Hamilton's Philosophy (London, 1878), p. 611.*

812. It is easier to square the circle than to get round a mathematician.—DE MORGAN, A.
Budget of Paradoxes (London, 1872), p. 90.

813. Mathematicians are like Frenchmen: whatever you say to them they translate into their own language and forthwith it is something entirely different.—GOETHE.
Maximen und Reflexionen, Sechste Abtheilung.

814. What I chiefly admired, and thought altogether unaccountable, was the strong disposition I observed in them [the mathematicians of Laputa] towards news and politics; perpetually inquiring into public affairs; giving their judgments in matters of state; and passionately disputing every inch of party opinion. I have indeed observed the same disposition among most of the mathematicians I have known in Europe, although I could never discover the least analogy between the two sciences.—SWIFT, JONATHAN.
Gulliver's Travels, Part 3, chap. 2.

815. The great mathematician, like the great poet or naturalist or great administrator, is born. My contention shall be that where the mathematic endowment is found, there will usually be found associated with it, as essential implications in it, other endowments in generous measure, and that the appeal of the science is to the whole mind, direct no doubt to the central powers of thought, but indirectly through sympathy of all, rousing, enlarging, developing, emancipating all, so that the faculties of will, of intellect and feeling learn to respond, each in its appropriate order and degree, like the parts of an orchestra to the "urge and ardor" of its leader and lord.—KEYSER, C. J.
Lectures on Science, Philosophy and Art (New York, 1908), p. 22.

816. Whoever limits his exertions to the gratification of others, whether by personal exhibition, as in the case of the actor and of the mimic, or by those kinds of literary composition which are calculated for no end but to please or to entertain, renders himself, in some measure, dependent on their caprices and humours. The diversity among men, in their judgments concerning the objects of taste, is incomparably greater than in their speculative conclusions; and accordingly, a mathematician will publish to the world a geometrical demonstration, or a philosopher, a process of abstract reasoning, with a confidence very different from what a poet would feel, in communicating one of his productions even to a friend.—STEWART, DUGALD.

> Elements of the Philosophy of the Human Mind, Part 3, chap. 1, sect. 3.

817. Considering that, among all those who up to this time made discoveries in the sciences, it was the mathematicians alone who had been able to arrive at demonstrations—that is to say, at proofs certain and evident—I did not doubt that I should begin with the same truths that they have investigated, although I had looked for no other advantage from them than to accustom my mind to nourish itself upon truths and not to be satisfied with false reasons.—DESCARTES.

> Discourse upon Method, Part 2; Philosophy of Descartes [Torrey] (New York, 1892), p. 48.

818. When the late Sophus Lie . . . was asked to name the characteristic endowment of the mathematician, his answer was the following quaternion: Phantasie, Energie, Selbstvertrauen, Selbstkritik.—KEYSER, C. J.

> Lectures on Philosophy, Science and Art (New York, 1908), p. 31.

819. The existence of an extensive Science of Mathematics, requiring the highest scientific genius in those who contributed to its creation, and calling for the most continued and vigorous exertion of intellect in order to appreciate it when created, etc.

> MILL, J. S.
> System of Logic, Bk. 2, chap. 4, sect. 4.

820. It may be true, that men, who are *mere* mathematicians, have certain specific shortcomings, but that is not the fault of mathematics, for it is equally true of every other exclusive occupation. So there are *mere* philologists, *mere* jurists, *mere* soldiers, *mere* merchants, etc. To such idle talk it might further be added: that whenever a certain exclusive occupation is *coupled* with specific shortcomings, it is likewise almost certainly divorced from certain *other* shortcomings.—GAUSS.

Gauss-Schumacher Briefwechsel, Bd. 4,
(Altona, 1862), p. 387.

821. Mathematical studies . . . when combined, as they now generally are, with a taste for physical science, enlarge infinitely our views of the wisdom and power displayed in the universe. The very intimate connexion indeed, which, since the date of the Newtonian philosophy, has existed between the different branches of mathematical and physical knowledge, renders such a character as that of a *mere mathematician* a very rare and scarcely possible occurrence.—STEWART, DUGALD.

Elements of the Philosophy of the Human
Mind, part 3, chap. 1, sect. 3.

822. Once when lecturing to a class he [Lord Kelvin] used the word "mathematician," and then interrupting himself asked his class: "Do you know what a mathematician is?" Stepping to the blackboard he wrote upon it:—

$$\int_{-\infty}^{+\infty} e^{-x^2}\, dx = \sqrt{\pi}$$

Then putting his finger on what he had written, he turned to his class and said: "A mathematician is one to whom *that* is as obvious as that twice two makes four is to you. Liouville was a mathematician —THOMPSON, S. P.

Life of Lord Kelvin (London, 1910), p. 1139.

823. It is not surprising, in view of the polydynamic constitution of the genuinely mathematical mind, that many of the major heros of the science, men like Desargues and Pascal, Descartes and Leibnitz, Newton, Gauss and Bolzano, Helmholtz and Clifford, Riemann and Salmon and Plücker and Poincaré, have attained to high distinction in other fields not only of science but of philosophy and letters too. And when we reflect that the very greatest mathematical achievements have been due, not alone to the peering, microscopic, histologic vision of men like Weierstrass, illuminating the hidden recesses, the minute and intimate structure of logical reality, but to the larger vision also of men like Klein who survey the kingdoms of geometry and analysis for the endless variety of things that flourish there, as the eye of Darwin ranged over the flora and fauna of the world, or as a commercial monarch contemplates its industry, or as a statesman beholds an empire; when we reflect not only that the Calculus of Probability is a creation of mathematics but that the master mathematician is constantly required to exercise judgment—judgment, that is, in matters not admitting of certainty—balancing probabilities not yet reduced nor even reducible perhaps to calculation; when we reflect that he is called upon to exercise a function analogous to that of the comparative anatomist like Cuvier, comparing theories and doctrines of every degree of similarity and dissimilarity of structure; when, finally, we reflect that he seldom deals with a single idea at a time, but is for the most part engaged in wielding organized hosts of them, as a general wields at once the division of an army or as a great civil administrator directs from his central office diverse and scattered but related groups of interests and operations; then, I say, the current opinion that devotion to mathematics unfits the devotee for practical affairs should be known for false on *a priori* grounds. And one should be thus prepared to find that as a fact Gaspard Monge, creator of descriptive geometry, author of the classic "Applications de l'analyse à la géométrie"; Lazare Carnot, author of the celebrated works, "Géométrie de position," and "Réflections sur la Métaphysique du Calcul infinitesimal"; Fourier, immortal creator of the "Théorie analytique de la chaleur"; Arago, rightful inheritor of Monge's chair of geometry; Poncelet, creator of pure projective geometry; one should not be surprised, I say, to find that these and other mathematicians in a land sagacious enough to invoke their aid, rendered, alike in peace and in war, eminent public service.

KEYSER, C. J.

Lectures on Science, Philosophy and Art (New York, 1908), pp. 32–33.

824. If in Germany the goddess *Justitia* had not the unfortunate habit of depositing the ministerial portfolios only in the cradles of her own progeny, who knows how many a German mathematician might not also have made an excellent minister.

PRINGSHEIM, A.

Jahresbericht der Deutschen Mathematiker Vereinigung, Bd. 13 (1904), p. 372.

825. We pass with admiration along the great series of mathematicians, by whom the science of theoretical mechanics has been cultivated, from the time of Newton to our own. There is no group of men of science whose fame is higher or brighter. The great discoveries of Copernicus, Galileo, Newton, had fixed all eyes on those portions of human knowledge on which their successors employed their labors. The certainty belonging to this line of speculation seemed to elevate mathematicians above the students of other subjects; and the beauty of mathematical relations and the subtlety of intellect which may be shown in dealing with them, were fitted to win unbounded applause. The successors of Newton and the Bernoullis, as Euler, Clairaut, D'Alembert, Lagrange, Laplace, not to introduce living names, have been some of the most remarkable men of talent which the world has seen.—WHEWELL. W.

History of the Inductive Sciences, Vol. 1, Bk. 4, chap. 6, sect. 6.

826. The persons who have been employed on these problems of applying the properties of matter and the laws of motion to the explanation of the phenomena of the world, and who have brought to them the high and admirable qualities which such an office requires, have justly excited in a very eminent degree the admiration which mankind feels for great intellectual powers. Their names occupy a distinguished place in literary history; and probably there are no scientific reputations of the last century higher, and none more merited, than those earned by great mathematicians who have laboured with such wonderful success in unfolding the mechanism of the heavens; such for instance as D'Alembert, Clairaut, Euler, Lagrange, Laplace.

WHEWELL, W.

Astronomy and General Physics (London, 1833), Bk. 3, chap. 4, p. 327.

827. Two extreme views have always been held as to the use of mathematics. To some, mathematics is only measuring and calculating instruments, and their interest ceases as soon as discussions arise which cannot benefit those who use the instruments for the purposes of application in mechanics, astronomy, physics, statistics, and other sciences. At the other extreme we have those who are animated exclusively by the love of pure science. To them pure mathematics, with the theory of numbers at the head, is the only real and genuine science, and the applications have only an interest in so far as they contain or suggest problems in pure mathematics.

Of the two greatest mathematicians of modern times, Newton and Gauss, the former can be considered as a representative of the first, the latter of the second class; neither of them was exclusively so, and Newton's inventions in the science of pure mathematics were probably equal to Gauss's work in applied mathematics. Newton's reluctance to publish the method of fluxions invented and used by him may perhaps be attributed to the fact that he was not satisfied with the logical foundations of the Calculus; and Gauss is known to have abandoned his electro-dynamic speculations, as he could not find a satisfying physical basis. . . .

Newton's greatest work, the " Principia ", laid the foundation of mathematical physics; Gauss's greatest work, the " Disquisitiones Arithmeticae ", that of higher arithmetic as distinguished from algebra. Both works, written in the synthetic style of the ancients, are difficult, if not deterrent, in their form, neither of them leading the reader by easy steps to the results. It took twenty or more years before either of these works received due recognition; neither found favour at once before that great tribunal of mathematical thought, the Paris Academy of Sciences. . . .

The country of Newton is still pre-eminent for its culture of mathematical physics, that of Gauss for the most abstract work in mathematics.—MERZ, J. T.

History of European Thought in the Nineteenth Century (Edinburgh and London, 1903), p. 630.

828. As there is no study which may be so advantageously enter, d upon with a less stock of preparatory knowledge than mathematics, so there is none in which a greater number of uneducated men have raised themselves, by their own exertions, to distinction and eminence. . . . Many of the intellectual defects which, in such cases, are commonly placed to the account of mathematical studies, ought to be ascribed to the want of a liberal education in early youth.—STEWART, DUGALD.

Elements of the Philosophy of the Human Mind, Part 3, chap. 1, sect. 3.

829. I know, indeed, and can conceive of no pursuit so antagonistic to the cultivation of the oratorical faculty . . . as the study of Mathematics. An eloquent mathematician must, from the nature of things, ever remain as rare a phenomenon as a talking fish, and it is certain that the more anyone gives himself up to the study of oratorical effect the less will he find himself in a fit state to mathematicize. It is the constant aim of the mathematician to reduce all his expressions to their lowest terms, to retrench every superfluous word and phrase, and to condense the Maximum of meaning into the Minimum of language. He has to turn his eye ever inwards, to see everything in its dryest light, to train and inure himself to a habit of internal and impersonal reflection and elaboration of abstract thought, which makes it most difficult for him to touch or enlarge upon any of those themes which appeal to the emotional nature of his fellow-men. When called upon to speak in public he feels as a man might do who has passed all his life in peering through a microscope, and is suddenly called upon to take charge of a astronomical observatory. He has to get out of himself, as it were, and change the habitual focus of his vision.

SYLVESTER, J. J.

Baltimore Address; Mathematical Papers, Vol. 3, pp. 72–73.

830. An accomplished mathematician, i. e. a most wretched orator.—BARROW, ISAAC.

Mathematical Lectures (London, 1734), p. 32.

831. *Nemo mathematicus genium indemnatus habebit.* [No mathematician * is esteemed a genius until condemned.]
Juvenal, Liberii, Satura VI, 562.

832. Taking . . . the mathematical faculty, probably fewer than one in a hundred really possess it, the great bulk of the population having no natural ability for the study, or feeling the slightest interest in it.† And if we attempt to measure the amount of variation in the faculty itself between a first-class mathematician and the ordinary run of people who find any kind of calculation confusing and altogether devoid of interest, it is probable that the former could not be estimated at less than a hundred times the latter, and perhaps a thousand times would more nearly measure the difference between them.
WALLACE, A. R.
Darwinism, chap. 15.

833. . . . the present gigantic development of the mathematical faculty is wholly unexplained by the theory of natural selection, and must be due to some altogether distinct cause.
WALLACE, A. R.
Darwinism, chap. 15.

834. Dr. Wallace, in his " Darwinism ", declares that he can find no ground for the existence of pure scientists, especially mathematicians, on the hypothesis of natural selection. If we put aside the fact that great power in theoretical science is correlated with other developments of increasing brain-activity, we may, I think, still account for the existence of pure scientists as Dr. Wallace would himself account for that of worker-bees. Their function may not fit them individually to survive in the struggle for existence, but they are a source of strength and efficiency to the society which produces them.—PEARSON, KARL.
Grammar of Science (London, 1911), Part 1,
p. 221.

* Used here in the sense of astrologer, or soothsayer.
† This is the estimate furnished me by two mathematical masters in one of our great public schools of the proportion of boys who have any special taste or capacity for mathematical studies. Many more, of course, can be drilled into a fair knowledge of elementary mathematics, but only this small proportion possess the natural faculty which renders it possible for them ever to rank high as mathematicians, to take any pleasure in it, or to do any original mathematical work.

835. It is only in mathematics, and to some extent in poetry, that originality may be attained at an early age, but even then it is very rare (Newton and Keats are examples), and it is not notable until adolescence is completed.—ELLIS, HAVELOCK.
A Study of British Genius (London, 1904), p. 142.

836. The Anglo-Dane appears to possess an aptitude for mathematics which is not shared by the native of any other English district as a whole, and it is in the exact sciences that the Anglo-Dane triumphs.*—ELLIS, HAVELOCK.
A Study of British Genius (London, 1904), p. 69.

837. In the whole history of the world there was never a race with less liking for abstract reasoning than the Anglo-Saxon. . . . Common-sense and compromise are believed in, logical deductions from philosophical principles are looked upon with suspicion, not only by legislators, but by all our most learned professional men.—PERRY, JOHN.
The Teaching of Mathematics (London, 1902), pp. 20–21.

838. The degree of exactness of the intuition of space may be different in different individuals, perhaps even in different races. It would seem as if a strong naïve space-intuition were an attribute pre-eminently of the Teutonic race, while the critical, purely logical sense is more fully developed in the Latin and Hebrew races. A full investigation of this subject, somewhat on the lines suggested by *Francis Galton* in his researches on heredity, might be interesting.—KLEIN, FELIX.
The Evanston Colloquium Lectures (New York, 1894), p. 46.

839. This [the fact that the pursuit of mathematics brings into harmonious action all the faculties of the human mind] accounts for the extraordinary longevity of all the greatest masters of the Analytic art, the Dii Majores of the mathematical

---

* The mathematical tendencies of Cambridge are due to the fact that Cambridge drains the ability of nearly the whole Anglo-Danish district.

Pantheon. Leibnitz lived to the age of 70; Euler to 76; Lagrange to 77; Laplace to 78; Gauss to 78; Plato, the supposed inventor of the conic sections, who made mathematics his study and delight, who called them the handles or aids to philosophy, the medicine of the soul, and is said never to have let a day go by without inventing some new theorems, lived to 82; Newton, the crown and glory of his race, to 85; Archimedes, the nearest akin, probably, to Newton in genius, was 75, and might have lived on to be 100, for aught we can guess to the contrary, when he was slain by the impatient and ill-mannered sergeant, sent to bring him before the Roman general, in the full vigour of his faculties, and in the very act of working out a problem; Pythagoras, in whose school, I believe, the word mathematician (used, however, in a somewhat wider than its present sense) originated, the second founder of geometry, the inventor of the matchless theorem which goes by his name, the pre-cognizer of the undoubtedly mis-called Copernican theory, the discoverer of the regular solids and the musical canon who stands at the very apex of this pyramid of fame, (if we may credit the tradition) after spending 22 years studying in Egypt, and 12 in Babylon, opened school when 56 or 57 years old in Magna Grӕcia, married a young wife when past 60, and died, carrying on his work with energy unspent to the last, at the age of 99. The mathematician lives long and lives young; the wings of his soul do not early drop off, nor do its pores become clogged with the earthy particles blown from the dusty highways of vulgar life.—SYLVESTER, J. J.

> *Presidential Address to the British Association;*
> *Collected Mathematical Papers, Vol. 2 (1908),*
> *p. 658.*

840. The game of chess has always fascinated mathematicians, and there is reason to suppose that the possession of great powers of playing that game is in many features very much like the possession of great mathematical ability. There are the different pieces to learn, the pawns, the knights, the bishops, the castles, and the queen and king. The board possesses certain possible combinations of squares, as in rows, diagonals, etc. The pieces are subject to certain rules by which their motions are governed, and there are other rules governing the players. . . .

One has only to increase the number of pieces, to enlarge the field of the board, and to produce new rules which are to govern either the pieces or the player, to have a pretty good idea of what mathematics consists.—SHAW, J. B.

What is Mathematics? *Bulletin American Mathematical Society Vol. 18 (1912), pp. 386–387.*

841. Every man is ready to join in the approval or condemnation of a philosopher or a statesman, a poet or an orator, an artist or an architect. But who can judge of a mathematician? Who will write a review of Hamilton's Quaternions, and show us wherein it is superior to Newton's Fluxions?—HILL, THOMAS.

Imagination in Mathematics; North American Review, Vol. 85, p. 224.

842. The pursuit of mathematical science makes its votary appear singularly indifferent to the ordinary interests and cares of men. Seeking eternal truths, and finding his pleasures in the realities of form and number, he has little interest in the disputes and contentions of the passing hour. His views on social and political questions partake of the grandeur of his favorite contemplations, and, while careful to throw his mite of influence on the side of right and truth, he is content to abide the workings of those general laws by which he doubts not that the fluctuations of human history are as unerringly guided as are the perturbations of the planetary hosts.—HILL, THOMAS.

Imagination in Mathematics; North American Review, Vol. 85, p. 227.

843. There is something sublime in the secrecy in which the really great deeds of the mathematician are done. No popular applause follows the act; neither contemporary nor succeeding generations of the people understand it. The geometer must be tried by his peers, and those who truly deserve the title of geometer or analyst have usually been unable to find so many as twelve living peers to form a jury. Archimedes so far outstripped his competitors in the race, that more than a thousand years elapsed before any man appeared, able to sit in judgment on his work, and to say how far he had really gone. And in judging of those men whose names are worthy of being mentioned in connection with his,—Galileo, Descartes, Leibnitz, Newton, and the mathematicians created by Leibnitz and Newton's calculus,—we are forced to depend upon their testimony of one another. They are too far above our reach for us to judge of them.—HILL, THOMAS.

Imagination in Mathematics; North American Review, Vol. 85, p. 223.

844. To think the thinkable—that is the mathematician's aim.—KEYSER, C. J.

The Universe and Beyond; Hibbert Journal, Vol. 3 (1904–1905), p. 312.

845. Every common mechanic has something to say in his craft about good and evil, useful and useless, but these practical considerations never enter into the purview of the mathematician.—ARISTIPPUS THE CYRENAIC.

Quoted in Hicks, R. D., Stoic and Epicurean, (New York, 1910) p. 210.

CHAPTER IX

(A–M)

901. Alexander is said to have asked Menæchmus to teach him geometry concisely, but Menæchmus replied: "O king, through the country there are royal roads and roads for common citizens, but in geometry there is one road for all."

Stobæus (*Edition Wachsmuth, Berlin, 1884*),
Ecl. 2, p. 30.

902. Alexander the king of the Macedonians, began like a wretch to learn geometry, that he might know how little the earth was, whereof he had possessed very little. Thus, I say, like a wretch for this, because he was to understand that he did bear a false surname. For who can be great in so small a thing? Those things that were delivered were subtile, and to be learned by diligent attention: not which that mad man could perceive, who sent his thoughts beyond the ocean sea. Teach me, saith he, easy things. To whom his master said: These things be the same, and alike difficult unto all. Think thou that the nature of things saith this. These things whereof thou complainest, they are the same unto all: more easy things can be given unto none; but whosoever will, shall make those things more easy unto himself. How? With uprightness of mind.

SENECA.
Epistle 91 [*Thomas Lodge*].

903. Archimedes . . . had stated that given the force, any given weight might be moved, and even boasted, we are told, relying on the strength of demonstration, that if there were another earth, by going into it he could remove this. Hiero being struck with amazement at this, and entreating him to make good this problem by actual experiment, and show some great weight moved by a small engine, he fixed accordingly upon a ship of burden out of the king's arsenal, which could not be drawn out of the dock without great labor and many men; and, loading her with many passengers and a full freight, sitting himself the while far off with no great endeavor, but only holding the head of the pulley in his hand and drawing the cords by degrees, he drew the ship in a straight line, as smoothly and evenly, as if she had been in the sea. The king, astonished at this, and convinced of the power of the art, prevailed upon Archimedes to make him engines accommodated to all the purposes, offensive and defensive, of a siege. . . . the apparatus was, in most opportune time, ready at hand for the Syracusans, and with it also the engineer himself.—PLUTARCH.

Life of Marcellus [Dryden].

904. These machines [used in the defense of the Syracusans against the Romans under Marcellus] he [Archimedes] had designed and contrived, not as matters of any importance, but as mere amusements in geometry; in compliance with king Hiero's desire and request, some time before, that he should reduce to practice some part of his admirable speculation in science, and by accommodating the theoretic truth to sensation and ordinary use, bring it more within the appreciation of people in general. Eudoxus and Archytas had been the first originators of this far-famed and highly-prized art of mechanics, which they employed as an elegant illustration of geometrical truths, and as means of sustaining experimentally, to the satisfaction of the senses, conclusions too intricate for proof by words and diagrams. As, for example, to solve the problem, so often required in constructing geometrical figures, given the two extremes, to find the two mean lines of a proportion, both these mathematicians had recourse to the aid of instruments, adapting to their purpose certain curves and sections of lines. But what with Plato's indignation at it, and his invectives against it as the mere corruption and annihilation of the one good of geometry,—which was thus shamefully turning its back upon the unembodied objects of pure intelligence to recur to sensation, and to ask help (not to be obtained without base supervisions and depravation) from matter; so it was that mechanics came to be separated from geometry, and, repudiated and neglected by philosophers, took its place as a military art.

PLUTARCH.
Life of Marcellus [Dryden].

905. Archimedes was not free from the prevailing notion that geometry was degraded by being employed to produce anything useful. It was with difficulty that he was induced to stoop from speculation to practice. He was half ashamed of those inventions which were the wonder of hostile nations, and always spoke of them slightingly as mere amusements, as trifles in which a mathematician might be suffered to relax his mind after intense application to the higher parts of his science.

MACAULAY.

Lord Bacon; Edinburgh Review, July 1837;
Critical and Miscellaneous Essays (New York,
1879), Vol. 1, p. 380.

906. Call Archimedes from his buried tomb
Upon the plain of vanished Syracuse,
And feelingly the sage shall make report
How insecure, how baseless in itself,
Is the philosophy, whose sway depends
On mere material instruments—how weak
Those arts, and high inventions, if unpropped
By virtue.—WORDSWORTH.

The Excursion.

907. Zu Archimedes kam einst ein wissbegieriger Jüngling.
"Weihe mich," sprach er zu ihm, "ein in die göttliche
Kunst,
Die so herrliche Frucht dem Vaterlande getragen,
Und die Mauern der Stadt vor der Sambuca bes-
chützt!"
"Göttlich nennst du die Kunst? Sie ists," versetzte der
Weise;
"Aber das war sie, mein Sohn, eh sie dem Staat noch
gedient.
Willst du nur Früchte von ihr, die kann auch die Ster-
bliche zeugen;
Wer um die Göttin freit, suche in ihr nicht das Weib."

SCHILLER.

Archimedes und der Schüler.

[To Archimedes once came a youth intent upon knowledge.

Said he "Initiate me into the Science divine,
Which to our country has borne glorious fruits in abundance,
And which the walls of the town 'gainst the Sambuca
protects."
"Callst thou the science divine? It is so," the wise man
responded;
"But so it was, my son, ere the state by her service was
blest.
Would'st thou have fruit of her only? Mortals with that
can provide thee,
He who the goddess would woo, seek not the woman in
her."]

908. Archimedes possessed so high a spirit, so profound a
soul, and such treasures of highly scientific knowledge, that
though these inventions [used to defend Syracuse against the
Romans] had now obtained him the renown of more than human
sagacity, he yet would not deign to leave behind him any com-
mentary or writing on such subjects; but, repudiating as sordid
and ignoble the whole trade of engineering, and every sort of
art that lends itself to mere use and profit, he placed his whole
affection and ambition in those purer speculations where there
can be no reference to the vulgar needs of life; studies, the
superiority of which to all others is unquestioned, and in which
the only doubt can be whether the beauty and grandeur of the
subjects examined, or the precision and cogency of the methods
and means of proof, most deserve our admiration.—PLUTARCH.
Life of Marcellus [*Dryden*].

909. Nothing afflicted Marcellus so much as the death of
Archimedes, who was then, as fate would have it, intent upon
working out some problem by a diagram, and having fixed his
mind alike and his eyes upon the subject of his speculation, he
never noticed the incursion of the Romans, nor that the city was
taken. In this transport of study and contemplation, a soldier,
unexpectedly coming up to him, commanded him to follow to

Marcellus, which he declined to do before he had worked out his problem to a demonstration; the soldier, enraged, drew his sword and ran him through. Others write, that a Roman soldier, running upon him with a drawn sword, offered to kill him; and that Archimedes, looking back, earnestly besought him to hold his hand a little while, that he might not leave what he was at work upon inconclusive and imperfect; but the soldier, nothing moved by his entreaty, instantly killed him. Others again relate, that as Archimedes was carrying to Marcellus mathematical instruments, dials, spheres, and angles, by which the magnitude of the sun might be measured to the sight, some soldiers seeing him, and thinking that he carried gold in a vessel, slew him. Certain it is, that his death was very afflicting to Marcellus; and that Marcellus ever after regarded him that killed him as a murderer; and that he sought for his kindred and honoured them with signal favours.—PLUTARCH.

Life of Marcellus [Dryden].

910. [Archimedes] is said to have requested his friends and relations that when he was dead, they would place over his tomb a sphere containing a cylinder, inscribing it with the ratio which the containing solid bears to the contained.—PLUTARCH.

Life of Marcellus [Dryden].

911. Archimedes, who combined a genius for mathematics with a physical insight, must rank with Newton, who lived nearly two thousand years later, as one of the founders of mathematical physics. . . . The day (when having discovered his famous principle of hydrostatics he ran through the streets shouting Eureka! Eureka!) ought to be celebrated as the birthday of mathematical physics; the science came of age when Newton sat in his orchard.—WHITEHEAD, A. N.

An Introduction to Mathematics (New York, 1911), p. 38.

912. It is not possible to find in all geometry more difficult and more intricate questions or more simple and lucid explanations [than those given by Archimedes]. Some ascribe this to his natural genius; while others think that incredible effort and toil produced these, to all appearance, easy and unlaboured results. No amount of investigation of yours would succeed in attaining the proof, and yet, once seen, you immediately believe you would have discovered it; by so smooth and so rapid a path he leads you to the conclusion required.—PLUTARCH.

Life of Marcellus [*Dryden*].

913. One feature which will probably most impress the mathematician accustomed to the rapidity and directness secured by the generality of modern methods is the *deliberation* with which Archimedes approaches the solution of any one of his main problems. Yet this very characteristic, with its incidental effects, is calculated to excite the more admiration because the method suggests the tactics of some great strategist who foresees everything, eliminates everything not immediately conducive to the execution of his plan, masters every position in its order, and then suddenly (when the very elaboration of the scheme has almost obscured, in the mind of the spectator, its ultimate object) strikes the final blow. Thus we read in Archimedes proposition after proposition the bearing of which is not immediately obvious but which we find infallibly used later on; and we are led by such easy stages that the difficulties of the original problem, as presented at the outset, are scarcely appreciated. As Plutarch says: "It is not possible to find in geometry more difficult and troublesome questions, or more simple and lucid explanations." But it is decidedly a rhetorical exaggeration when Plutarch goes on to say that we are deceived by the easiness of the successive steps into the belief that anyone could have discovered them for himself. On the contrary, the studied simplicity and the perfect finish of the treatises involve at the same time an element of mystery. Though each step depends on the preceding ones, we are left in the dark as to how they were suggested to Archimedes. There is, in fact, much truth in a remark by Wallis to the effect that he seems "as it were of set purpose to have covered up the traces of his investigation as if he had grudged posterity the secret of his method of inquiry while he wished to extort from them assent to his results." Wallis adds with equal reason that not only Archimedes but nearly all the ancients so hid away from posterity their method of Analysis (though it is certain that they had one) that more modern mathematicians found it easier to invent a new Analysis than to seek out the old.—HEATH, T. L.

The Works of Archimedes (Cambridge, 1897), Preface.

914. It is a great pity Aristotle had not understood mathematics as well as Mr. Newton, and made use of it in his natural philosophy with good success: his example had then authorized the accommodating of it to material things.—LOCKE, JOHN.

Second Reply to the Bishop of Worcester.

915. The opinion of Bacon on this subject [geometry] was diametrically opposed to that of the ancient philosophers. He valued geometry chiefly, if not solely, on account of those uses, which to Plato appeared so base. And it is remarkable that the longer Bacon lived the stronger this feeling became. When in 1605 he wrote the two books on the Advancement of Learning, he dwelt on the advantages which mankind derived from mixed mathematics; but he at the same time admitted that the beneficial effect produced by mathematical study on the intellect, though a collateral advantage, was "no less worthy than that which was principal and intended." But it is evident that his views underwent a change. When near twenty years later, he published the *De Augmentis*, which is the Treatise on the Advancement of Learning, greatly expanded and carefully corrected, he made important alterations in the part which related to mathematics. He condemned with severity the pretensions of the mathematicians, "*delicias et fastum mathematicorum.*" Assuming the well-being of the human race to be the end of knowledge, he pronounced that mathematical science could claim no higher rank than that of an appendage or an auxiliary to other sciences. Mathematical science, he says, is the handmaid of natural philosophy; she ought to demean herself as such; and he declares that he cannot conceive by what ill chance it has happened that she presumes to claim precedence over her mistress.—MACAULAY.

Lord Bacon: Edinburgh Review, July, 1837; Critical and Miscellaneous Essays (New York, 1879), Vol. 1, p. 380.

916. If Bacon erred here [in valuing mathematics only for its uses], we must acknowledge that we greatly prefer his error to the opposite error of Plato. We have no patience with a philosophy which, like those Roman matrons who swallowed abortives in order to preserve their shapes, takes pains to be barren for fear of being homely.—MACAULAY.

> Lord Bacon, Edinburgh Review, July, 1837;
> Critical and Miscellaneous Essays (New York,
> 1879), Vol. 2, p. 381.

917. He [Lord Bacon] appears to have been utterly ignorant of the discoveries which had just been made by Kepler's calculations . . . he does not say a word about Napier's Logarithms, which had been published only nine years before and reprinted more than once in the interval. He complained that no considerable advance had been made in Geometry beyond Euclid, without taking any notice of what had been done by Archimedes and Apollonius. He saw the importance of determining accurately the specific gravities of different substances, and himself attempted to form a table of them by a rude process of his own, without knowing of the more scientific though still imperfect methods previously employed by Archimedes, Ghetaldus and Porta. He speaks of the εὕρηκα of Archimedes in a manner which implies that he did not clearly appreciate either the problem to be solved or the principles upon which the solution depended. In reviewing the progress of Mechanics, he makes no mention either of Archimedes, or Stevinus, Galileo, Guldinus, or Ghetaldus. He makes no allusion to the theory of Equilibrium. He observes that a ball of one pound weight will fall nearly as fast through the air as a ball of two, without alluding to the theory of acceleration of falling bodies, which had been made known by Galileo more than thirty years before. He proposed an inquiry with regard to the lever,—namely, whether in a balance with arms of different length but equal weight the distance from the fulcrum has any effect upon the inclination—though the theory of the lever was as well understood in his own time as it is now. . . . He speaks of the poles of the earth as fixed, in a manner which seems to imply that he was not acquainted with the precession of the equinoxes; and in another place, of the north pole being above and the south pole below, as a reason why in our hemisphere the north winds predominate over the south.—SPEDDING, J.

Works of Francis Bacon (Boston), Preface to De Interpretatione Naturae Prooemium.

918. Bacon himself was very ignorant of all that had been done by mathematics; and, strange to say, he especially objected to astronomy being handed over to the mathematicians. Leverrier and Adams, calculating an unknown planet into a visible existence by enormous heaps of algebra, furnish the last comment of note on this specimen of the goodness of Bacon's view. . . . Mathematics was beginning to be the great instrument of exact inquiry: Bacon threw the science aside, from ignorance, just at the time when his enormous sagacity, applied to knowledge, would have made him see the part it was to play. If Newton had taken Bacon for his master, not he, but somebody else, would have been Newton.—DE MORGAN, A.

Budget of Paradoxes (London, 1872), pp. 53–54.

919. Daniel Bernoulli used to tell two little adventures, which he said had given him more pleasure than all the other honours he had received. Travelling with a learned stranger, who, being pleased with his conversation, asked his name; "I am Daniel Bernoulli," answered he with great modesty; "and I," said the stranger (who thought he meant to laugh at him) "am Isaac Newton." Another time, having to dine with the celebrated Koenig, the mathematician, who boasted, with some degree of self-complacency, of a difficult problem he had solved with much trouble, Bernoulli went on doing the honours of his table, and when they went to drink coffee he presented Koenig with a solution of the problem more elegant than his own.

HUTTON, CHARLES.
A Philosophical and Mathematical Dictionary (London, 1815), Vol. 1, p. 226.

920. Following the example of Archimedes who wished his tomb decorated with his most beautiful discovery in geometry and ordered it inscribed with a cylinder circumscribed by a sphere, James Bernoulli requested that his tomb be inscribed with his logarithmic spiral together with the words, *"Eadem* *mutata resurgo,"* a happy allusion to the hope of the Christians, which is in a way symbolized by the properties of that curve.

FONTENELLE.
*Eloge de M. Bernoulli; Oeuvres de Fontenelle,
t. 5 (1758), p. 112.*

921. This formula [for computing Bernoulli's numbers] was first given by James Bernoulli. He gave no general demonstration; but was quite aware of the importance of his theorem, for he boasts that by means of it he calculated *intra semiquadrantem horae!* the sum of the 10th powers of the first thousand integers, and found it to be

91,409,924,241,424,243,424,241,924,242,500.

CHRYSTAL, G.
Algebra, Part 2 (Edinburgh, 1879), p. 209.

922. In the year 1692, James Bernoulli, discussing the logarithmic spiral [or equiangular spiral, $\rho = a^{\theta}$] . . . shows that it reproduces itself in its evolute, its involute, and its caustics of both reflection and refraction, and then adds: "But since this marvellous spiral, by such a singular and wonderful peculiarity, pleases me so much that I can scarce be satisfied with thinking about it, I have thought that it might not be inelegantly used for a symbolic representation of various matters. For since it always produces a spiral similar to itself, indeed precisely the same spiral, however it may be involved or evolved, or reflected or refracted, it may be taken as an emblem of a progeny always in all things like the parent, *simillima filia matri.* Or, if it is not forbidden ·to compare a theorem of eternal truth to the mysteries of our faith, it may be taken as an emblem of the eternal generation of the Son, who as an image of the Father, emanating from him, as light from light, remains ὁμοούσιος with him, howsoever overshadowed. Or, if you prefer, since our *spira mirabilis* remains, amid all changes, most persistently itself, and exactly the same as ever, it may be used as a symbol, either of fortitude and constancy in adversity, or, of the human body, which after all its changes, even after death, will be restored to its exact and perfect self, so that, indeed, if the fashion of Archimedes were allowed in these days, I should gladly have my tombstone bear this spiral, with the motto, " Though changed, I arise again exactly the same, *Eadem numero mutata resurgo.*"

HILL, THOMAS.
The Uses of Mathesis; Bibliotheca Sacra, Vol. 32, pp. 515–516.

923. Babbage was one of the founders of the Cambridge Analytical Society whose purpose he stated was to advocate "the principles of pure *d*-ism as opposed to the *dot*-age of the university."—BALL, W. W. R.
History of Mathematics (London, 1901), p. 451.

924. Bolyai [Janos] when in garrison with cavalry officers, was provoked by thirteen of them and accepted all their challenges on condition that he be permitted after each duel to play a bit on his violin. He came out victor from his thirteen duels, leaving his thirteen adversaries on the square.—HALSTED. G. B.
Bolyai's Science Absolute of Space (Austin, 1896), Introduction, p. 29.

925. Bolyai [Janos] projected a universal language for speech as we have it for music and mathematics.—HALSTED, G. B.
Bolyai's Science Absolute of Space (Austin, 1896), Introduction, p. 29.

926. [Bolyai's Science Absolute of Space]—the most extraordinary two dozen pages in the history of thought!

HALSTED, G. B.
Bolyai's Science Absolute of Space (Austin, 1896), Introduction, p. 18.

927. [Wolfgang Bolyai] was extremely modest. No monument, said he, should stand over his grave, only an apple-tree, in memory of the three apples: the two of Eve and Paris, which made hell out of earth, and that of Newton, which elevated the earth again into the circle of the heavenly bodies.—CAJORI, F.
History of Elementary Mathematics (New York, 1910), p. 273.

928. Bernard Bolzano dispelled the clouds that throughout all the foregone centuries had enveloped the notion of Infinitude

in darkness, completely sheared the great term of its vagueness without shearing it of its strength, and thus rendered it forever available for the purposes of logical discourse.—KEYSER, C. J.
Lectures on Science, Philosophy and Art (New York, 1908), p. 42.

929. Let me tell you how at one time the famous mathematician *Euclid* became a physician. It was during a vacation, which I spent in Prague as I most always did, when I was attacked by ̗an illness never before experienced, which manifested itself in chilliness and painful weariness of the whole body. In order to ease my condition I took up *Euclid's Elements* and read for the first time his doctrine of *ratio*, which I found treated there in a manner entirely new to me. The ingenuity displayed in Euclid's presentation filled me with such vivid pleasure, that forthwith I felt as well as ever.

BOLZANO, BERNARD.
Selbstbiographie (Wien, 1875), p. 20.

930. Mr. Cayley, of whom it may be so truly said, whether the matter he takes in hand be great or small, *"nihil tetigit quod non ornavit,"* . . . —SYLVESTER, J. J.
Philosophic Transactions of the Royal Society, Vol. 17 (1864), p. 605.

931. It is not *Cayley's* way to analyze concepts into their ultimate elements. . . . But he is master of the *empirical* utilization of the material: in the way he combines it to form a single abstract concept which he generalizes and then subjects to computative tests, in the way the newly acquired data are made to yield at a single stroke the general comprehensive idea to the subsequent numerical verification of which years of labor are devoted. *Cayley* is thus the *natural philosopher* among mathematicians.—NOETHER, M.
Mathematische Annalen, Bd. 46 (1895), p. 479.

932. When Cayley had reached his most advanced generalizations he proceeded to establish them directly by some method or other, though he seldom gave the clue by which they had first been obtained: a proceeding which does not tend to make his papers easy reading. . . .

His literary style is direct, simple and clear. His legal training had an influence, not merely upon his mode of arrangement but also upon his expression; the result is that his papers are severe and present a curious contrast to the luxuriant enthusiasm which pervades so many of Sylvester's papers. He used to prepare his work for publication as soon as he carried his investigations in any subject far enough for his immediate purpose. . . . A paper once written out was promptly sent for publication; this practice he maintained throughout life. . . . The consequence is that he has left few arrears of unfinished or unpublished papers; his work has been given by himself to the world.—FORSYTH, A. R.

> *Proceedings of London Royal Society, Vol. 58*
> *(1895), pp. 23–24.*

933. Cayley was singularly learned in the work of other men, and catholic in his range of knowledge. Yet he did not read a memoir completely through: his custom was to read only so much as would enable him to grasp the meaning of the symbols and understand its scope. The main result would then become to him a subject of investigation: he would establish it (or test it) by algebraic analysis and, not infrequently, develop it so to obtain other results. This faculty of grasping and testing rapidly the work of others, together with his great knowledge, made him an invaluable referee; his services in this capacity were used through a long series of years by a number of societies to which he was almost in the position of standing mathematical advisor.—FORSYTH, A. R.

> *Proceedings London Royal Society, Vol. 58*
> *(1895), pp. 11–12.*

934. Bertrand, Darboux, and Glaisher have compared Cayley to Euler, alike for his range, his analytical power, and, not least, for his prolific production of new views and fertile theories. There is hardly a subject in the whole of pure mathematics at which he has not worked.—FORSYTH, A. R.

> *Proceedings London Royal Society, Vol. 58*
> *(1895), p. 21.*

935. The mathematical talent of Cayley was characterized by clearness and extreme elegance of analytical form; it was reenforced by an incomparable capacity for work which has caused the distinguished scholar to be compared with Cauchy.

HERMITE, C.
Comptes Rendus, t. 120 (1895), p. 234.

936. J. J. Sylvester was an enthusiastic supporter of reform [in the teaching of geometry]. The difference in attitude on this question between the two foremost British mathematicians, J. J. Sylvester, the algebraist, and Arthur Cayley, the algebraist and geometer, was grotesque. Sylvester wished to bury Euclid "deeper than e'er plummet sounded" out of the schoolboy's reach; Cayley, an ardent admirer of Euclid, desired the retention of Simson's *Euclid*. When reminded that this treatise was a mixture of Euclid and Simson, Cayley suggested striking out Simson's additions and keeping strictly to the original treatise.—CAJORI, F.

History of Elementary Mathematics (New York, 1910), p. 285.

937. Tait once urged the advantage of Quaternions on Cayley (who never used them), saying: "You know Quaternions are just like a pocket-map." "That may be," replied Cayley, "but you've got to take it out of your pocket, and unfold it, before it's of any use." And he dismissed the subject with a smile.—THOMPSON, S. P.

Life of Lord Kelvin (London, 1910), p. 1137.

938. As he [Clifford] spoke he appeared not to be working out a question, but simply telling what he saw. Without any diagram or symbolic aid he described the geometrical conditions on which the solution depended, and they seemed to stand out visibly in space. There were no longer consequences to be deduced, but real and evident facts which only required to be seen. . . . So whole and complete was his vision that for the time the only strange thing was that anybody should fail to see it in the same way. When one endeavored to call it up again, and not till then, it became clear that the magic of genius had been at work, and that the common sight had been raised to that higher perception by the power that makes and transforms ideas, the conquering and masterful quality of the human mind which Goethe called in one word *das Dämonische.*—POLLOCK, F.

Clifford's Lectures and Essays (New York, 1901), Vol. 1, Introduction, pp. 5–6.

939. Much of his [Clifford's] best work was actually spoken before it was written. He gave most of his public lectures with no visible preparation beyond very short notes, and the outline seemed to be filled in without effort or hesitation. Afterwards he would revise the lecture from a shorthand writer's report, or sometimes write down from memory almost exactly what he had said. It fell out now and then, however, that neither of these things was done; in such cases there is now no record of the lecture at all.—POLLOCK, F.

Clifford's Lectures and Essays (New York, 1901), Vol. 1, Introduction, p. 10.

940. I cannot find anything showing early aptitude for acquiring languages; but that he [Clifford] had it and was fond of exercising it in later life is certain. One practical reason for it was the desire of being able to read mathematical papers in foreign journals; but this would not account for his taking up Spanish, of which he acquired a competent knowledge in the course of a tour to the Pyrenees. When he was at Algiers in 1876 he began Arabic, and made progress enough to follow in a general way a course of lessons given in that language. He read modern Greek fluently, and at one time he was furious about Sanskrit. He even spent some time on hieroglyphics. A new language is a riddle before it is conquered, a power in the hand afterwards: to Clifford every riddle was a challenge, and every chance of new power a divine opportunity to be seized. Hence he was likewise interested in the various modes of conveying and expressing language invented for special purposes, such as the Morse alphabet and shorthand. . . . I have forgotten to mention his command of French and German, the former of which he knew very well, and the latter quite sufficiently; . . .

POLLOCK, F.

Clifford's Lectures and Essays (New York, 1901), Vol. 1, Introduction, pp. 11–12.

941. The most remarkable thing was his [Clifford's] great strength as compared with his weight, as shown in some exercises. At one time he could pull up on the bar with either hand, which is well known to be one of the greatest feats of strength. His nerve at dangerous heights was extraordinary. I am appalled now to think that he climbed up and sat on the cross bars of the weathercock on a church tower, and when by way of doing something worse I went up and hung by my toes to the bars he did the same.

Quoted from a letter by one of Clifford's friends to Pollock, F.: Clifford's Lectures and Essays (New York, 1901), Vol. 1, Introduction, p. 8.

942. [Comte] may truly be said to have created the philosophy of higher mathematics.—MILL, J. S.

System of Logic (New York, 1846), p. 369.

943. These specimens, which I could easily multiply, may suffice to justify a profound distrust of Auguste Comte, wherever he may venture to speak as a mathematician. But his vast *general* ability, and that personal intimacy with the great Fourier, which I most willingly take his own word for having enjoyed, must always give an interest to his *views* on any subject of pure or applied mathematics.—HAMILTON, W. R.

Graves' Life of W. R. Hamilton (New York, 1882–1889), Vol. 3, p. 475.

944. The manner of Demoivre's death has a certain interest for psychologists. Shortly before it, he declared that it was necessary for him to sleep some ten minutes or a quarter of an hour longer each day than the preceding one: the day after he had thus reached a total of something over twenty-three hours he slept up to the limit of twenty-four hours, and then died in his sleep.—BALL, W. W. R.

History of Mathematics (London, 1911), p. 394.

945. De Morgan was explaining to an actuary what was the chance that a certain proportion of some group of people would at the end of a given time be alive; and quoted the actuarial formula, involving π, which, in answer to a question, he explained stood for the ratio of the circumference of a circle to its diameter. His acquaintance, who had so far listened to the explanation with interest, interrupted him and exclaimed, "My dear friend, that must be a delusion, what can a circle have to do with the number of people alive at a given time?"

BALL, W. W. R.
Mathematical Recreations and Problems (London, 1896), p. 180; See also De Morgan's Budget of Paradoxes (London, 1872), p. 172.

946. A few days afterwards, I went to him [the same actuary referred to in 945] and very gravely told him that I had discovered the law of human mortality in the Carlisle Table, of which he thought very highly. I told him that the law was involved in this circumstance. Take the table of the expectation of life, choose any age, take its expectation and make the nearest integer a new age, do the same with that, and so on; begin at what age you like, you are sure to end at the place where the age past is equal, or most nearly equal, to the expectation to come. "You don't mean that this always happens?"—"Try it." He did try, again and again; and found it as I said. "This is, indeed, a curious thing; this *is* a discovery!" I might have sent him about trumpeting the law of life: but I contented myself with informing him that the same thing would happen with any table whatsoever in which the first column goes up and the second goes down; . . .—DE MORGAN, A.
Budget of Paradoxes (London, 1872), p. 172.

947. [De Morgan relates that some person had made up 800 anagrams on his name, of which he had seen about 650. Commenting on these he says:]

Two of these I have joined in the title-page:

[Ut agendo surgamus arguendo gustamus.]

A few of the others are personal remarks.

Great gun! do us a sum!

is a sneer at my pursuit; but,

Go! great sum! $\int a^u du$

is more dignified. . . .

Adsum, nugator, suge!

is addressed to a student who continues talking after the lecture has commenced: . . .

Graduatus sum! nego
applies to one who declined to subscribe for an M. A. degree.
DE MORGAN, AUGUSTUS.
Budget of Paradoxes (London, 1872), p. 82.

948. Descartes is the completest type which history presents of the purely mathematical type of mind—that in which the tendencies produced by mathematical cultivation reign unbalanced and supreme.—MILL, J. S.
An Examination of Sir W. Hamilton's Philosophy (London, 1878), p. 626.

949. To *Descartes*, the great philosopher of the 17th century, is due the undying credit of having removed the bann which until then rested upon geometry. The *analytical geometry*, as Descartes' method was called, soon led to an abundance of new theorems and principles, which far transcended everything that ever could have been reached upon the path pursued by the ancients.—HANKEL, H.
Die Entwickelung der Mathematik in den letzten Jahrhunderten (Tübingen, 1884), p. 10.

950. [The application of algebra has] far more than any of his metaphysical speculations, immortalized the name of Descartes, and constitutes the greatest single step ever made in the progress of the exact sciences.—MILL, J. S.
An Examination of Sir W. Hamilton's Philosophy (London, 1878), p. 617.

951. . . . καί φασιν ὅτι Πτολεμαῖος ἤρετό ποτε αὐτόν [Εὐκλείδην], εἴ τίς ἐστιν περὶ γεωμετρίαν ὁδὸς συντομωτέρα τῆς στοιχειώσεως· ὁδὲ ἀπεκρίνατο, μὴ εἶναι βασιλικὴν ἀτραπὸν ἐπὶ γεωμετρίαν.
[. . . they say that Ptolemy once asked him (Euclid) whether there was in geometry no shorter way than that of the elements and he replied, "There is no royal road to geometry."]
PROCLUS.
(Edition Friedlein, 1873), Prol. II, 39.

952. Someone who had begun to read geometry with Euclid, when he had learned the first proposition, asked Euclid, "But

what shall I get by learning these things?" whereupon Euclid called his slave and said, "Give him three-pence, since he must make gain out of what he learns."—STOBÆUS.
(Edition Wachsmuth, 1884), Ecl. II

953. The sacred writings excepted, no Greek has been so much read and so variously translated as Euclid.*
DE MORGAN, A.
Smith's Dictionary of Greek and Roman Biology and Mythology (London, 1902), Article, "Eucleides."

954. The thirteen books of Euclid must have been a tremendous advance, probably even greater than that contained in the "Principia" of Newton.—DE MORGAN, A.
Smith's Dictionary of Greek and Roman Biography and Mythology (London, 1902), Article, "Eucleides."

955. To suppose that so perfect a system as that of Euclid's Elements was produced by one man, without any preceding model or materials, would be to suppose that Euclid was more than man. We ascribe to him as much as the weakness of human understanding will permit, if we suppose that the inventions in geometry, which had been made in a tract of preceding ages, were by him not only carried much further, but digested into so admirable a system, that his work obscured all that went before it, and made them be forgot and lost.—REID, THOMAS.
Essay on the Powers of the Human Mind (Edinburgh, 1812), Vol. 2, p. 368.

956. It is the invaluable merit of the great Basle mathematician Leonhard *Euler*, to have freed the analytical calculus from all geometrical bonds, and thus to have established *analysis* as an independent science, which from his time on has maintained an unchallenged leadership in the field of mathematics.
HANKEL, H.
Die Entwickelung der Mathematik in den letzten Jahrhunderten (Tübingen, 1884), p. 12.

* Riccardi's Bibliografia Euclidea (Bologna, 1887), lists nearly two thousand editions.

957. We may safely say, that the whole form of modern mathematical thinking was created by Euler. It is only with the greatest difficulty that one is able to follow the writings of any author immediately preceding Euler, because it was not yet known how to let the formulas speak for themselves. This art Euler was the first one to teach.—Rudio, F.

> *Quoted by Ahrens W.: Scherz und Ernst in der Mathematik (Leipzig, 1904), p. 251.*

958. The general knowledge of our author [Leonhard Euler] was more extensive than could well be expected, in one who had pursued, with such unremitting ardor, mathematics and astronomy as his favorite studies. He had made a very considerable progress in medical, botanical, and chemical science. What was still more extraordinary, he was an excellent scholar, and possessed in a high degree what is generally called erudition. He had attentively read the most eminent writers of ancient Rome; the civil and literary history of all ages and all nations was familiar to him; and foreigners, who were only acquainted with his works, were astonished to find in the conversation of a man, whose long life seemed solely occupied in mathematical and physical researches and discoveries, such an extensive acquaintance with the most interesting branches of literature. In this respect, no doubt, he was much indebted to an uncommon memory, which seemed to retain every idea that was conveyed to it, either from reading or from meditation.

> Hutton, Charles.
> *Philosophical and Mathematical Dictionary (London, 1815), pp. 493–494.*

959. Euler could repeat the Aeneid from the beginning to the end, and he could even tell the first and last lines in every page of the edition which he used. In one of his works there is a learned memoir on a question in mechanics, of which, as he himself informs us, a verse of Aeneid * gave him the first idea.

> Brewster, David.
> *Letters of Euler (New York, 1872), Vol. 1, p. 24.*

* The line referred to is:
  "The anchor drops, the rushing keel is staid."

960. Most of his [Euler's] memoirs are contained in the transactions of the Academy of Sciences at St. Petersburg, and in those of the Academy at Berlin. From 1728 to 1783 a large portion of the Petropolitan transactions were filled by his writings. He had engaged to furnish the Petersburg Academy with memoirs in sufficient number to enrich its acts for twenty years—a promise more than fulfilled, for down to 1818 [Euler died in 1793] the volumes usually contained one or more papers of his. It has been said that an edition of Euler's complete works would fill 16,000 quarto pages.—CAJORI, F.

> *History of Mathematics (New York, 1897), pp. 253–254.*

961. Euler who could have been called almost without metaphor, and certainly without hyperbole, analysis incarnate.

ARAGO.

> *Oeuvres, t. 2 (1854), p. 443.*

962. Euler calculated without any apparent effort, just as men breathe, as eagles sustain themselves in the air.—ARAGO.

> *Oeuvres, t. 2 (1854), p. 133.*

963. Two of his [Euler's] pupils having computed to the 17th term, a complicated converging series, their results differed one unit in the fiftieth cipher; and an appeal being made to Euler, he went over the calculation in his mind, and his decision was found correct.—BREWSTER, DAVID.

> *Letters of Euler (New York, 1872), Vol. 2, p. 22.*

964. In 1735 the solving of an astronomical problem, proposed by the Academy, for which several eminent mathematicians had demanded several months' time, was achieved in three days by Euler with aid of improved methods of his own. . . . With still superior methods this same problem was solved by the illustrious Gauss in one hour.—CAJORI, F.

> *History of Mathematics (New York, 1897), p. 248.*

965. Euler's *Tentamen novae theorae musicae* had no great success, as it contained too much geometry for musicians, and too much music for geometers.—FUSS, N.

> *Quoted by Brewster: Letters of Euler (New York, 1872), Vol. 1, p. 26.*

966. Euler was a believer in God, downright and straight-forward. The following story is told by Thiebault, in his *Souvenirs de vingt ans de séjour à Berlin*, . . . Thiebault says that he has no personal knowledge of the truth of the story, but that it was believed throughout the whole of the north of Europe. Diderot paid a visit to the Russian Court at the invitation of the Empress. He conversed very freely, and gave the younger members of the Court circle a good deal of lively atheism. The Empress was much amused, but some of her counsellors suggested that it might be desirable to check these expositions of doctrine. The Empress did not like to put a direct muzzle on her guest's tongue, so the following plot was contrived. Diderot was informed that a learned mathematician was in possession of an algebraical demonstration of the exist-ence of God, and would give it him before all the Court, if he desired to hear it. Diderot gladly consented: though the name of the mathematician is not given, it was Euler. He advanced toward Diderot, and said gravely, and in a tone of perfect con-viction:

$$Monsieur, \frac{a + b^n}{n} = x, donc\ Dieu\ existe;\ repondez!$$

Diderot, to whom algebra was Hebrew, was embarrassed and disconcerted; while peals of laughter rose on all sides. He asked permission to return to France at once, which was granted.

> DE MORGAN, A.
> *Budget of Paradoxes (London, 1872), p. 251.*

967. Fermat died with the belief that he had found a long-sought-for law of prime numbers in the formula $2^{2^n} + 1 = a$ prime, but he admitted that he was unable to prove it rigor-ously. The law is not true, as was pointed out by Euler in the example $2^{2^5} + 1 = 4,294,967,297 = 6,700,417$ times 641. The American lightning calculator *Zerah Colburn*, when a boy, readily found the factors but was unable to explain the method by which he made his marvellous mental computation.

CAJORI, F.
History of Mathematics (New York, 1897), p. 180.

968. I crave the liberty to conceal my name, not to suppress it. I have composed the letters of it written in Latin in this sentence—

In Mathesi a sole fundes.*—FLAMSTEED, J.
Macclesfield: Correspondence of Scientific Men (Oxford, 1841), Vol. 2, p. 90.

969.   *To the Memory of Fourier*

Fourier! with solemn and profound delight,
Joy born of awe, but kindling momently
To an intense and thrilling ecstacy,
I gaze upon thy glory and grow bright:
As if irradiate with beholden light;
As if the immortal that remains of thee
Attuned me to thy spirit's harmony,
Breathing serene resolve and tranquil might.
Revealed appear thy silent thoughts of youth,
As if to consciousness, and all that view
Prophetic, of the heritage of truth
To thy majestic years of manhood due:
Darkness and error fleeing far away,
And the pure mind enthroned in perfect day.

HAMILTON, W. R.
Graves' Life of W. R. Hamilton, (New York, 1882), Vol. 1, p. 596.

970. Astronomy and Pure Mathematics are the magnetic poles toward which the compass of my mind ever turns.

GAUSS TO BOLYAI.
Briefwechsel (Schmidt-Stakel), (1899), p. 55.

971. [Gauss calculated the elements of the planet Ceres] and his analysis proved him to be the first of theoretical astronomers no less than the greatest of "arithmeticians."—BALL, W. W. R.
History of Mathematics (London, 1901), p. 458.

* Johannes Flamsteedius.

972. The mathematical giant [Gauss], who from his lofty heights embraces in one view the stars and the abysses . . .

BOLYAI, W.
Kurzer Grundriss eines Versuchs (Maros Vasarhely, 1851), p. 44.

973. Almost everything, which the mathematics of our century has brought forth in the way of original scientific ideas, attaches to the name of Gauss.—KRONECKER, L.
Zahlentheorie, Teil 1 (Leipzig, 1901), p. 43.

974. I am giving this winter two courses of lectures to three students, of which one is only moderately prepared, the other less than moderately, and the third lacks both preparation and ability. Such are the onera of a mathematical profession.

GAUSS TO BESSEL, 1810.
Gauss-Bessel Briefwechsel (1880), p. 107.

975. Gauss once said "Mathematics is the queen of the sciences and number-theory the queen of mathematics." If this be true we may add that the Disquisitiones is the Magna Charta of number-theory. The advantage which science gained by Gauss' long-lingering method of publication is this: What he put into print is as true and important today as when first published; his publications are statutes, superior to other human statutes in this, that nowhere and never has a single error been detected in them. This justifies and makes intelligible the pride with which Gauss said in the evening of his life of the first larger work of his youth: "The Disquisitiones arithmeticae belong to history."—CANTOR, M.
Allgemeine Deutsche Biographie, Bd. 8 (1878), p. 435.

976. Here I am at the limit which God and nature has assigned to my individuality. I am compelled to depend upon word, language and image in the most precise sense, and am wholly unable to operate in any manner whatever with symbols and numbers which are easily intelligible to the most highly gifted minds.—GOETHE.
Letter to Naumann (1826); Vogel: Goethe's Selbstzeugnisse (Leipzig, 1903), p. 56.

977. Dirichlet was not satisfied to study Gauss' "Disquisitiones arithmeticae" once or several times, but continued throughout life to keep in close touch with the wealth of deep mathematical thoughts which it contains by perusing it again and again. For this reason the book was never placed on the shelf but had an abiding place on the table at which he worked. . . . Dirichlet was the first one, who not only fully understood this work, but made it also accessible to others.—KUMMER, E. E.

Dirichlet: Werke, Bd. 2, p. 315.

978. [The famous attack of Sir William Hamilton on the tendency of mathematical studies] affords the most express evidence of those fatal *lacunae* in the circle of his knowledge, which unfitted him for taking a comprehensive or even an accurate view of the processes of the human mind in the establishment of truth. If there is any pre-requisite which all must see to be indispensable in one who attempts to give laws to the human intellect, it is a thorough acquaintance with the modes by which human intellect has proceeded, in the case where, by universal acknowledgment, grounded on subsequent direct verification, it has succeeded in ascertaining the greatest number of important and recondite truths. This requisite Sir W. Hamilton had not, in any tolerable degree, fulfilled. Even of pure mathematics he apparently knew little but the rudiments. Of mathematics as applied to investigating the laws of physical nature; of the mode in which the properties of number, extension, and figure, are made instrumental to the ascertainment of truths other than arithmetical or geometrical—it is too much to say that he had even a superficial knowledge: there is not a line in his works which shows him to have had any knowledge at all.—MILL, J. S.

Examination of Sir William Hamilton's Philosophy (London, 1878), p. 607.

979. Helmholtz—the physiologist who learned physics for the sake of his physiology, and mathematics for the sake of his physics, and is now in the first rank of all three.

CLIFFORD, W. K.
Aims and Instruments of Scientific Thought; Lectures and Essays, Vol. 1 (London, 1901), p. 165.

980. It is said of Jacobi, that he attracted the particular attention and friendship of Böckh, the director of the philological seminary at Berlin, by the great talent he displayed for philology, and only at the end of two years' study at the University, and after a severe mental struggle, was able to make his final choice in favor of mathematics.—SYLVESTER, J. J.

> Collected Mathematical Papers, Vol. 2 (Cambridge, 1908), p. 651.

981. When Dr. Johnson felt, or fancied he felt, his fancy disordered, his constant recurrence was to the study of arithmetic.

> BOSWELL, J.
> Life of Johnson (Harper's Edition, 1871), Vol. 2, p. 264.

982. Endowed with two qualities, which seemed incompatible with each other, a volcanic imagination and a pertinacity of intellect which the most tedious numerical calculations could not daunt, Kepler conjectured that the movements of the celestial bodies must be connected together by simple laws, or, to use his own expression, by harmonic laws. These laws he undertook to discover. A thousand fruitless attempts, errors of calculation inseparable from a colossal undertaking, did not prevent him a single instant from advancing resolutely toward the goal of which he imagined he had obtained a glimpse. Twenty-two years were employed by him in this investigation, and still he was not weary of it! What, in reality, are twenty-two years of labor to him who is about to become the legislator of worlds; who shall inscribe his name in ineffaceable characters upon the frontispiece of an immortal code; who shall be able to exclaim in dithyrambic language, and without incurring the reproach of anyone, "The die is cast; I have written my book; it will be read either in the present age or by posterity, it matters not which; it may well await a reader, since God has waited six thousand years for an interpreter of his words."—ARAGO.

> Eulogy on Laplace: [Baden Powell] Smithsonian Report, 1874, p. 132.

983. The great masters of modern analysis are Lagrange, Laplace, and Gauss, who were contemporaries. It is interesting to note the marked contrast in their styles. Lagrange is perfect both in form and matter, he is careful to explain his procedure, and though his arguments are general they are easy to follow. Laplace on the other hand explains nothing, is indifferent to style, and, if satisfied that his results are correct, is content to leave them either with no proof or with a faulty one. Gauss is as exact and elegant as Lagrange, but even more difficult to follow than Laplace, for he removes every trace of the analysis by which he reached his results, and studies to give a proof which while rigorous shall be as concise and synthetical as possible.

BALL, W. W. R.
History of Mathematics (London, 1901), p. 463.

984. Lagrange, in one of the later years of his life, imagined that he had overcome the difficulty [of the parallel axiom]. He went so far as to write a paper, which he took with him to the Institute, and began to read it. But in the first paragraph something struck him which he had not observed: he muttered *Il faut que j'y songe encore*, and put the paper in his pocket.

DE MORGAN, A.
Budget of Paradoxes (London, 1872), p. 173.

985. I never come across one of Laplace's "*Thus it plainly appears*" without feeling sure that I have hours of hard work before me to fill up the chasm and find out and show *how* it plainly appears.—BOWDITCH, N.
Quoted by Cajori: Teaching and History of Mathematics in the U. S. (Washington, 1896), p. 104.

986. Biot, who assisted Laplace in revising it [The Mécanique Céleste] for the press, says that Laplace himself was frequently unable to recover the details in the chain of reasoning, and if satisfied that the conclusions were correct, he was content to insert the constantly recurring formula, "*Il est àisé a voir.*"—BALL, W. W. R.
History of Mathematics (London, 1901), p 427.

987. It would be difficult to name a man more remarkable for the greatness and the universality of his intellectual powers than Leibnitz.—MILL, J. S.
System of Logic, Bk. 2, chap. 5, sect. 6.

988. The influence of his [Leibnitz's] genius in forming that peculiar taste both in pure and in mixed mathematics which has prevailed in France, as well as in Germany, for a century past, will be found, upon examination, to have been incomparably greater than that of any other individual.—STEWART, DUGALD.
Philosophy of the Human Mind, Part 3, chap. 1, sect. 3.

989. Leibnitz's discoveries lay in the direction in which all modern progress in science lies, in establishing order, symmetry, and harmony, i. e., comprehensiveness and perspicuity,—rather than in dealing with single problems, in the solution of which followers soon attained greater dexterity than himself.
MERZ, J. T.
Leibnitz, Chap. 6.

990. It was his [Leibnitz's] love of method and order, and the conviction that such order and harmony existed in the real world, and that our success in understanding it depended upon the degree and order which we could attain in our own thoughts, that originally was probably nothing more than a habit which by degrees grew into a formal rule.* This habit was acquired by early occupation with legal and mathematical questions. We have seen how the theory of combinations and arrangements of elements had a special interest for him. We also saw how mathematical calculations served him as a type and model of clear and orderly reasoning, and how he tried to introduce method and system into logical discussions, by reducing to a small number of terms the multitude of compound notions he had to deal with. This tendency increased in strength, and even in those early years he elaborated the idea of a general arithmetic, with a universal language of symbols, or a characteristic which would be applicable to all reasoning processes, and reduce philosophical investigations to that simplicity and certainty which the use of algebraic symbols had introduced into mathematics.

A mental attitude such as this is always highly favorable for mathematical as well as for philosophical investigations. Wher-

* This sentence has been reworded for the purpose of this quotation.

ever progress depends upon precision and clearness of thought, and wherever such can be gained by reducing a variety of investigations to a general method, by bringing a multitude of notions under a common term or symbol, it proves inestimable. It necessarily imports the special qualities of number—viz., their continuity, infinity and infinite divisibility—like mathematical quantities—and destroys the notion that irreconcilable contrasts exist in nature, or gaps which cannot be bridged over. Thus, in his letter to Arnaud, Leibnitz expresses it as his opinion that geometry, or the philosophy of space, forms a step to the philosophy of motion—i. e., of corporeal things—and the philosophy of motion a step to the philosophy of mind.

MERZ, J. T.
Leibnitz (Philadelphia,), pp. 44–45.

991. Leibnitz believed he saw the image of creation in his binary arithmetic in which he employed only two characters, unity and zero. Since God may be represented by unity, and nothing by zero, he imagined that the Supreme Being might have drawn all things from nothing, just as in the binary arithmetic all numbers are expressed by unity with zero. This idea was so pleasing to Leibnitz, that he communicated it to the Jesuit Grimaldi, President of the Mathematical Board of China, with the hope that this emblem of the creation might convert to Christianity the reigning emperor who was particularly attached to the sciences.—LAPLACE.

Essai Philosophique sur les Probabilités; Oeuvres (Paris, 1896), t. 7, p. 119.

992. Sophus Lie, great comparative anatomist of geometric theories.—KEYSER, C. J.

Lectures on Science, Philosophy and Art (New York, 1908), p. 31.

993. It has been the final aim of Lie from the beginning to make progress in the theory of differential equations; as subsidiary to this may be regarded both his geometrical developments and the theory of continuous groups.—KLEIN, F.

Lectures on Mathematics (New York, 1911), p. 24.

994. To fully understand the mathematical genius of Sophus Lie, one must not turn to books recently published by him in collaboration with Dr. Engel, but to his earlier memoirs, written during the first years of his scientific career. There Lie shows himself the true geometer that he is, while in his later publications, finding that he was but imperfectly understood by the mathematicians accustomed to the analytic point of view, he adopted a very general analytic form of treatment that is not always easy to follow.—KLEIN, F.

Lectures on Mathematics (New York, 1911), p. 9.

995. It is said that the composing of the Lilawati was occasioned by the following circumstance. Lilawati was the name of the author's [Bhascara] daughter, concerning whom it appeared, from the qualities of the ascendant at her birth, that she was destined to pass her life unmarried, and to remain without children. The father ascertained a lucky hour for contracting her in marriage, that she might be firmly connected and have children. It is said that when that hour approached, he brought his daughter and his intended son near him. He left the hour cup on the vessel of water and kept in attendance a time-knowing astrologer, in order that when the cup should subside in the water, those two precious jewels should be united. But, as the intended arrangement was not according to destiny, it happened that the girl, from a curiosity natural to children, looked into the cup, to observe the water coming in at the hole, when by chance a pearl separated from her bridal dress, fell into the cup, and, rolling down to the hole, stopped the influx of water. So the astrologer waited in expectation of the promised hour. When the operation of the cup had thus been delayed beyond all moderate time, the father was in consternation, and examining, he found that a small pearl had stopped the course of the water, and that the long-expected hour was passed. In short, the father, thus disappointed, said to his unfortunate daughter, I will write a book of your name, which shall remain to the latest times—for a good name is a second life, and the ground-work of eternal existence.—FIZI.

Preface to the Lilawati. Quoted by A. Hutton:
A Philosophical and Mathematical Dictionary,
Article "Algebra" (London, 1815).

996. Is there anyone whose name cannot be twisted into either praise or satire? I have had given to me,

Thomas Babington Macaulay
Mouths big: a Cantab anomaly.

DE MORGAN, A.
Budget of Paradoxes (London, 1872), p. 83.

CHAPTER X

1001. When he had a few moments for diversion, he [Napoleon] not unfrequently employed them over a book of logarithms, in which he always found recreation.—ABBOTT, J. S. C.
> Napoleon Bonaparte (New York, 1904), Vol. 1, chap. 10.

1002. The name of Sir Isaac Newton has by general consent been placed at the head of those great men who have been the ornaments of their species. . . . The philosopher [Laplace], indeed, to whom posterity will probably assign a place next to Newton, has characterized the Principia as pre-eminent above all the productions of human intellect.—BREWSTER, D.
> Life of Sir Isaac Newton (London, 1831), pp. 1, 2.

1003. Newton and Laplace need myriads of ages and thick-strewn celestial areas. One may say a gravitating solar system is already prophesied in the nature of Newton's mind.
> EMERSON.
> Essay on History.

1004. The law of gravitation is indisputably and incomparably the greatest scientific discovery ever made, whether we look at the advance which it involved, the extent of truth disclosed, or the fundamental and satisfactory nature of this truth.—WHEWELL, W.
> History of the Inductive Sciences, Bk. 7, chap. 2, sect. 5.

1005. Newton's theory is the circle of generalization which includes all the others [as Kepler's laws, Ptolemy's theory, etc.];—the highest point of the inductive ascent;—the catastrophe of the philosophic drama to which Plato had prologized;—

166

the point to which men's minds had been journeying for two thousand years.—WHEWELL, W.
History of the Inductive Sciences, Bk. 7, chap. 2, sect. 5.

1006. The efforts of the great philosopher [Newton] were always superhuman; the questions which he did not solve were incapable of solution in his time.—ARAGO.
Eulogy on Laplace, [Baden Powell] Smithsonian Report, 1874, p. 133.

1007. Nature and Nature's laws lay hid in night:
God said, " Let Newton be! " and all was light.
POPE, A.
Epitaph intended for Sir Isaac Newton.

1008. There Priest of Nature! dost thou shine,
Newton! a King among the Kings divine.—SOUTHEY.
Translation of a Greek Ode on Astronomy.

1009. O'er Nature's laws God cast the veil of night,
Out-blaz'd a Newton's soul—and all was light.
HILL, AARON.
On Sir Isaac Newton.

1010. Taking mathematics from the beginning of the world to the time when Newton lived, what he had done was much the better half.—LEIBNITZ.
Quoted by F. R. Moulton: Introduction to Astronomy (New York, 1906), p. 199.

1011. Newton was the greatest genius that ever existed, and the most fortunate, for we cannot find more than once a system of the world to establish.—LAGRANGE.
Quoted by F. R. Moulton: Introduction to Astronomy (New York, 1906), p. 199.

1012. A monument to Newton! a monument to Shakespeare! Look up to Heaven—look into the Human Heart. Till the planets and the passions—the affections and the fixed stars are extinguished—their names cannot die.—WILSON, JOHN.
Noctes Ambrosianae.

1013. Such men as Newton and Linnæus are incidental, but august, teachers of religion.—WILSON, JOHN.
Essays: Education of the People.

1014. Sir Isaac Newton, the supreme representative of Anglo-Saxon genius.—ELLIS, HAVELOCK.
Study of British Genius (London, 1904), p. 49.

1015. Throughout his life Newton must have devoted at least as much attention to chemistry and theology as to mathematics. . . .—BALL, W. W. R.
History of Mathematics (London, 1901), p. 335.

1016. There was a time when he [Newton] was possessed with the old fooleries of astrology; and another when he was so far gone in those of chemistry, as to be upon the hunt after the philosopher's stone.—REV. J. SPENCE.
Anecdotes, Observations, and Characters of Books and Men (London, 1858), p. 54.

1017. For several years this great man [Newton] was intensely occupied in endeavoring to discover a way of changing the base metals into gold. . . . There were periods when his furnace fires were not allowed to go out for six weeks; he and his secretary sitting up alternate nights to replenish them.
PARTON, JAMES.
Sir Isaac Newton.

1018. On the day of Cromwell's death, when Newton was sixteen, a great storm raged all over England. He used to say, in his old age, that on that day he made his first purely scientific experiment. To ascertain the force of the wind, he first jumped with the wind and then against it; and, by comparing these distances with the extent of his own jump on a calm day, he was enabled to compute the force of the storm. When the wind blew thereafter, he used to say it was so many feet strong.
PARTON, JAMES.
Sir Isaac Newton.

1019. Newton lectured now and then to the few students who chose to hear him; and it is recorded that very frequently he came to the lecture-room and found it empty. On such occasions he would remain fifteen minutes, and then, if no one came, return to his apartments.—PARTON, JAMES.

Sir Isaac Newton.

1020. Sir Isaac Newton, though so deep in algebra and fluxions, could not readily make up a common account: and, when he was Master of the Mint, used to get somebody else to make up his accounts for him.—REV. J. SPENCE.

Anecdotes, Observations, and Characters of Books and Men (London, 1858), p. 132.

1021. We have one of his [Newton's] college memorandum-books, which is highly interesting. The following are some of the entries: "Drills, gravers, a hone, a hammer, and a mandril, 5s.;" "a magnet, 16s.;" "compasses, 2s.;" "glass bubbles, 4s.;" "at the tavern several other times, £1;" "spent on my cousin, 12s.;" "on other acquaintances, 10s.;" "Philosophical Intelligences, 9s. 6d.;" "lost at cards twice, 15s.;" "at the tavern twice, 3s. 6d.;" "to three prisms, £3;" "four ounces of putty, 1s. 4d.;" "Bacon's Miscellanies, 1s. 6d.;" "a bible binding, 3s.;" "for oranges to my sister, 4s. 2d.;" "for aquafortis, sublimate, oyle pink, fine silver, antimony, vinegar, spirit of wine, white lead, salt of tartar, £2;" "Theatrum chemicum, £1 8s."—PARTON, JAMES.

Sir Isaac Newton.

1022. On one occasion, when he was giving a dinner to some friends at the university, he left the table to get them a bottle of wine; but, on his way to the cellar, he fell into reflection, forgot his errand and his company, went to his chamber, put on his surplice, and proceeded to the chapel. Sometimes he would go into the street half dressed, and on discovering his condition, run back in great haste, much abashed. Often, while strolling in his garden, he would suddenly stop, and then run rapidly to his room, and begin to write, standing, on the first piece of paper that presented itself. Intending to dine in the public hall, he would go out in a brown study, take the wrong turn, walk a while, and then return to his room, having totally forgotten the dinner. Once having dismounted from his horse to lead him up a hill, the horse slipped his head out of the bridle; but Newton, oblivious, never discovered it till, on reaching a tollgate at the top of the hill, he turned to remount and perceived that the bridle which he held in his hand had no horse attached to it. His secretary records that his forgetfulness of his dinner was an excellent thing for his old housekeeper, who "sometimes found both dinner and supper scarcely tasted of, which the old woman has very pleasantly and mumpingly gone away with." On getting out of bed in the morning, he has been discovered to sit on his bedside for hours without dressing himself, utterly absorbed in thought.—PARTON, JAMES.

> *Sir Isaac Newton.*

1023. I don't know what I may seem to the world, but, as to myself, I seem to have been only as a boy playing on the sea-shore, and diverting myself in now and then finding a smoother pebble or a prettier shell than ordinary, whilst the great ocean of truth lay all undiscovered before me.—NEWTON, I.

> *Quoted by Rev. J. Spence: Anecdotes, Observations, and Characters of Books and Men (London, 1858), p. 40.*

1024. If I have seen farther than Descartes, it is by standing on the shoulders of giants.—NEWTON, I.

> *Quoted by James Parton: Sir Isaac Newton.*

1025. Newton could not admit that there was any difference between him and other men, except in the possession of such habits as . . . perseverance and vigilance. When he was asked how he made his discoveries, he answered, "by always thinking about them;" and at another time he declared that if he had done anything, it was due to nothing but industry and patient thought: "I keep the subject of my inquiry constantly before me, and wait till the first dawning opens gradually, by little and little, into a full and clear light." WHEWELL, W.

> *History of the Inductive Sciences, Bk. 7, chap. 2, sect. 5.*

1026. Newton took no exercise, indulged in no amusements, and worked incessantly, often spending eighteen or nineteen hours out of the twenty-four in writing.—BALL, W. W. R.

> *History of Mathematics (London, 1901), p. 358.*

1027. Foreshadowings of the principles and even of the language of [the infinitesimal] calculus can be found in the writings of Napier, Kepler, Cavalieri, Pascal, Fermat, Wallis, and Barrow. It was Newton's good luck to come at a time when everything was ripe for the discovery, and his ability enabled him to construct almost at once a complete calculus.

BALL, W. W. R.
History of Mathematics (London, 1901), p. 356.

1028. Kepler's suggestion of gravitation with the inverse distance, and Bouillaud's proposed substitution of the inverse square of the distance, are things which Newton knew better than his modern readers. I have discovered two anagrams on his name, which are quite conclusive: the notion of gravitation was *not new;* but Newton *went on.*—DE MORGAN, A.
Budget of Paradoxes (London, 1872), p. 82.

1029. For other great mathematicians or philosophers, he [Gauss] used the epithets magnus, or clarus, or clarissimus; for Newton alone he kept the prefix summus.—BALL, W. W. R.
History of Mathematics (London, 1901), p. 362.

1030. To know him [Sylvester] was to know one of the historic figures of all time, one of the immortals; and when he was really moved to speak, his eloquence equalled his genius.

HALSTED, G. B.
F. Cajori's Teaching and History of Mathematics in the U. S. (Washington, 1890), p. 265.

1031. Professor Sylvester's first high class at the new university Johns Hopkins consisted of only one student, G. B. Halsted, who had persisted in urging Sylvester to lecture on the modern algebra. The attempt to lecture on this subject led him into new investigations in quantics.—CAJORI, F.
Teaching and History of Mathematics in the U. S. (Washington, 1890), p. 264.

1032. But for the persistence of a student of this university in urging upon me his desire to study with me the modern algebra I should never have been led into this investigation; and the new facts and principles which I have discovered in regard to it (important facts, I believe), would, so far as I am concerned, have remained still hidden in the womb of time. In vain I represented to this inquisitive student that he would do better to take up some other subject lying less off the beaten track of study, such as the higher parts of the calculus or elliptic functions, or the theory of substitutions, or I wot not what besides. He stuck with perfect respectfulness, but with invincible pertinacity, to his point. He would have the new algebra (Heaven knows where he had heard about it, for it is almost unknown in this continent), that or nothing. I was obliged to yield, and what was the consequence? In trying to throw light upon an obscure explanation in our text-book, my brain took fire, I plunged with re-quickened zeal into a subject which I had for years abandoned, and found food for thoughts which have engaged my attention for a considerable time past, and will probably occupy all my powers of contemplation advantageously for several months to come.—SYLVESTER, J. J.

> Johns Hopkins Commemoration Day Address; Collected Mathematical Papers, Vol. 3, p. 76.

1033. Sylvester was incapable of reading mathematics in a purely receptive way. Apparently a subject either fired in his brain a train of active and restless thought, or it would not retain his attention at all. To a man of such a temperament, it would have been peculiarly helpful to live in an atmosphere in which his human associations would have supplied the stimulus which he could not find in mere reading. The great modern work in the theory of functions and in allied disciplines, he never became acquainted with . . .

What would have been the effect if, in the prime of his powers, he had been surrounded by the influences which prevail in Berlin or in Göttingen? It may be confidently taken for granted that he would have done splendid work in those domains of analysis, which have furnished the laurels of the great mathematicians of Germany and France in the second half of the present century.

FRANKLIN, F

> Johns Hopkins University Circulars 16 (1897), p. 54.

1034. If we survey the mathematical works of Sylvester, we recognize indeed a considerable abundance, but in contradistinction to Cayley—not a versatility toward separate fields, but, with few exceptions—a confinement to arithmetic-algebraic branches. . . .

The concept of *Function* of a continuous variable, the fundamental concept of modern mathematics, plays no role, is indeed scarcely mentioned in the entire work of Sylvester—Sylvester was combinatorist [combinatoriker].—NOETHER, M.

Mathematische Annalen, Bd.50 (1898), pp.134–135.

1035. Sylvester's *methods!* He had none. "Three lectures will be delivered on a New Universal Algebra," he would say; then, " The course must be extended to twelve." It did last all the rest of that year. The following year the course was to be *Substitutions-Theorie*, by Netto. We all got the text. He lectured about three times, following the text closely and stopping sharp at the end of the hour. Then he began to think about matrices again. " I must give one lecture a week on those," he said. He could not confine himself to the hour, nor to the one lecture a week. Two weeks were passed, and Netto was forgotten entirely and never mentioned again. Statements like the following were not unfrequent in his lectures: " I haven't proved this, but I am as sure as I can be of anything that it must be so. From this it will follow, etc." At the next lecture it turned out that what he was so sure of was false. Never mind, he kept on forever guessing and trying, and presently a wonderful discovery followed, then another and another. Afterward he would go back and work it all over again, and surprise us with all sorts of side lights. He then made another leap in the dark, more treasures were discovered, and so on forever.

DAVIS, E. W.
Cajori's Teaching and History of Mathematics in the U. S. (Washington, 1890), pp. 265–266.

1036. I can see him [Sylvester] now, with his white beard and few locks of gray hair, his forehead wrinkled o'er with thoughts, writing rapidly his figures and formulae on the board, sometimes explaining as he wrote, while we, his listeners, caught the reflected sounds from the board. But stop, something is not right, he pauses, his hand goes to his forehead to help his thought, he goes over the work again, emphasizes the leading points, and finally discovers his difficulty. Perhaps it is some error in his figures, perhaps an oversight in the reasoning. Sometimes, however, the difficulty is not elucidated, and then there is not much to the rest of the lecture. But at the next lecture we would hear of some new discovery that was the outcome of that difficulty, and of some article for the Journal, which he had begun. If a text-book had been taken up at the beginning, with the intention of following it, that text-book was most likely doomed to oblivion for the rest of the term, or until the class had been made listeners to every new thought and principle that had sprung from the laboratory of his mind, in consequence of that first difficulty. Other difficulties would soon appear, so that no text-book could last more than half of the term. In this way his class listened to almost all of the work that subsequently appeared in the Journal. It seemed to be the quality of his mind that he must adhere to one subject. He would think about it, talk about it to his class, and finally write about it for the Journal. The merest accident might start him, but once started, every moment, every thought was given to it, and, as much as possible, he read what others had done in the same direction; but this last seemed to be his real point; he could not read without finding difficulties in the way of understanding the author. Thus, often his own work reproduced what had been done by others, and he did not find it out until too late.

A notable example of this is in his theory of cyclotomic functions, which he had reproduced in several foreign journals, only to find that he had been greatly anticipated by foreign authors. It was manifest, one of the critics said, that the learned professor had not read Kummer's elementary results in the theory of ideal primes. Yet Professor Smith's report on the theory of numbers, which contained a full synopsis of Kummer's theory, was Professor Sylvester's constant companion.

This weakness of Professor Sylvester, in not being able to read what others had done, is perhaps a concomitant of his peculiar genius. Other minds could pass over little difficulties and not be troubled by them, and so go on to a final understanding of the results of the author. But not so with him. A difficulty, however small, worried him, and he was sure to have difficulties until the subject had been worked over in his own way, to correspond with his own mode of thought. To read the work of others, meant therefore to him an almost independent development of it. Like the man whose pleasure in life is to pioneer the way for society into the forests, his rugged mind could derive satisfaction only in hewing out its own paths; and only when his efforts brought him into the uncleared fields of mathematics did he find his place in the Universe.

HATHAWAY, A. S.
F. Cajori's Teaching and History of Mathematics in the U. S. (Washington, 1890), pp. 266–267.

1037. Professor Cayley has since informed me that the theorem about whose origin I was in doubt, will be found in Schläfli's " De Eliminatione." This is not the first unconscious plagiarism I have been guilty of towards this eminent man whose friendship I am proud to claim. A more glaring case occurs in a note by me in the " Comptes Rendus," on the twenty-seven straight lines of cubic surfaces, where I believe I have followed (like one walking in his sleep), down to the very nomenclature and notation, the substance of a portion of a paper inserted by Schläfli in the " Mathematical Journal," which bears my name as one of the editors upon the face.

SYLVESTER, J. J.
Philosophical Transactions of the Royal Society (1864), p. 642.

1038. He [Sylvester] had one remarkable peculiarity. He seldom remembered theorems, propositions, etc., but had always to deduce them when he wished to use them. In this he was the very antithesis of Cayley, who was thoroughly conversant with everything that had been done in every branch of mathematics.

I remember once submitting to Sylvester some investigations that I had been engaged on, and he immediately denied my first statement, saying that such a proposition had never been heard of, let alone proved. To his astonishment, I showed him a paper of his own in which he had proved the proposition; in fact, I believe the object of his paper had been the very proof which was so strange to him.—Durfee, W. P.

F. Cajori's Teaching and History of Mathematics in the U. S. (Washington, 1890), p. 268.

1039. A short, broad man of tremendous vitality, the physical type of Hereward, the last of the English, and his brother-in-arms, Winter, Sylvester's capacious head was ever lost in the highest cloud-lands of pure mathematics. Often in the dead of night he would get his favorite pupil, that he might communicate the very last product of his creative thought. Everything he saw suggested to him something new in the higher algebra. This transmutation of everything into new mathematics was a revelation to those who knew him intimately. They began to do it themselves. His ease and fertility of invention proved a constant encouragement, while his contempt for provincial stupidities, such as the American hieroglyphics for π and e, which have even found their way into Webster's Dictionary, made each young worker apply to himself the strictest tests.

Halsted, G. B.

F. Cajori's Teaching and History of Mathematics in the U. S. (Washington, 1890), p. 265.

1040. Sylvester's writings are flowery and eloquent. He was able to make the dullest subject bright, fresh and interesting. His enthusiasm is evident in every line. He would get quite close up to his subject, so that everything else looked small in comparison, and for the time would think and make others think that the world contained no finer matter for contemplation. His handwriting was bad, and a trouble to his printers. His papers were finished with difficulty. No sooner was the manuscript in the editor's hands than alterations, corrections, ameliorations and generalizations would suggest themselves to his mind, and every post would carry further directions to the editors and printers.—MacMahon. P. A.

Nature, Vol. 55 (1897), p. 494.

1041. The enthusiasm of Sylvester for his own work, which manifests itself here as always, indicates one of his characteristic qualities: a high degree of *subjectivity* in his productions and publications. Sylvester was so fully possessed by the matter which for the time being engaged his attention, that it appeared to him and was designated by him as the summit of all that is important, remarkable and full of future promise. It would excite his phantasy and power of imagination in even a greater measure than his power of reflection, so much so that he could never marshal the ability to master his subject-matter, much less to present it in an orderly manner.

Considering that he was also somewhat of a poet, it will be easier to overlook the poetic flights which pervade his writing, often bombastic, sometimes furnishing apt illustrations; more damaging is the complete lack of form and orderliness of his publications and their sketchlike character, . . . which must be accredited at least as much to lack of objectivity as to a superfluity of ideas. Again, the text is permeated with associated emotional expressions, bizarre utterances and paradoxes and is everywhere accompanied by notes, which constitute an essential part of Sylvester's method of presentation, embodying relations, whether proximate or remote, which momentarily suggested themselves. These notes, full of inspiration and occasional flashes of genius, are the more stimulating owing to their incompleteness. But none of his works manifest a desire to penetrate the subject from all sides and to allow it to mature; each mere surmise, conceptions which arose during publication, immature thoughts and even errors were ushered into publicity at the moment of their inception, with utmost carelessness, and always with complete unfamiliarity of the literature of the subject. Nowhere is there the least trace of self-criticism. No one can be expected to read the treatises entire, for in the form in which they are available they fail to give a clear view of the matter under contemplation.

Sylvester's was not a harmoniously gifted or well-balanced mind, but rather an instinctively active and creative mind, free from egotism. His reasoning moved in generalizations, was frequently influenced by analysis and at times was guided even by mystical numerical relations. His reasoning consists less frequently of pure intelligible conclusions than of inductions, or rather conjectures incited by individual observations and verifications. In this he was guided by an algebraic sense, developed through long occupation with processes of forms, and this led him luckily to general fundamental truths which in some instances remain veiled. His lack of system is here offset by the advantage of freedom from purely mechanical logical activity.

The exponents of his essential characteristics are an intuitive talent and a faculty of invention to which we owe a series of ideas of lasting value and bearing the germs of fruitful methods. To no one more fittingly than to Sylvester can be applied one of the mottos of the Philosophic Magazine:

"Admiratio generat quaestionem, quaestio investigationem investigatio inventionem."—NOETHER, M.

> *Mathematische Annalen, Bd. 50 (1898), pp. 155–160.*

1042. Perhaps I may without immodesty lay claim to the appellation of Mathematical Adam, as I believe that I have given more names (passed into general circulation) of the creatures of the mathematical reason than all the other mathematicians of the age combined.—SYLVESTER, J. J.

> *Nature, Vol. 37 (1887–1888), p. 162.*

1043. Tait dubbed Maxwell dp/dt, for according to thermodynamics dp/dt = JCM (where C denotes Carnot's function) the initials of (J. C.) Maxwell's name. On the other hand Maxwell denoted Thomson by T and Tait by T'; so that it became customary to quote Thomson and Tait's Treatise on Natural Philosophy as T and T'.—MACFARLANE, A.

> *Bibliotheca Mathematica, Bd. 3 (1903), p. 187.*

1044. In future times Tait will be best known for his work in the quaternion analysis. Had it not been for his expositions, developments and applications, Hamilton's invention would be today, in all probability, a mathematical curiosity.

> MACFARLANE, A.
> *Bibliotheca Mathematica, Bd. 3 (1903), p. 189.*

1045. Not seldom did he [Sir William Thomson], in his writings, set down some mathematical statement with the prefacing remark "it is obvious that" to the perplexity of mathematical readers, to whom the statement was anything but obvious from such mathematics as preceded it on the page. To him it was obvious for physical reasons that might not suggest themselves at all to the mathematician, however competent.

THOMPSON, S. P.
Life of Lord Kelvin (London, 1910), p. 1136.

1046. The following is one of the many stories told of "old Donald McFarlane" the faithful assistant of Sir William Thomson.

The father of a new student when bringing him to the University, after calling to see the Professor [Thomson] drew his assistant to one side and besought him to tell him what his son must do that he might stand well with the Professor. "You want your son to stand weel with the Profeessorr?" asked McFarlane. "Yes." "Weel, then, he must just have a guid bellyful o' mathematics!"—THOMPSON, S. P.
Life of Lord Kelvin (London, 1910), p. 420.

1047. The following story (here a little softened from the vernacular) was narrated by Lord Kelvin himself when dining at Trinity Hall:—

A certain rough Highland lad at the university had done exceedingly well, and at the close of the session gained prizes both in mathematics and in metaphysics. His old father came up from the farm to see his son receive the prizes, and visited the College. Thomson was deputed to show him round the place. "Weel, Mr. Thomson," asked the old man, "and what may these mathematics be, for which my son has getten a prize?" "I told him," replied Thomson, "that mathematics meant reckoning with figures, and calculating." "Oo ay," said the old man, "he'll ha' getten that fra' me: I were ever a braw hand at the countin'." After a pause he resumed: "And what, Mr. Thomson, might these metapheesics be?" "I endeavoured," replied Thomson, "to explain how metaphysics was the attempt to express in language the indefinite." The old Highlander stood still and scratched his head. "Oo ay: may be he'll ha' getten that fra' his mither. She were aye a bletherin' body."

THOMPSON, S. P.
Life of Lord Kelvin (London, 1910), p. 1124.

1048. Lord Kelvin, unable to meet his classes one day, posted the following notice on the door of his lecture room,—

"Professor Thomson will not meet his classes today."

The disappointed class decided to play a joke on the professor. Erasing the "c" they left the legend to read,—

"Professor Thomson will not meet his lasses today."

When the class assembled the next day in anticipation of the effect of their joke, they were astonished and chagrined to find that the professor had outwitted them. The legend of yesterday was now found to read,—

"Professor Thomson will not meet his asses today." *

NORTHRUP, CYRUS.
University of Washington Address, November 2, 1908.

1049. One morning a great noise proceeded from one of the classrooms [of the Braunsberger gymnasium] and on investigation it was found that Weierstrass, who was to give the recitation, had not appeared. The director went in person to Weierstrass' dwelling and on knocking was told to come in. There sat Weierstrass by a glimmering lamp in a darkened room though it was daylight outside. He had worked the night through and had not noticed the approach of daylight. When the director reminded him of the noisy throng of students who were waiting for him, his only reply was that he could impossibly interrupt his work; that he was about to make an important discovery which would attract attention in scientific circles.—LAMPE, E.

Karl Weierstrass: Jahrbuch der Deutschen Mathematiker Vereinigung, Bd. 6 (1897), pp. 38–39.

1050. Weierstrass related . . . that he followed Sylvester's papers on the theory of algebraic forms very attentively until Sylvester began to employ Hebrew characters. That was more than he could stand and after that he quit him.—LAMPE, E.

Naturwissenschaftliche Rundschau, Bd. 12 (1897), p. 361.

* Author's note. My colleague, Dr. E. T. Bell, informs me that this same anecdote is associated with the name of J. S. Blackie, Professor of Greek at Aberdeen and Edinburgh.

CHAPTER XI

1101. The world of idea which it discloses or illuminates, the contemplation of divine beauty and order which it induces, the harmonious connexion of its parts, the infinite hierarchy and absolute evidence of the truths with which it is concerned, these, and such like, are the surest grounds of the title of mathematics to human regard, and would remain unimpeached and unimpaired were the plan of the universe unrolled like a map at our feet, and the mind of man qualified to take in the whole scheme of creation at a glance.—Sylvester, J. J.

> *Presidential Address, British Association Report (1869); Collected Mathematical Papers, Vol. 2, p. 659.*

1102. Mathematics has a triple end. It should furnish an instrument for the study of nature. Furthermore it has a philosophic end, and, I venture to say, an end esthetic. It ought to incite the philosopher to search into the notions of number, space, and time; and, above all, adepts find in mathematics delights analogous to those that painting and music give. They admire the delicate harmony of number and of forms; they are amazed when a new discovery discloses for them an unlooked for perspective; and the joy they thus experience, has it not the esthetic character although the senses take no part in it? Only the privileged few are called to enjoy it fully, it is true; but is it not the same with all the noblest arts? Hence I do not hesitate to say that mathematics deserves to be cultivated for its own sake, and that the theories not admitting of application to physics deserve to be studied as well as others.

Poincaré, Henri.

> *The Relation of Analysis and Mathematical Physics; Bulletin American Mathematical Society, Vol. 4 (1899), p. 248.*

1103. I like to look at mathematics almost more as an art than as a science; for the activity of the mathematician, constantly creating as he is, guided though not controlled by the external world of the senses, bears a resemblance, not fanciful I believe but real, to the activity of an artist, of a painter let us say. Rigorous deductive reasoning on the part of the mathematician may be likened here to technical skill in drawing on the part of the painter. Just as no one can become a good painter without a certain amount of skill, so no one can become a mathematician without the power to reason accurately up to a certain point. Yet these qualities, fundamental though they are, do not make a painter or mathematician worthy of the name, nor indeed are they the most important factors in the case. Other qualities of a far more subtle sort, chief among which in both cases is imagination, go to the making of a good artist or good mathematician.—BÔCHER, MAXIME.

Fundamental Conceptions and Methods in Mathematics; Bulletin American Mathematical Society, Vol. 9 (1904), p. 133.

1104. Mathematics, rightly viewed, possesses not only truth, but supreme beauty—a beauty cold and austere, like that of sculpture, without appeal to any part of our weaker nature, without the gorgeous trappings of painting or music, yet sublimely pure, and capable of a stern perfection such as only the greatest art can show. The true spirit of delight, the exaltation, the sense of being more than man, which is the touchstone of the highest excellence, is to be found in mathematics as surely as in poetry. What is best in mathematics deserves not merely to be learned as a task, but to be assimilated as a part of daily thought, and brought again and again before the mind with ever-renewed encouragement. Real life is, to most men, a long second-best, a perpetual compromise between the real and the possible; but the world of pure reason knows no compromise, no practical limitations, no barrier to the creative activity embodying in splendid edifices the passionate aspiration after the perfect from which all great work springs. Remote from human passions, remote even from the pitiful facts of nature, the generations have gradually created an ordered cosmos, where pure thought can dwell as in its natural home, and where one, at least, of our nobler impulses can èscape from the dreary exile of the natural world.—RUSSELL, BERTRAND.

The Study of Mathematics: Philosophical Essays (London, 1910), p. 73.

1105. It was not alone the striving for universal culture which attracted the great masters of the Renaissance, such as Brunellesco, Leonardo de Vinci, Raphael, Michael Angelo and especially Albrecht Dürer, with irresistible power to the mathematical sciences. They were conscious that, with all the freedom of the individual phantasy, art is subject to necessary laws, and conversely, with all its rigor of logical structure, mathematics follows esthetic laws.—RUDIO, F.

Virchow-Holtzendorf: Sammlung gemeinverständliche wissenschaftliche Vorträge, Heft 142, p. 19.

1106. Surely the claim of mathematics to take a place among the liberal arts must now be admitted as fully made good. Whether we look at the advances made in modern geometry, in modern integral calculus, or in modern algebra, in each of these three a free handling of the material employed is now possible, and an almost unlimited scope is left to the regulated play of fancy. It seems to me that the whole of aesthetic (so far as at present revealed) may be regarded as a scheme having four centres, which may be treated as the four apices of a tetrahedron, namely Epic, Music, Plastic, and Mathematic. There will be found a *common* plane to every three of these, *outside* of which lies the fourth; and through every two may be drawn a common axis *opposite* to the axis passing through the other two. So far is certain and demonstrable. I think it also possible that there is a centre of gravity to each set of three, and that the line joining each such centre with the outside apex will intersect in a common point—the centre of gravity of the whole body of aesthetic; but what that centre is or must be I have not had time to think out.—SYLVESTER, J. J.

Proof of the hitherto undemonstrated Fundamental Theorem of Invariants: Collected Mathematical Papers, Vol. 3, p. 123.

1107. It is with mathematics not otherwise than it is with music, painting or poetry. Anyone can become a lawyer, doctor or chemist, and as such may succeed well, provided he is clever and industrious, but not every one can become a painter, or a musician, or a mathematician: general cleverness and industry alone count here for nothing.—MOEBIUS, P. J.

> *Ueber die Anlage zur Mathematik (Leipzig, 1900), p. 5.*

1108. The true mathematician is always a good deal of an artist, an architect, yes, of a poet. Beyond the real world, though perceptibly connected with it, mathematicians have intellectually created an ideal world, which they attempt to develop into the most perfect of all worlds, and which is being explored in every direction. None has the faintest conception of this world, except he who knows it.—PRINGSHEIM, A.

> *Jahresbericht der Deutschen Mathematiker Vereinigung, Bd. 32, p. 381.*

1109. Who has studied the works of such men as Euler, Lagrange, Cauchy, Riemann, Sophus Lie, and Weierstrass, can doubt that a great mathematician is a great artist? The faculties possessed by such men, varying greatly in kind and degree with the individual, are analogous with those requisite for constructive art. Not every mathematician possesses in a specially high degree that critical faculty which finds its employment in the perfection of form, in conformity with the ideal of logical completeness; but every great mathematician possesses the rarer faculty of constructive imagination.—HOBSON, E. W.

> *Presidential Address British Association for the Advancement of Science (1910) Nature, Vol. 84, p. 290.*

1110. Mathematics has beauties of its own—a symmetry and proportion in its results, a lack of superfluity, an exact adaptation of means to ends, which is exceedingly remarkable and to be found elsewhere only in the works of the greatest beauty. It was a felicitous expression of Goethe's to call a noble cathedral "frozen music," but it might even better be called "petrified mathematics." The beauties of mathematics—of simplicity, of symmetry, of completeness—can and should be exemplified even to young children. When this subject is properly and concretely presented, the mental emotion should be that of enjoyment of beauty, not that of repulsion from the ugly and the unpleasant.—YOUNG, J. W. A.

> The Teaching of Mathematics (New York, 1907), p. 44.

1111. A peculiar beauty reigns in the realm of mathematics, a beauty which resembles not so much the beauty of art as the beauty of nature and which affects the reflective mind, which has acquired an appreciation of it, very much like the latter.

KUMMER, E. E.

> Berliner Monatsberichte (1867), p. 395.

1112. Mathematics make the mind attentive to the objects which it considers. This they do by entertaining it with a great variety of truths, which are delightful and evident, but not obvious. Truth is the same thing to the understanding as music to the ear and beauty to the eye. The pursuit of it does really as much gratify a natural faculty implanted in us by our wise Creator as the pleasing of our senses: only in the former case, as the object and faculty are more spiritual,the delight is more pure, free from regret, turpitude, lassitude, and intemperance that commonly attend sensual pleasures.—ARBUTHNOT, JOHN.

> Usefulness of Mathematical Learning.

1113. However far the calculating reason of the mathematician may seem separated from the bold flight of the artist's phantasy, it must be remembered that these expressions are but momentary images snatched arbitrarily from among the activities of both. In the projection of new theories the mathematician needs as bold and creative a phantasy as the productive artist, and in the execution of the details of a composition the artist too must calculate dispassionately the means which are necessary for the successful consummation of the parts. Common to both is the creation, the generation, of forms out of mind.—LAMPE, E.

> Die Entwickelung der Mathematik, etc. (Berlin, 1893), p. 4.

1114. As pure truth is the polar star of our science [mathematics], so it is the great advantage of our science over others that it awakens more easily the love of truth in our pupils. . . . If Hegel justly said, " Whoever does not know the works of the ancients, has lived without knowing *beauty,*" Schellbach responds with equal right, " Who does not know mathematics, and the results of recent scientific investigation, dies without knowing *truth.*"—SIMON, MAX.
> *Quoted in J. W. A. Young: Teaching of Mathematics (New York, 1907), p. 44.*

1115. Büchsel in his reminiscences from the life of a country parson relates that he sought his recreation in Lacroix's Differential Calculus and thus found intellectual refreshment for his calling. Instances like this make manifest the great advantage which occupation with mathematics affords to one who lives remote from the city and is compelled to forego the pleasures of art. The entrancing charm of mathematics, which captivates every one who devotes himself to it, and which is comparable to the fine frenzy under whose ban the poet completes his work, has ever been incomprehensible to the spectator and has often caused the enthusiastic mathematician to be held in derision. A classic illustration is the example of Archimedes, . . .—LAMPE, E.
> *Die Entwickelung der Mathematik, etc. (Berlin 1893), p. 22.*

1116. Among the memoirs of Kirchhoff are some of uncommon beauty. Beauty, I hear you ask, do not the Graces flee where integrals stretch forth their necks? Can anything be beautiful, where the author has no time for the slightest external embellishment? . . . Yet it is this very simplicity, the indispensableness of each word, each letter, each little dash, that among all artists raises the mathematician nearest to the World-creator; it establishes a sublimity which is equalled in no other art,—something like it exists at most in symphonic music. The Pythagoreans recognized already the similarity between the most subjective and the most objective of the arts. . . . *Ultima se tangunt.* How expressive, how nicely characterizing withal is mathematics! As the musician recognizes Mozart, Beethoven, Schubert in the first chords, so the mathematician would distinguish his Cauchy, Gauss, Jacobi, Helmholtz in a few pages. Extreme external elegance, sometimes a somewhat weak skeleton of conclusions characterizes the French; the English, above all Maxwell, are distinguished by the greatest dramatic bulk. Who does not know Maxwell's dynamic theory of gases? At first there is the majestic development of the variations of velocities, then enter from one side the equations of condition and from the other the equations of central motions,—higher and higher surges the chaos of formulas,—suddenly four words burst forth: "Put $n = 5$." The evil demon V disappears like the sudden ceasing of the basso parts in music, which hitherto wildly permeated the piece; what before seemed beyond control is now ordered as by magic. There is no time to state why this or that substitution was made, he who cannot feel the reason may as well lay the book aside; Maxwell is no program-musician who explains the notes of his composition. Forthwith the formulas yield obediently result after result, until the temperature-equilibrium of a heavy gas is reached as a surprising final climax and the curtain drops. . . .

Kirchhoff's whole tendency, and its true counterpart, the form of his presentation, was different. . . . He is characterized by the extreme precision of his hypotheses, minute execution, a quiet rather than epic development with utmost rigor, never concealing a difficulty, always dispelling the faintest obscurity. To return once more to my allegory, he resembled Beethoven, the thinker in tones.—He who doubts that mathematical compositions can be beautiful, let him read his memoir on Absorption and Emission (Gesammelte Abhandlungen, Leipzig, 1882, p. 571–598) or the chapter of his mechanics devoted to Hydrodynamics.—BOLTZMANN, L.

Gustav Robert Kirchhoff (Leipzig 1888), pp. 28–30.

1117.   On poetry and geometric truth,
And their high privilege of lasting life,
From all internal injury exempt,
I mused; upon these chiefly: and at length,
My senses yielding to the sultry air,
Sleep seized me, and I passed into a dream.

WORDSWORTH.
The Prelude, Bk. 5.

1118. Geometry seems to stand for all that is practical, poetry for all that is visionary, but in the kingdom of the imagination you will find them close akin, and they should go together as a precious heritage to every youth.—MILNER, FLORENCE.
School Review, 1898, p. 114.

1119. The beautiful has its place in mathematics as elsewhere. The prose of ordinary intercourse and of business correspondence might be held to be the most practical use to which language is put, but we should be poor indeed without the literature of imagination. Mathematics too has its triumphs of the creative imagination, its beautiful theorems, its proofs and processes whose perfection of form has made them classic. He must be a "practical" man who can see no poetry in mathematics.—WHITE, W. F.
A Scrap-book of Elementary Mathematics (Chicago, 1908), p. 208.

1120. I venture to assert that the feelings one has when the beautiful symbolism of the infinitesimal calculus first gets a meaning, or when the delicate analysis of Fourier has been mastered, or while one follows Clerk Maxwell or Thomson into the strange world of electricity, now growing so rapidly in form and being, or can almost feel with Stokes the pulsations of light that gives nature to our eyes, or track with Clausius the courses of molecules we can measure, even if we know with certainty that we can never see them—I venture to assert that these feelings are altogether comparable to those aroused in us by an exquisite poem or a lofty thought.—WORKMAN, W. P.
F. Spencer: Aim and Practice of Teaching (New York, 1897), p. 194.

1121. It is an open secret to the few who know it, but a mystery and stumbling block to the many, that Science and Poetry are own sisters; insomuch that in those branches of scientific inquiry which are most abstract, most formal, and most remote from the grasp of the ordinary sensible imagination, a higher power of imagination akin to the creative insight of the poet is most needed and most fruitful of lasting work.

POLLOCK, F.
Clifford's Lectures and Essays (New York, 1901), Vol. 1, Introduction, p. 1.

1122. It is as great a mistake to maintain that a high development of the imagination is not essential to progress in mathematical studies as to hold with Ruskin and others that science and poetry are antagonistic pursuits.—HOFFMAN, F. S.

Sphere of Science (London, 1898), p. 107.

1123. We have heard much about the poetry of mathematics, but very little of it has as yet been sung. The ancients had a juster notion of their poetic value than we. The most distinct and beautiful statements of any truth must take at last the mathematical form. We might so simplify the rules of moral philosophy, as well as of arithmetic, that one formula would express them both.—THOREAU, H. D.

A Week on the Concord and Merrimac Rivers (Boston, 1893), p. 477.

1124. We do not listen with the best regard to the verses of a man who is only a poet, nor to his problems if he is only an algebraist; but if a man is at once acquainted with the geometric foundation of things and with their festal splendor, his poetry is exact and his arithmetic musical.—EMERSON, R. W.

Society and Solitude, Chap. 7, Works and Days.

1125. Mathesis and Poetry are . . . the utterance of the same power of imagination, only that in the one case it is addressed to the head, and in the other, to the heart.

HILL, THOMAS.
North American Review, Vol. 85, p. 230.

1126. The Mathematics are usually considered as being the very antipodes of Poesy. Yet Mathesis and Poesy are of the closest kindred, for they are both works of the imagination. Poesy is a creation, a making, a fiction; and the Mathematics have been called, by an admirer of them, the sublimest and most stupendous of fictions. It is true, they are not only μάθησις, learning, but ποίησις, a creation.—HILL, THOMAS.

North American Review, Vol. 85, p. 229.

1127. Music and poesy used to quicken you:
The mathematics, and the metaphysics,
Fall to them as you find your stomach serves you.
No profit grows, where is no pleasure ta'en:—
In brief, sir, study what you most affect.

SHAKESPEARE.
Taming of the Shrew, Act 1, Scene 1.

1128. Music has much resemblance to algebra.—NOVALIS.
Schriften, Teil 2 (Berlin, 1901), p. 549.

1129. I do present you with a man of mine,
Cunning in music and in mathematics,
To instruct her fully in those sciences,
Whereof, I know, she is not ignorant.—SHAKESPEARE.
Taming of the Shrew, Act 2, Scene 1.

1130. Saturated with that speculative spirit then pervading the Greek mind, he [Pythagoras] endeavoured to discover some principle of homogeneity in the universe. Before him, the philosophers of the Ionic school had sought it in the matter of things; Pythagoras looked for it in the structure of things. He observed the various numerical relations or analogies between numbers and the phenomena of the universe. Being convinced that it was in numbers and their relations that he was to find the foundation to true philosophy, he proceeded to trace the origin of all things to numbers. Thus he observed that musical strings of equal lengths stretched by weights having the proportion of $\frac{1}{2}$, $\frac{2}{3}$, $\frac{3}{4}$, produced intervals which were an octave, a fifth and a fourth. Harmony, therefore, depends on musical proportion; it is nothing but a mysterious numerical relation. Where harmony is, there are numbers. Hence the order and beauty of the universe have their origin in numbers. There are seven intervals in the musical scale, and also seven planets crossing the heavens. The same numerical relations which underlie the former must underlie the latter. But where number is, there is harmony. Hence his spiritual ear discerned in the planetary motions a wonderful "Harmony of spheres."

CAJORI, F.
History of Mathematics (New York, 1897), p. 67.

1131. May not Music be described as the Mathematic of sense, Mathematic as Music of the reason? the soul of each the same! Thus the musician *feels* Mathematic, the mathematician *thinks* Music,—Music the dream, Mathematic the working life—each to receive its consummation from the other when the human intelligence, elevated to its perfect type, shall shine forth glorified in some future Mozart-Dirichlet or Beethoven-Gauss—a union already not indistinctly foreshadowed in the genius and labours of a Helmholtz!—SYLVESTER, J. J.

> *On Newton's Rule for the Discovery of Imaginary Roots; Collected Mathematical Papers, Vol. 2, p. 419.*

1132. Just as the musician is able to form an acoustic image of a composition which he has never heard played by merely looking at its score, so the equation of a curve, which he has never seen, furnishes the mathematician with a complete picture of its course. Yea, even more: as the score frequently reveals to the musician niceties which would escape his ear because of the complication and rapid change of the auditory impressions, so the insight which the mathematician gains from the equation of a curve is much deeper than that which is brought about by a mere inspection of the curve.

> PRINGSHEIM, A.
> *Jahresbericht der Deutschen Mathematiker Vereiningung, Bd. 13, p. 364.*

1133. Mathematics and music, the most sharply contrasted fields of scientific activity which can be found, and yet related, supporting each other, as if to show forth the secret connection which ties together all the activities of our mind, and which leads us to surmise that the manifestations of the artist's genius are but the unconscious expressions of a mysteriously acting rationality.—HELMHOLTZ, H.

> *Vorträge und Reden, Bd. 1 (Braunschweig, 1884), p. 82.*

1134. Among all highly civilized peoples the golden age of art has always been closely coincident with the golden age of the pure sciences, particularly with mathematics, the most ancient among them.

This coincidence must not be looked upon as accidental, but as natural, due to an inner necessity. Just as art can thrive only when the artist, relieved of the anxieties of existence, can listen to the inspirations of his spirit and follow in their lead, so mathematics, the most ideal of the sciences, will yield its choicest blossoms only when life's dismal phantom dissolves and fades away, when the striving after naked truth alone predominates, conditions which prevail only in nations while in the prime of their development.—LAMPE, E.

> Die Entwickelung der Mathematik etc. (Berlin, 1893), p. 4.

1135. Till the fifteenth century little progress appears to have been made in the science or practice of music; but since that era it has advanced with marvelous rapidity, its progress being curiously parallel with that of mathematics, inasmuch as great musical geniuses appeared suddenly among different nations, equal in their possession of this special faculty to any that have since arisen. As with the mathematical so with the musical faculty—it is impossible to trace any connection between its possession and survival in the struggle for existence.

> WALLACE, A. R.
> Darwinism, Chap. 15.

1136. In my opinion, there is absolutely no trustworthy proof that talents have been improved by their exercise through the course of a long series of generations. The Bach family shows that musical talent, and the Bernoulli family that mathematical power, can be transmitted from generation to generation, but this teaches us nothing as to the origin of such talents. In both families the high-watermark of talent lies, not at the end of the series of generations, as it should do if the results of practice are transmitted, but in the middle. Again, talents frequently appear in some member of a family which has not been previously distinguished.

Gauss was not the son of a mathematician; Handel's father was a surgeon, of whose musical powers nothing is known; Titian was the son and also the nephew of a lawyer, while he and his brother, Francesco Vecellio, were the first painters in a family which produced a succession of seven other artists with diminishing talents. These facts do not, however, prove that the condition of the nerve-tracts and centres of the brain, which determine the specific talent, appeared for the first time in these men: the appropriate condition surely existed previously in their parents, although it did not achieve expression. They prove, as it seems to me, that a high degree of endowment in a special direction, which we call talent, cannot have arisen from the experience of previous generations, that is, by the exercise of the brain in the same specific direction.

WEISMANN, AUGUST.
Essays upon Heredity [*A. E. Shipley*], (*Oxford, 1891*), *Vol. 1, p. 97.*

CHAPTER XII

MATHEMATICS AS A LANGUAGE

1201. The new mathematics is a sort of supplement to language, affording a means of thought about form and quantity and a means of expression, more exact, compact, and ready than ordinary language. The great body of physical science, a great deal of the essential facts of financial science, and endless social and political problems are only accessible and only thinkable to those who have had a sound training in mathematical analysis, and the time may not be very remote when it will be understood that for complete initiation as an efficient citizen of one of the new great complex world wide states that are now developing, it is as necessary to be able to compute, to think in averages and maxima and minima, as it is now to be able to read and to write.

WELLS, H. G.
Mankind in the Making (*London, 1904*),
pp. 191–192.

1202. Mathematical language is not only the simplest and most easily understood of any, but the shortest also.

BROUGHAM, H. L.
Works (*Edinburgh, 1872*), *Vol. 7, p. 317.*

1203. Mathematics is the science of definiteness, the necessary vocabulary of those who know.—WHITE, W. F.
A Scrap-book of Elementary Mathematics
(*Chicago, 1908*), *p. 7.*

1204. Mathematics, too, is a language, and as concerns its structure and content it is the most perfect language which exists, superior to any vernacular; indeed, since it is understood by every people, mathematics may be called the language of languages. Through it, as it were, nature herself speaks; through it the Creator of the world has spoken, and through it the Preserver of the world continues to speak.—DILLMANN, C.
Die Mathematik die Fackelträgerin einer neuen Zeit (*Stuttgart, 1889*), *p. 5.*

1205. Would it sound too presumptuous to speak of perception as a quintessence of sensation, language (that is, communicable thought) of perception, mathematics of language? We should then have four terms differentiating from inorganic matter and from each other the Vegetable, Animal, Rational, and Supersensual modes of existence.—SYLVESTER, J. J.

Presidential Address, British Association; Collected Mathematical Papers, Vol. 2, p. 652.

1206. Little could Plato have imagined, when, indulging his instinctive love of the true and beautiful for their own sakes, he entered upon these refined speculations and revelled in a world of his own creation, that he was writing the grammar of the language in which it would be demonstrated in after ages that the pages of the universe are written.—SYLVESTER, J. J.

A Probationary Lecture on Geometry; Collected Mathematical Papers, Vol. 2, p. 7.

1207. It is the symbolic language of mathematics only which has yet proved sufficiently accurate and comprehensive to demand familiarity with this conception of an inverse process.

VENN, JOHN.

Symbolic Logic (London and New York, 1894), p. 74.

1208. Without this language [mathematics] most of the intimate analogies of things would have remained forever unknown to us; and we should forever have been ignorant of the internal harmony of the world, which is the only true objective reality. . . .

This harmony . . . is the sole objective reality, the only truth we can attain; and when I add that the universal harmony of the world is the source of all beauty, it will be understood what price we should attach to the slow and difficult progress which little by little enables us to know it better.—POINCARÉ, H.

The Value of Science [Halsted] Popular Science Monthly, 1906, pp. 195–196.

1209. The most striking characteristic of the written language of algebra and of the higher forms of the calculus is the sharpness of definition, by which we are enabled to reason upon the symbols by the mere laws of verbal logic, discharging our minds entirely of the meaning of the symbols, until we have reached a stage of the process where we desire to interpret our results. The ability to attend to the symbols, and to perform the verbal, visible changes in the position of them permitted by the logical rules of the science, without allowing the mind to be perplexed with the meaning of the symbols until the result is reached which you wish to interpret, is a fundamental part of what is called analytical power. Many students find themselves perplexed by a perpetual attempt to interpret not only the result, but each step of the process. They thus lose much of the benefit of the labor-saving machinery of the calculus and are, indeed, frequently incapacitated for using it.—Hill, Thomas.

Uses of Mathesis; Bibliotheca Sacra, Vol. 32, p. 505.

1210. The prominent reason why a mathematician can be judged by none but mathematicians, is that he uses a peculiar language. The language of mathesis is special and untranslatable. In its simplest forms it can be translated, as, for instance, we say a right angle to mean a square corner. But you go a little higher in the science of mathematics, and it is impossible to dispense with a peculiar language. It would defy all the power of Mercury himself to explain to a person ignorant of the science what is meant by the single phrase "functional exponent." How much more impossible, if we may say so, would it be to explain a whole treatise like Hamilton's Quaternions, in such a wise as to make it possible to judge of its value! But to one who has learned this language, it is the most precise and clear of all modes of expression. It discloses the thought exactly as conceived by the writer, with more or less beauty of form, but never with obscurity. It may be prolix, as it often is among French writers; may delight in mere verbal metamorphoses, as in the Cambridge University of England; or adopt the briefest and clearest forms, as under the pens of the geometers of our Cambridge; but it always reveals to us precisely the writer's thought.—Hill, Thomas.

North American Review, Vol. 85, pp. 224-225.

1211. The domain, over which the language of analysis extends its sway, is, indeed, relatively limited, but within this domain it so infinitely excels ordinary language that its attempt to follow the former must be given up after a few steps. The mathematician, who knows how to think in this marvelously condensed language, is as different from the mechanical computer as heaven from earth.—PRINGSHEIM, A.

> *Jahresberichte der Deutschen Mathematiker Vereinigung, Bd. 13, p. 367.*

1212. The results of systematic symbolical reasoning must *always* express general truths, by their nature; and do not, for their justification, require each of the steps of the process to represent some definite operation upon quantity. The *absolute universality of the interpretation of symbols* is the fundamental principle of their use.—WHEWELL, WILLIAM.

> *The Philosophy of the Inductive Sciences, Part I, Bk. 2, chap. 12, sect. 2 (London, 1858).*

1213. Anyone who understands algebraic notation, reads at a glance in an equation results reached arithmetically only with great labour and pains.—COURNOT, A.

> *Theory of Wealth [N. T. Bacon], (New York, 1897), p. 4.*

1214. As arithmetic and algebra are sciences of great clearness, certainty, and extent, which are immediately conversant about signs, upon the skilful use whereof they entirely depend, so a little attention to them may possibly help us to judge of the progress of the mind in other sciences, which, though differing in nature, design, and object, may yet agree in the general methods of proof and inquiry.—BERKELEY, GEORGE.

> *Alciphron, or the Minute Philosopher, Dialogue 7, sect. 12.*

1215. In general the position as regards all such new calculi is this—That one cannot accomplish by them anything that could not be accomplished without them. However, the advantage is, that, provided such a calculus corresponds to the inmost nature of frequent needs, anyone who masters it thoroughly is able—without the unconscious inspiration of genius which no one can command—to solve the respective problems, yea, to solve them mechanically in complicated cases in which, without such aid, even genius becomes powerless. Such is the case with the invention of general algebra, with the differential calculus, and in a more limited region with Lagrange's calculus of variations, with my calculus of congruences, and with Möbius's calculus. Such conceptions unite, as it were, into an organic whole countless problems which otherwise would remain isolated and require for their separate solution more or less application of inventive genius.—GAUSS, C. J.

Werke, Bd. 8, p. 298.

1216. The invention of what we may call primary or fundamental notation has been but little indebted to analogy, evidently owing to the small extent of ideas in which comparison can be made useful. But at the same time analogy should be attended to, even if for no other reason than that, by making the invention of notation an art, the exertion of individual caprice ceases to be allowable. Nothing is more easy than the invention of notation, and nothing of worse example and consequence than the confusion of mathematical expressions by unknown symbols. If new notation be advisable, permanently or temporarily, it should carry with it some mark of distinction from that which is already in use, unless it be a demonstrable extension of the latter.—DE MORGAN, A.

Calculus of Functions; Encyclopedia Metropolitana, Addition to Article 26.

1217. Before the introduction of the Arabic notation, multiplication was difficult, and the division even of integers called into play the highest mathematical faculties. Probably nothing in the modern world could have more astonished a Greek mathematician than to learn that, under the influence of compulsory education, the whole population of Western Europe, from the highest to the lowest, could perform the operation of division for the largest numbers. This fact would have seemed to him a sheer impossibility. . . . Our modern power of easy reckoning

with decimal fractions is the most miraculous result of a perfect notation.—WHITEHEAD, A. N.
Introduction to Mathematics (New York, 1911), p. 59.

1218. Mathematics is often considered a difficult and mysterious science, because of the numerous symbols which it employs. Of course, nothing is more incomprehensible than a symbolism which we do not understand. Also a symbolism, which we only partially understand and are unaccustomed to use, is difficult to follow. In exactly the same way the technical terms of any profession or trade are incomprehensible to those who have never been trained to use them. But this is not because they are difficult in themselves. On the contrary they have invariably been introduced to make things easy. So in mathematics, granted that we are giving any serious attention to mathematical ideas, the symbolism is invariably an immense simplification.—WHITEHEAD, A. N.
Introduction to Mathematics (New York, 1911), pp. 59–60.

1219. Symbolism is useful because it makes things difficult. Now in the beginning everything is self-evident, and it is hard to see whether one self-evident proposition follows from another or not. Obviousness is always the enemy to correctness. Hence we must invent a new and difficult symbolism in which nothing is obvious. . . . Thus the whole of Arithmetic and Algebra has been shown to require three indefinable notions and five indemonstrable propositions.—RUSSELL, BERTRAND.
International Monthly, 1901, p. 85.

1220. The employment of mathematical symbols is perfectly natural when the relations between magnitudes are under discussion; and even if they are not rigorously necessary, it would hardly be reasonable to reject them, because they are not equally familiar to all readers and because they have sometimes been wrongly used, if they are able to facilitate the exposition of problems, to render it more concise, to open the way to more extended developments, and to avoid the digressions of vague argumentation.—COURNOT, A.
Theory of Wealth [N. T. Bacon], (New York, 1897), pp. 3–4.

1221. An all-inclusive geometrical symbolism, such as Hamilton and Grassmann conceived of, is impossible.

BURKHARDT, H.
Jahresbericht der Deutschen Mathematiker Vereinigung, Bd. 5, p. 52.

1222. The language of analysis, most perfect of all, being in itself a powerful instrument of discoveries, its notations, especially when they are necessary and happily conceived, are so many germs of new calculi.—LAPLACE.

Oeuvres, t. 7 (Paris, 1896), p. xl.

CHAPTER XIII

1301. Mathematics belongs to every inquiry, moral as well as physical. Even the rules of logic, by which it is rigidly bound, could not be deduced without its aid. The laws of argument admit of simple statement, but they must be curiously transposed before they can be applied to the living speech and verified by observation. In its pure and simple form the syllogism cannot be directly compared with all experience, or it would not have required an Aristotle to discover it. It must be transmuted into all the possible shapes in which reasoning loves to clothe itself. The transmutation is the mathematical process in the establishment of the law.—PEIRCE, BENJAMIN.

Linear Associative Algebra; American Journal of Mathematics, Vol. 4 (1881), p. 97.

1302. In mathematics we see the conscious logical activity of our mind in its purest and most perfect form; here is made manifest to us all the labor and the great care with which it progresses, the precision which is necessary to determine exactly the source of the established general theorems, and the difficulty with which we form and comprehend abstract conceptions; but we also learn here to have confidence in the certainty, breadth, and fruitfulness of such intellectual labor.—HELMHOLTZ, H.

Vorträge und Reden, Bd. 1 (Braunschweig, 1896), p. 176.

1303. Mathematical demonstrations are a logic of as much or more use, than that commonly learned at schools, serving to a just formation of the mind, enlarging its capacity, and strengthening it so as to render the same capable of exact reasoning, and discerning truth from falsehood in all occurrences, even in subjects not mathematical. For which reason it is said, the Egyptians, Persians, and Lacedaemonians seldom elected any new kings, but such as had some knowledge in the mathe-

matics, imagining those, who had not, men of imperfect judgments, and unfit to rule and govern.—FRANKLIN, BENJAMIN.
> *Usefulness of Mathematics; Works (Boston,*
> *1840), Vol. 2, p. 68.*

1304. The mathematical conception is, from its very nature,
abstract; indeed its abstractness is usually of a higher order
than the abstractness of the logician.—CHRYSTAL, GEORGE.
> *Encyclopedia Britannica (Ninth Edition),*
> *Article "Mathematics."*

1305. Mathematics, that giant pincers of scientific logic . . .
> HALSTED, G. B.
> *Science (1905), p. 161.*

1306. Logic has borrowed the rules of geometry without
understanding its power. . . . I am far from placing logicians
by the side of geometers who teach the true way to guide the
reason. . . . The method of avoiding error is sought by every
one. The logicians profess to lead the way, the geometers alone
reach it, and aside from their science there is no true demonstration.—PASCAL.
> *Quoted by A. Rebière: Mathématiques et*
> *Mathématiciens (Paris, 1898), pp. 162–163.*

1307. Mathematics, like dialectics, is an organ of the higher
sense, in its execution it is an art like eloquence. To both
nothing but the form is of value; neither cares anything for
content. Whether mathematics considers pennies or guineas,
whether rhetoric defends truth or error, is perfectly immaterial
to either.—GOETHE.
> *Sprüche in Prosa, Natur IV, 946.*

1308. Confined to its true domain, mathematical reasoning is
admirably adapted to perform the universal office of sound
logic: to induce in order to deduce, in order to construct. . . .
It contents itself to furnish, in the most favorable domain, a
model of clearness, of precision, and consistency, the close
contemplation of which is alone able to prepare the mind to
render other conceptions also as perfect as their nature permits. Its general reaction, more negative than positive, must

consist, above all, in inspiring us everywhere with an invincible aversion for vagueness, inconsistency, and obscurity, which may always be really avoided in any reasoning whatsoever, if we make sufficient effort.—COMTE, A.

Subjective Synthesis.

1309. Formal thought, consciously recognized as such, is the means of all exact knowledge; and a correct understanding of the main formal sciences, Logic and Mathematics, is the proper and only safe foundation for a scientific education.

LEFEVRE, ARTHUR.
Number and its Algebra (Boston, Sect. 222.)

1310. It has come to pass, I know not how, that Mathematics and Logic, which ought to be but the handmaids of Physic, nevertheless presume on the strength of the certainty which they possess to exercise dominion over it.

BACON, FRANCIS.
De Augmentis, Bk. 3.

1311. We may regard geometry as a practical logic, for the truths which it considers, being the most simple and most sensible of all, are, for this reason, the most susceptible to easy and ready application of the rules of reasoning.—D'ALEMBERT.

Quoted in A. Rebière: Mathématiques et Mathématiciens (Paris, 1898), pp. 151–152.

1312. There are notable examples enough of demonstration outside of mathematics, and it may be said that Aristotle has already given some in his "Prior Analytics." In fact logic is as susceptible of demonstration as geometry, . . . Archimedes is the first, whose works we have, who has practised the art of demonstration upon an occasion where he is treating of physics, as he has done in his book on Equilibrium. Furthermore, jurists may be said to have many good demonstrations; especially the ancient Roman jurists, whose fragments have been preserved to us in the Pandects.—LEIBNITZ, G. W.

New Essay on Human Understanding [Langley], Bk. 4, chap. 2, sect. 12.

1313. It is commonly considered that mathematics owes its certainty to its reliance on the immutable principles of formal logic. This . . . is only half the truth imperfectly expressed. The other half would be that the principles of formal logic owe such a degree of permanence as they have largely to the fact that they have been tempered by long and varied use by mathematicians. "A vicious circle!" you will perhaps say. I should rather describe it as an example of the process known by mathematicians as the method of successive approximation.

BÔCHER, MAXIME.
Bulletin of the American Mathematical Society, Vol. 11, p. 120.

1314. Whatever advantage can be attributed to logic in directing and strengthening the action of the understanding is found in a higher degree in mathematical study, with the immense added advantage of a determinate subject, distinctly circumscribed, admitting of the utmost precision, and free from the danger which is inherent in all abstract logic,—of leading to useless and puerile rules, or to vain ontological speculations. The positive method, being everywhere identical, is as much at home in the art of reasoning as anywhere else: and this is why no science, whether biology or any other, can offer any kind of reasoning, of which mathematics does not supply a simpler and purer counterpart. Thus, we are enabled to eliminate the only remaining portion of the old philosophy which could even appear to offer any real utility; the logical part, the value of which is irrevocably absorbed by mathematical science.—COMTE, A.
Positive Philosophy, [Martineau], (London, 1875), Vol. 1, pp. 321–322.

1315. We know that mathematicians care no more for logic than logicians for mathematics. The two eyes of exact science are mathematics and logic: the mathematical sect puts out the logical eye, the logical sect puts out the mathematical eye; each believing that it can see better with one eye than with two.

DE MORGAN, A.
Quoted in F. Cajori: History of Mathematics (New York, 1897), p. 316.

1316. The progress of the art of rational discovery depends in a great part upon the art of characteristic (ars characteristica). The reason why people usually seek demonstrations only in numbers and lines and things represented by these is none other than that there are not, outside of numbers, convenient characters corresponding to the notions.—LEIBNITZ, G. W.

Philosophische Schriften [Gerhardt] Bd. 8, p. 198.

1317. The influence of the mathematics of Leibnitz upon his philosophy appears chiefly in connection with his law of continuity and his prolonged efforts to establish a Logical Calculus. . . . To find a Logical Calculus (implying a universal philosophical language or system of signs) is an attempt to apply in theological and philosophical investigations an analytic method analogous to that which had proved so successful in Geometry and Physics. It seemed to Leibnitz that if all the complex and apparently disconnected ideas which make up our knowledge could be analysed into their simple elements, and if these elements could each be represented by a definite sign, we should have a kind of " alphabet of human thoughts." By the combination of these signs (letters of the alphabet of thought) a system of true knowledge would be built up, in which reality would be more and more adequately represented or symbolized. . . . In many cases the analysis may result in an infinite series of elements; but the principles of the Infinitesimal Calculus in mathematics have shown that this does not necessarily render calculation impossible or inaccurate. Thus it seemed to Leibnitz that a synthetic calculus, based upon a thorough analysis, would be the most effective instrument of knowledge that could be devised. " I feel," he says, " that controversies can never be finished, nor silence imposed upon the Sects, unless we give up complicated reasonings in favor of simple *calculations*, words of vague and uncertain meaning in favor of fixed symbols." Thus it will appear that " every paralogism is nothing but *an error of calculation.*" " When controversies arise, there will be no more necessity of disputation between two philosophers than between two accountants. Nothing will be needed but that they should take pen in hand, sit down with

their counting-tables, and (having summoned a friend, if they like) say to one another: *Let us calculate.*"—LATTA, ROBERT.
> *Leibnitz, The Monadology, etc. (Oxford, 1898), p. 85.*

1318. Pure mathematics was discovered by Boole in a work which he called "The Laws of Thought". . . . His work was concerned with formal logic, and this is the same thing as mathematics.—RUSSELL, BERTRAND.
> *International Monthly, 1901, p. 83.*

1319. Mathematics is but the higher development of Symbolic Logic.—WHETHAM, W. C. D.
> *Recent Development of Physical Science (Philadelphia, 1904), p. 34.*

1320. Symbolic Logic has been disowned by many logicians on the plea that its interest is mathematical, and by many mathematicians on the plea that its interest is logical.
> WHITEHEAD, A. N.
> *Universal Algebra (Cambridge, 1898), Preface, p. 6.*

1321. . . . the two great components of the critical movement, though distinct in origin and following separate paths, are found to converge at last in the thesis: Symbolic Logic is Mathematics, Mathematics is Symbolic Logic, the twain are one.
> KEYSER, C. J.
> *Lectures on Science, Philosophy and Art (New York, 1908), p. 19.*

1322. The emancipation of logic from the yoke of Aristotle very much resembles the emancipation of geometry from the bondage of Euclid; and, by its subsequent growth and diversification, logic, less abundantly perhaps but not less certainly than geometry, has illustrated the blessings of freedom.
> KEYSER, C. J.
> *Science, Vol. 35 (1912), p. 108.*

1323. I would express it as my personal view, which is probably not yet shared generally, that pure mathematics seems to

me merely a *branch of general logic;* that branch which is based
on the concept of *numbers,* to whose economic advantages is to
be attributed the tremendous development which this particular
branch has undergone as compared with the remaining branches
of logic, which until the most recent times have remained almost stationary.—SCHRÖDER, E.

> *Ueber Pasigraphie etc.; Verhandlungen des 1. In-*
> *ternationalen Mathematiker-Kongresses (Leipzig,*
> *1898), p. 149.*

1324. If logical training is to consist, not in repeating barbarous scholastic formulas or mechanically tacking together
empty majors and minors, but in acquiring dexterity in the use
of trustworthy methods of advancing from the known to the
unknown, then mathematical investigation must ever remain
one of its most indispensable instruments. Once inured to the
habit of accurately imagining abstract relations, recognizing the
true value of symbolic conceptions, and familiarized with a
fixed standard of proof, the mind is equipped for the consideration of quite other objects than lines and angles. The twin
treatises of Adam Smith on social science, wherein, by deducing
all human phenomena first from the unchecked action of selfish-
ness and then from the unchecked action of sympathy, he
arrives at mutually-limiting conclusions of transcendent practical importance, furnish for all time a brilliant illustration of the
value of mathematical methods and mathematical discipline.

FISKE, JOHN.

> *Darwinism and other Essays (Boston, 1893),*
> *pp. 297–298.*

1325. No irrational exaggeration of the claims of Mathematics can ever deprive that part of philosophy of the property
of being the natural basis of all logical education, through its
simplicity, abstractness, generality, and freedom from dis-
turbance by human passion. There, and there alone, we find in
full development the art of reasoning, all the resources of
which, from the most spontaneous to the most sublime, are
continually applied with far more variety and fruitfulness than
elsewhere; . . . The more abstract portion of mathematics

may in fact be regarded as an immense repository of logical resources, ready for use in scientific deduction and co-ordination.

COMTE, A.

Positive Philosphy [Martineau], (London, 1875), Vol. 2, p. 439.

1326. Logic it is called [referring to Whitehead and Russell's Principia Mathematica] and logic it is, the logic of propositions and functions and classes and relations, by far the greatest (not merely the biggest) logic that our planet has produced, so much that is new in matter and in manner; but it is also mathematics, a prolegomenon to the science, yet itself mathematics in its most genuine sense, differing from other parts of the science only in the respects that it surpasses these in fundamentality, generality and precision, and lacks traditionality. Few will read it, but all will feel its effect, for behind it is the urgence and push of a magnificent past: two thousand five hundred years of record and yet longer tradition of human endeavor to think aright.—KEYSER, C. J.

Science, Vol. 35 (1912), p. 110.

CHAPTER XIV

1401. Socrates is praised by all the centuries for having called philosophy from heaven to men on earth; but if, knowing the condition of our science, he should come again and should look once more to heaven for a means of curing men, he would there find that to mathematics, rather than to the philosophy of today, had been given the crown because of its industry and its most happy and brilliant successes.—HERBART, J. F.

> *Werke [Kehrbach], (Langensalza, 1890), Bd. 5, p. 95.*

1402. It is the embarrassment of metaphysics that it is able to accomplish so little with the many things that mathematics offers her.—KANT, E.

> *Metaphysische Anfangsgründe der Naturwissenschaft, Vorrede.*

1403. Philosophers, when they have possessed a thorough knowledge of mathematics, have been among those who have enriched the science with some of its best ideas. On the other hand it must be said that, with hardly an exception, all the remarks on mathematics made by those philosophers who have possessed but a slight or hasty or late-acquired knowledge of it are entirely worthless, being either trivial or wrong.

> WHITEHEAD, A. N.
> *Introduction to Mathematics (New York, 1911), p. 113.*

1404. The union of philosophical and mathematical productivity, which besides in Plato we find only in Pythagoras, Descartes and Leibnitz, has always yielded the choicest fruits to mathematics: To the first we owe scientific mathematics in general, Plato discovered the analytic method, by means of which mathematics was elevated above the view-point of the elements, Descartes created the analytical geometry, our own

illustrious countryman discovered the infinitesimal calculus—
and just these are the four greatest steps in the development of
mathematics.—HANKEL, HERMANN.
> Geschichte der Mathematik im Altertum und
> im Mittelalter (Leipzig, 1874), pp. 149–150.

1405. Without mathematics one cannot fathom the depths
of philosophy; without philosophy one cannot fathom the
depths of mathematics; without the two one cannot fathom
anything.—BORDAS-DEMOULINS.
> Quoted in A. Rebière: Mathématiques et Mathé-
> maticiens (Paris, 1898), p. 147.

1406. In the end mathematics is but simple philosophy, and
philosophy, higher mathematics in general.—NOVALIS.
> Schriften (Berlin, 1901), Teil 2, p. 443.

1407. It is a safe rule to apply that, when a mathematical or
philosophical author writes with a misty profundity, he is
talking nonsense.—WHITEHEAD, A. N.
> Introduction to Mathematics (New York, 1911),
> p. 227.

1408. The real finisher of our education is philosophy, but it is
the office of mathematics to ward off the dangers of philosophy.
> HERBART, J. F.
> Pestalozzi's Idee eines ABC der Anschauung;
> Werke [Kehrbach], (Langensalza, 1890),
> Bd. 1, p. 168.

1409. Since antiquity mathematics has been regarded as the
most indispensable school for philosophic thought and in its
highest spheres the research of the mathematician is indeed most
closely related to pure speculation. Mathematics is the most
perfect union between exact knowledge and theoretical thought.
> CURTIUS, E.
> Berliner Monatsberichte (1873), p. 517.

1410. Geometry has been, throughout, of supreme importance
in the history of knowledge.—RUSSELL, BERTRAND.
> Foundations of Geometry (Cambridge, 1897),
> p. 54.

1411. He is unworthy of the name of man who is ignorant of the fact that the diagonal of a square is incommensurable with its side.—PLATO.

> *Quoted by Sophie Germain: Mémoire sur les surfaces élastiques.*

1412. Mathematics, considered as a science, owes its origin to the *idealistic* needs of the Greek philosophers, and not as fable has it, to the *practical* demands of Egyptian economics. . . . Adam was no zoölogist when he gave names to the beasts of the field, nor were the Egyptian surveyors mathematicians.

> HANKEL, H.
> *Die Entwickelung der Mathematik in den letzten Jahrhunderten (Tübingen, 1884), p. 7.*

1413. There are only two ways open to man for attaining a certain knowledge of truth: clear intuition and necessary deduction.—DESCARTES.

> *Rules for the Direction of the Mind; Torrey's The Philosophy of Descartes (New York, 1892), p. 104.*

1414. Mathematicians have, in many cases, proved some things to be possible and others to be impossible, which, without demonstration, would not have been believed . . . Mathematics afford many instances of impossibilities in the nature of things, which no man would have believed, if they had not been strictly demonstrated. Perhaps, if we were able to reason demonstratively in other subjects, to as great extent as in mathematics, we might find many things to be impossible, which we conclude, without hesitation, to be possible.

> REID, THOMAS.
> *Essay on the Intellectual Powers of Man, Essay 4, chap. 3.*

1415. If philosophers understood mathematics, they would know that indefinite speech, which permits each one to think what he pleases and produces a constantly increasing difference of opinion, is utterly unable, in spite of all fine words and even in spite of the magnitude of the objects which are under contemplation, to maintain a balance against a science which in-

structs and advances through every word which it utters and
which at the same time wins for itself endless astonishment, not
through its survey of immense spaces, but through the exhibition of the most prodigious human ingenuity which surpasses all
power of description.—HERBART, J. F.

> Werke Kehrbach (Langensalza, 1890), Bd. 5,
> p. 105.

1416. German intellect is an excellent thing, but when a
German product is presented it must be analysed. Most
probably it is a combination of intellect (I) and tobacco-smoke
(T). Certainly I_3T_1, and I_2T_1, occur; but I_1T_3 is more common, and I_2T_{15} and I_1T_{20} occur. In many cases metaphysics (M)
occurs and I hold that $I_aT_bM_c$ never occurs without b + c > 2a.
N. B.—Be careful, in analysing the compounds of the three,
not to confound T and M, which are strongly suspected to be
isomorphic. Thus, $I_1T_3M_3$ may easily be confounded with
I_1T_6. As far as I dare say anything, those who have placed
Hegel, Fichte, etc., in the rank of the extenders of *Kant* have
imagined T and M to be identical.—DE MORGAN, A.

> Graves' Life of W. R. Hamilton (New York,
> 1882–1889), Vol. 13, p. 446.

1417. The discovery [of Ceres] was made by G. Piazzi of
Palermo; and it was the more interesting as its announcement
occurred simultaneously with a publication by Hegel in which
he severely criticized astronomers for not paying more attention
to philosophy, a science, said he, which would at once have
shown them that there could not possibly be more than seven
planets, and a study of which would therefore have prevented an
absurd waste of time in looking for what in the nature of things
could never be found.—BALL, W. W. R.

> History of Mathematics (London, 1901), p. 458.

1418. But who shall parcel out
　　His intellect by geometric rules,
　　Split like a province into round and square?

> WORDSWORTH.
> The Prelude. Bk. 2.

1419. And Proposition, gentle maid,
Who soothly ask'd stern Demonstration's aid, . . .

COLERIDGE, S. T.
A Mathematical Problem.

1420. Mathematics connect themselves on the one side with common life and physical science; on the other side with philosophy in regard to our notions of space and time, and in the questions which have arisen as to the universality and necessity of the truths of mathematics and the foundation of our knowledge of them.—CAYLEY, ARTHUR.

British Association Address (1883); Collected Mathematical Papers, Vol. 11, p. 430.

1427. Mathematical teaching . . . trains the mind to capacities, which . . . are of the closest kin to those of the greatest metaphysician and philosopher. There is some color of truth for the opposite doctrine in the case of elementary algebra. The resolution of a common equation can be reduced to almost as mechanical a process as the working of a sum in arithmetic. The reduction of the question to an equation, however, is no mechanical operation, but one which, according to the degree of its difficulty, requires nearly every possible grade of ingenuity: not to speak of the new, and in the present state of the science insoluble, equations, which start up at every fresh step attempted in the application of mathematics to other branches of knowledge.—MILL, J. S.

An Examination of Sir William Hamilton's Philosophy (London, 1878), p. 615.

1422. The value of mathematical instruction as a preparation for those more difficult investigations, consists in the applicability not of its doctrines, but of its methods. Mathematics will ever remain the most perfect type of the Deductive Method in general; and the applications of mathematics to the simpler branches of physics, furnish the only school in which philosophers can effectually learn the most difficult and important portion of their art, the employment of the laws of the simpler phenomena for explaining and predicting those of the more complex. These grounds are quite sufficient for deeming mathe-

matical training an indispensable basis of real scientific education, and regarding, with Plato, one who is ἀγεωμέτρητος, as
wanting in one of the most essential qualifications for the
successful cultivation of the higher branches of philosophy.

MILL, J. S.
System of Logic, Bk. 3, chap. 24, sect. 9.

1423. In metaphysical reasoning, the process is always short.
The conclusion is but a step or two, seldom more, from the first
principles or axioms on which it is grounded, and the different
conclusions depend not one upon another.

It is otherwise in mathematical reasoning. Here the field has
no limits. One proposition leads on to another, that to a third,
and so on without end. If it should be asked, why demonstrative reasoning has so wide a field in mathematics, while, in other
abstract subjects, it is confined within very narrow limits, I
conceive this is chiefly owing to the nature of quantity, . . .
mathematical quantities being made up of parts without number, can touch in innumerable points, and be compared in
innumerable different ways.—REID, THOMAS.
Essays on the Powers of the Human Mind
(Edinburgh, 1812), Vol. 2, pp. 422-423.

1424. The power of Reason . . . is unquestionably the most
important by far of those which are comprehended under the
general title of Intellectual. It is on the right use of this power
that our success in the pursuit of both knowledge and of happi-
ness depends; and it is by the exclusive possession of it that man
is distinguished, in the most essential respects, from the lower
animals. It is, indeed, from their subserviency to its operations,
that the other faculties . . . derive their chief value.
STEWART, DUGALD.
Philosophy of the Human Mind; Collected
Works (Edinburgh, 1854), Vol. 8, p. 5.

1425. When . . . I asked myself why was it then that the
earliest philosophers would admit to the study of wisdom only
those who had studied mathematics, as if this science was the
easiest of all and the one most necessary for preparing and
disciplining the mind to comprehend the more advanced, I

suspected that they had knowledge of a mathematical science different from that of our time. . . .

I believe I find some traces of these true mathematics in Pappus and Diophantus, who, although they were not of extreme antiquity, lived nevertheless in times long preceding ours. But I willingly believe that these writers themselves, by a culpable ruse, suppressed the knowledge of them; like some artisans who conceal their secret, they feared, perhaps, that the ease and simplicity of their method, if become popular, would diminish its importance, and they preferred to make themselves admired by leaving to us, as the product of their art, certain barren truths deduced with subtlety, rather than to teach us that art itself, the knowledge of which would end our admiration.

DESCARTES.

Rules for the Direction of the Mind; Philosophy of Descartes [*Torrey*], (*New York, 1892*), *pp. 70–71.*

1426. If we rightly adhere to our rule [that is, that we should occupy ourselves only with those subjects in reference to which the mind is capable of acquiring certain and indubitable knowledge] there will remain but few things to the study of which we can devote ourselves. There exists in the sciences hardly a single question upon which men of intellectual ability have not held different opinions. But whenever two men pass contrary judgment on the same thing, it is certain that one of the two is wrong. More than that, neither of them has the truth; for if one of them had a clear and precise insight into it, he could so exhibit it to his opponent as to end the discussion by compelling his conviction. . . . It follows from this, if we reckon rightly, that among existing sciences there remain only geometry and arithmetic, to which the observance of our rule would bring us.

DESCARTES.

Rules for the Direction of the Mind; Philosophy of Descartes [*Torrey*], (*New York, 1892*), *p. 62.*

1427. The same reason which led Plato to recommend the study of arithmetic led him to recommend also the study of geometry. The vulgar crowd of geometricians, he says, will not

understand him. They have practice always in view. They do
not know that the real use of the science is to lead men to the
knowledge of abstract, essential, eternal truth. (Plato's Republic, Book 7). Indeed if we are to believe Plutarch, Plato carried
his feeling so far that he considered geometry as degraded by
being applied to any purpose of vulgar utility. Archytas, it
seems, had framed machines of extraordinary power on mathematical principles. (Plutarch, Sympos., VIII., and Life of
Marcellus. The machines of Archytas are also mentioned by
Aulus Gellius and Diogenes Laertius). Plato remonstrated
with his friend, and declared that this was to degrade a noble
intellectual exercise into a low craft, fit only for carpenters and
wheelwrights. The office of geometry, he said, was to discipline
the mind, not to minister to the base wants of the body. His
interference was successful; and from that time according to
Plutarch, the science of mechanics was considered unworthy of
the attention of a philosopher.—MACAULAY.

Lord Bacon; Edinburgh Review, July, 1837.

1428. The intellectual habits of the Mathematicians are, in
some respects, the same with those [of the Metaphysicians] we
have been now considering; but, in other respects, they differ
widely. Both are favourable to the improvement of the power
of *attention*, but not in the same manner, nor in the same degree.

Those of the metaphysician give capacity of fixing the attention on the subjects of our consciousness, without being distracted by things external; but they afford little or no exercise
to that species of attention which enables us to follow long
processes of reasoning, and to keep in view all the various steps
of an investigation till we arrive at the conclusion. In mathematics, such processes are much longer than in any other
science; and hence the study of it is peculiarly calculated to
strengthen the power of steady and concatenated thinking,—
a power which, in all the pursuits of life, whether speculative or
active, is one of the most valuable endowments we can possess.
This command of attention, however, it may be proper to add,
is to be acquired, not by the practice of modern methods, but
by the study of Greek geometry, more particularly, by accustoming ourselves to pursue long trains of demonstration, without

availing ourselves of the aid of any sensible diagrams; the thoughts being directed solely by those ideal delineations which the powers of conception and of memory enable us to form.

STEWART, DUGALD.
Philosophy of the Human Mind, Part 3, chap. 1, sect. 3.

1429. They [the Greeks] speculated and theorized under a lively persuasion that a Science of every part of nature was possible, and was a fit object for the exercise of a man's best faculties; and they were speedily led to the conviction that such a science must clothe its conclusions in the language of mathematics. This conviction is eminently conspicuous in the writings of Plato. . . . Probably no succeeding step in the discovery of the Laws of Nature was of so much importance as the full adoption of this pervading conviction, that there must be Mathematical Laws of Nature, and that it is the business of Philosophy to discover these Laws. This conviction continues, through all the succeeding ages of the history of the science, to be the animating and supporting principle of scientific investigation and discovery.—WHEWELL, W.
History of the Inductive Sciences, Vol. 1, bk. 2, chap. 3.

1430. For to pass by those Ancients, the wonderful *Pythagoras,* the sagacious *Democritus,* the divine *Plato,* the most subtle and very learned *Aristotle,* Men whom every Age has hitherto acknowledged as deservedly honored, as the greatest Philosophers, the Ring-leaders of Arts; in whose Judgments how much these Studies [mathematics] were esteemed, is abundantly proclaimed in History and confirmed by their famous Monuments, which are everywhere interspersed and bespangled with Mathematical Reasonings and Examples, as with so many Stars; and consequently anyone not in some Degree conversant in these Studies will in vain expect to understand, or unlock their hidden Meanings, without the Help of a Mathematical Key: For who can play well on *Aristotle's* Instrument but with a Mathematical Quill; or not be altogether deaf to the Lessons of natural *Philosophy,* while ignorant of *Geometry?* Who void of (*Geometry* shall I say, or) *Arithmetic* can comprehend *Plato's*

Socrates lisping with Children concerning Square Numbers; or can conceive *Plato* himself treating not only of the Universe, but the Polity of Commonwealths regulated by the Laws of Geometry, and formed according to a Mathematical Plan?

BARROW, ISAAC.
Mathematical Lectures (London, 1734), pp. 26-27.

1431. And Reason now through number, time, and space
Darts the keen lustre of her serious eye;
And learns from facts compar'd the laws to trace
Whose long procession leads to Deity.

BEATTIE, JAMES.
The Minstrel, Bk. 2, stanza 47.

1432. That Egyptian and Chaldean wisdom mathematical wherewith Moses and Daniel were furnished, . . .

HOOKER, RICHARD.
Ecclesiastical Polity, Bk. 3, sect. 8.

1433. General and certain truths are only founded in the habitudes and relations of *abstract ideas.* A sagacious and methodical application of our thoughts, for the finding out of these relations, is the only way to discover all that can be put with truth and certainty concerning them into general propositions. By what steps we are to proceed in these, is to be learned in the schools of mathematicians, who, from very plain and easy beginnings, by gentle degrees, and a continued chain of reasonings, proceed to the discovery and demonstration of truths that appear at first sight beyond human capacity. The art of finding proofs, and the admirable method they have invented for the singling out and laying in order those intermediate ideas that demonstratively show the equality or inequality of unapplicable quantities, is that which has carried them so far and produced such wonderful and unexpected discoveries; but whether something like this, in respect of other ideas, as well as those of magnitude, may not in time be found out, I will not determine. This, I think, I may say, that if other ideas that are the real as well as the nominal essences of their species, were pursued in the way familiar to mathematicians, they would carry our thoughts further, and with greater evidence and clearness than possibly we are apt to imagine.

LOCKE, JOHN.
An Essay concerning Human Understanding,
Bk. 4, chap. 12, sect. 7.

1434. Those long chains of reasoning, quite simple and easy, which geometers are wont to employ in the accomplishment of their most difficult demonstrations, led me to think that everything which might fall under the cognizance of the human mind might be connected together in a similar manner, and that, provided only that one should take care not to receive anything as true which was not so, and if one were always careful to preserve the order necessary for deducing one truth from another, there would be none so remote at which he might not at last arrive, nor so concealed which he might not discover.

DESCARTES.
Discourse upon Method, part 2; The Philos-
ophy of Descartes [Torrey], (New York, 1892),
p. 47.

1435. If anyone wished to write in mathematical fashion in metaphysics or ethics, nothing would prevent him from so doing with vigor. Some have professed to do this, and we have a promise of mathematical demonstrations outside of mathematics; but it is very rare that they have been successful. This is, I believe, because they are disgusted with the trouble it is necessary to take for a small number of readers where they would ask as in Persius: *Quis leget haec,* and reply: *Vel duo vel nemo.*

LEIBNITZ.
New Essay concerning Human Understanding,
Langley, Bk 2, chap. 29, sect. 12.

1436. It is commonly asserted that mathematics and philosophy differ from one another according to their *objects,* the former treating of *quantity,* the latter of *quality.* All this is false. The difference between these sciences cannot depend on their object; for philosophy applies to everything, hence also to *quanta,* and so does mathematics in part, inasmuch as everything has magnitude. It is only the *different kind of rational knowledge or application* of reason in mathematics and philosophy which constitutes the specific difference between these two sciences. For philosophy is *rational knowledge from mere concepts*, mathematics, on the contrary, is *rational knowledge from the construction of concepts*.

We construct concepts when we represent them in intuition *a priori*, without experience, or when we represent in intuition the object which corresponds to our concept of it.—The mathematician can never apply his reason to mere concepts, nor the philosopher to the construction of concepts.—In mathematics the reason is employed *in concreto*, however, the intuition is not empirical, but the object of contemplation is something *a priori*.

In this, as we see, mathematics has an advantage over philosophy, the knowledge in the former being intuitive, in the latter, on the contrary, only *discursive*. But the reason why in mathematics we deal more with quantity lies in this, that magnitudes can be constructed in intuition *a priori*, while qualities, on the contrary, do not permit of being represented in intuition.

KANT, E.
Logik; Werke [Hartenstein], (Leipzig, 1868), Bd. 8, pp. 23–24.

1437. Kant has divided human ideas into the two categories of quantity and quality, which, if true, would destroy the universality of Mathematics; but Descartes' fundamental conception of the relation of the concrete to the abstract in Mathematics abolishes this division, and proves that all ideas of quality are reducible to ideas of quantity. He had in view geometrical phenomena only; but his successors have included in this generalization, first, mechanical phenomena, and, more recently, those of heat. There are now no geometers who do not consider it of universal application, and admit that every phenomenon may be as logically capable of being represented by an equation as a curve or a motion, if only we were always capable (which we are very far from being) of first discovering, and then resolving it.

The limitations of Mathematical science are not, then, in its nature. The limitations are in our intelligence: and by these we find the domain of the science remarkably restricted, in proportion as phenomena, in becoming special, become complex.—COMTE, A.   *Positive Philosophy [Martineau], Bk. 1, chap. 1.*

1438. The great advantage of the mathematical sciences over the moral consists in this, that the ideas of the former, being sensible, are always clear and determinate, the smallest distinction between them being immediately perceptible, and the same terms are still expressive of the same ideas, without ambiguity or variation. An oval is never mistaken for a circle, nor an hyperbola for an ellipsis. The isosceles and scalenum are distinguished by boundaries more exact than vice and virtue, right or wrong. If any term be defined in geometry, the mind readily, of itself, substitutes on all occasions, the definition for the thing defined: Or even when no definition is employed, the object itself may be represented to the senses, and by that means be steadily and clearly apprehended. But the finer sentiments of the mind, the operations of the understanding, the various agitations of the passions, though really in themselves distinct, easily escape us, when surveyed by reflection; nor is it in our power to recall the original object, so often as we have occasion to contemplate it. Ambiguity, by this means, is gradually introduced into our reasonings: Similar objects are readily taken to be the same: And the conclusion becomes at last very wide off the premises.—HUME, DAVID.

An Inquiry concerning Human Understanding,
sect. 7, part 1.

1439. One part of these disadvantages in moral ideas which has made them be thought not capable of demonstration, may in a good measure be remedied by definitions, setting down that collection of simple ideas, which every term shall stand for; and then using the terms steadily and constantly for that precise collection. And what methods algebra, or something of that kind, may hereafter suggest, to remove the other difficulties, it is not easy to foretell. Confident, I am, that if men would in the same method, and with the same indifferency, search after moral as they do mathematical truths, they would find them have a stronger connexion one with another, and a more necessary consequence from our clear and distinct ideas, and to come nearer perfect demonstration than is commonly imagined.

LOCKE, JOHN.
An Essay concerning Human Understanding,
Bk. 4, chap. 3, sect. 20.

1440. That which in this respect has given the advantage to the ideas of quantity, and made them thought more capable of certainty and demonstration [than moral ideas], is,

First, That they can be set down and represented by sensible marks, which have a greater and nearer correspondence with them than any words or sounds whatsoever. Diagrams drawn on paper are copies of the ideas in the mind, and not liable to the uncertainty that words carry in their signification. An angle, circle, or square, drawn in lines, lies open to the view, and cannot be mistaken: it remains unchangeable, and may at leisure be considered and examined, and the demonstration be revised, and all the parts of it may be gone over more than once, without any danger of the least change in the ideas. This cannot be done in moral ideas: we have no sensible marks that resemble them, whereby we can set them down; we have nothing but words to express them by; which, though when written they remain the same, yet the ideas they stand for may change in the same man; and it is seldom that they are not different in different persons.

Secondly, Another thing that makes the greater difficulty in ethics is, That moral ideas are commonly more complex than those of the figures ordinarily considered in mathematics. From whence these two inconveniences follow:—First, that their names are of more uncertain signification, the precise collection of simple ideas they stand for not being so easily agreed on; and so the sign that is used for them in communication always, and in thinking often, does not steadily carry with it the same idea. Upon which the same disorder, confusion, and error follow, as would if a man, going to demonstrate something of an heptagon, should, in the diagram he took to do it, leave out one of the angles, or by oversight make the figure with an angle more than the name ordinarily imported, or he intended it should when at first he thought of his demonstration. This often happens, and is hardly avoidable in very complex moral ideas, where the same name being retained, an angle, i. e. one simple idea is left out, or put in the complex one (still called by the same name) more at one time than another. Secondly, From the complexedness of these moral ideas there follows another inconvenience, viz., that the mind cannot easily retain

those precise combinations so exactly and perfectly as is necessary in the examination of the habitudes and correspondences, agreements or disagreements, of several of them one with another; especially where it is to be judged of by long deductions and the intervention of several other complex ideas to show the agreement or disagreement of two remote ones.—LOCKE, JOHN.
An Essay concerning Human Understanding,
Bk. 4, chap. 3, sect. 19.

1441. It has been generally taken for granted, that mathematics alone are capable of demonstrative certainty: but to have such an agreement or disagreement as may be intuitively perceived, being, as I imagine, not the privileges of the ideas of number, extension, and figure alone, it may possibly be the want of due method and application in us, and not of sufficient evidence in things, that demonstration has been thought to have so little to do in other parts of knowledge, and been scarce so much as aimed at by any but mathematicians. For whatever ideas we have wherein the mind can perceive the immediate agreement or disagreement that is between them, there the mind is capable of intuitive knowledge, and where it can perceive the agreement or disagreement of any two ideas, by an intuitive perception of the agreement or disagreement they have with any intermediate ideas, there the mind is capable of demonstration: which is not limited to the idea of extension, figure, number, and their modes.—LOCKE, JOHN.
An Essay concerning Human Understanding,
Bk. 4, chap. 2, sect. 9.

1442. Now I shall remark again what I have already touched upon more than once, that it is a common opinion that only mathematical sciences are capable of a demonstrative certainty; but as the agreement and disagreement which may be known intuitively is not a privilege belonging only to the ideas of numbers and figures, it is perhaps for want of application on our part that mathematics alone have attained to demonstrations.—LEIBNITZ.
New Essay concerning Human Understanding,
Bk. 4, chap. 2, sect. 9 [Langley].

CHAPTER XV

1501. How comes it about that the knowledge of other sciences, which depend upon this [mathematics], is painfully sought, and that no one puts himself to the trouble of studying this science itself? I should certainly be surprised, if I did not know that everybody regarded it as being very easy, and if I had not long ago observed that the human mind, neglecting what it believes to be easy, is always in haste to run after what is novel and advanced.—DESCARTES.

Rules for the Direction of the Mind; Philosophy of Descartes [Torrey], (New York, 1892), p. 72.

1502. All quantitative determinations are in the hands of mathematics, and it at once follows from this that all speculation which is heedless of mathematics, which does not enter into partnership with it, which does not seek its aid in distinguishing between the manifold modifications that must of necessity arise by a change of quantitative determinations, is either an empty play of thoughts, or at most a fruitless effort. In the field of speculation many things grow which do not start from mathematics nor give it any care, and I am far from asserting that all that thus grow are useless weeds, among them may be many noble plants, but without mathematics none will develop to complete maturity.—HERBART, J. F.

Werke (Kehrbach), (Langensalza, 1890), Bd. 5, p. 106.

1503. There are few things which we know, which are not capable of being reduc'd to a Mathematical Reasoning, and when they cannot, it's a sign our knowledge of them is very small and confus'd; and where a mathematical reasoning can be had, it's as great folly to make use of any other, as to grope for a thing in the dark, when you have a candle standing by you.

ARBUTHNOT.

Quoted in Todhunder's History of the Theory of Probability (Cambridge and London, 1865), p. 51.

1504. Mathematical Analysis is . . . the true rational basis of the whole system of our positive knowledge.—COMTE, A.
Positive Philosophy [Martineau], Bk. 1, chap. 1.

1505. It is only through Mathematics that we can thoroughly understand what true science is. Here alone we can find in the highest degree simplicity and severity of scientific law, and such abstraction as the human mind can attain. Any scientific education setting forth from any other point, is faulty in its basis.—COMTE, A.
Positive Philosophy [Martineau], Bk. 1, chap. 1.

1506. In the present state of our knowledge we must regard Mathematics less as a constituent part of natural philosophy than as having been, since the time of Descartes and Newton, the true basis of the whole of natural philosophy; though it is, exactly speaking, both the one and the other. To us it is of less use for the knowledge of which it consists, substantial and valuable as that knowledge is, than as being the most powerful instrument that the human mind can employ in the investigation of the laws of natural phenomena.—COMTE, A.
Positive Philosophy [Martineau], Introduction, chap. 2.

1507. The concept of mathematics is the concept of science in general.—NOVALIS.
Schriften (Berlin, 1901), Teil 2, p. 222.

1508. I contend, that each natural science is real science only in so far as it is mathematical. . . . It may be that a pure philosophy of nature in general (that is, a philosophy which concerns itself only with the general concepts of nature) is possible without mathematics, but a pure science of nature dealing with definite objects (physics or psychology), is possible only by means of mathematics, and since each natural science contains only as much real science as it contains *a priori* knowledge, each natural science becomes real science only to the extent that it permits the application of mathematics. —KANT, E.
Metaphysische Anfangsgründe der Naturwissenschaft, Vorrede.

1509. The theory most prevalent among teachers is that mathematics affords the best training for the reasoning powers; . . . The modern, and to my mind true, theory is that mathematics is the abstract form of the natural sciences; and that it is valuable as a training of the reasoning powers, not because it is abstract, but because it is a representation of actual things.—SAFFORD, T. H.
> *Mathematical Teaching etc. (Boston, 1886), p. 9.*

1510. It seems to me that no one science can so well serve to co-ordinate and, as it were, bind together all of the sciences as the queen of them all, mathematics.—DAVIS, E. W.
> *Proceedings Nebraska Academy of Sciences for 1896 (Lincoln, 1897), p. 282.*

1511. And as for Mixed Mathematics, I may only make this prediction, that there cannot fail to be more kinds of them, as nature grows further disclosed.—BACON, FRANCIS.
> *Advancement of Learning, Bk. 2; De Augmentis, Bk. 3.*

1512. Besides the exercise in keen comprehension and the certain discovery of truth, mathematics has another formative function, that of equipping the mind for the survey of a scientific system.—GRASSMANN, H.
> *Stücke aus dem Lehrbuche der Arithmetik; Werke (Leipzig, 1904), Bd. 2, p. 298.*

1513. Mathematicks may help the naturalists, both to frame hypotheses, and to judge of those that are proposed to them, especially such as relate to mathematical subjects in conjunction with others.—BOYLE, ROBERT.
> *Works (London, 1772), Vol. 3, p. 429.*

1514. The more progress physical sciences make, the more they tend to enter the domain of mathematics, which is a kind of centre to which they all converge. We may even judge of the degree of perfection to which a science has arrived by the facility with which it may be submitted to calculation.
> QUETELET.
> *Quoted in E. Mailly's Eulogy on Quetelet; Smithsonian Report, 1874, p. 173.*

1515. The mathematical formula is the point through which all the light gained by science passes in order to be of use to practice; it is also the point in which all knowledge gained by practice, experiment, and observation must be concentrated before it can be scientifically grasped. The more distant and marked the point, the more concentrated will be the light coming from it, the more unmistakable the insight conveyed. All scientific thought, from the simple gravitation formula of Newton, through the more complicated formulae of physics and chemistry, the vaguer so called laws of organic and animated nature, down to the uncertain statements of psychology and the data of our social and historical knowledge, alike partakes of this characteristic, that it is an attempt to gather up the scattered rays of light, the different parts of knowledge, in a focus, from whence it can be again spread out and analyzed, according to the abstract processes of the thinking mind. But only when this can be done with a mathematical precision and accuracy is the image sharp and well-defined, and the deductions clear and unmistakable. As we descend from the mechanical, through the physical, chemical, and biological, to the mental, moral, and social sciences, the process of focalization becomes less and less perfect,—the sharp point, the focus, is replaced by a larger or smaller circle, the contours of the image become less and less distinct, and with the possible light which we gain there is mingled much darkness, the sources of many mistakes and errors. But the tendency of all scientific thought is toward clearer and clearer definition; it lies in the direction of a more and more extended use of mathematical measurements, of mathematical formulae.—MERZ, J. T.

> *History of European Thought in the 19th Century (Edinburgh and London, 1904), Vol. 1, p. 333.*

1516. From the very outset of his investigations the physicist has to rely constantly on the aid of the mathematician, for even in the simplest cases, the direct results of his measuring operations are entirely without meaning until they have been submitted to more or less of mathematical discussion. And when in this way some interpretation of the experimental results has been arrived at, and it has been proved that two or more physical quantities stand in a definite relation to each other, the mathematician is very often able to infer, from the existence of this relation, that the quantities in question also fulfill some other relation, that was previously unsuspected. Thus when Coulomb, combining the functions of experimentalist and mathematician, had discovered the law of the force exerted between two particles of electricity, it became a purely mathematical problem, not requiring any further experiment, to ascertain how electricity is distributed upon a charged conductor and this problem has been solved by mathematicians in several cases.—FOSTER, G. C.

> *Presidential Address British Association for the Advancement of Science, Section A (1877); Nature, Vol. 16, p. 312–313.*

1517. Without consummate mathematical skill, on the part of some investigators at any rate, all the higher physical problems would be sealed to us; and without competent skill on the part of the ordinary student no idea can be formed of the nature and cogency of the evidence on which the solutions rest. Mathematics are not merely a gate through which we may approach if we please, but they are the only mode of approach to large and important districts of thought.—VENN, JOHN.

> *Symbolic Logic (London and New York, 1894), Introduction, p. xix.*

1518. Much of the skill of the true mathematical physicist and of the mathematical astronomer consists in the power of adapting methods and results carried out on an exact mathematical basis to obtain approximations sufficient for the purposes of physical measurements. It might perhaps be thought that a scheme of Mathematics on a frankly approximative basis would be sufficient for all the practical purposes of application in Physics, Engineering Science, and Astronomy, and no doubt it would be possible to develop, to some extent at least, a species of Mathematics on these lines. Such a system would, however, involve an intolerable awkwardness and prolixity in the statements of results, especially in view of the fact that the degree of approximation necessary for various purposes is very different, and thus that unassigned grades of approximation would have to be provided for. Moreover, the mathematician working on these lines would be cut off from the chief sources of inspiration, the ideals of exactitude and logical rigour, as well as from one of his most indispensable guides to discovery, symmetry, and permanence of mathematical form. The history of the actual movements of mathematical thought through the centuries shows that these ideals are the very life-blood of the science, and warrants the conclusion that a constant striving toward their attainment is an absolutely essential condition of vigorous growth. These ideals have their roots in irresistible impulses and deep-seated needs of the human mind, manifested in its efforts to introduce intelligibility in certain great domains of the world of thought.—HOBSON, E. W.

Presidential Address British Association for the Advancement of Science, Section A (1910); Nature, Vol. 84, pp. 285–286.

1519. The immense part which those laws [laws of number and extension] take in giving a deductive character to the other departments of physical science, is well known; and is not surprising, when we consider that all causes operate according to mathematical laws. The effect is always dependent upon, or in mathematical language, is a function of, the quantity of the agent; and generally of its position also. We cannot, therefore, reason respecting causation, without introducing considerations of quantity and extension at every step; and if the nature of the phenomena admits of our obtaining numerical data of sufficient accuracy, the laws of quantity become the grand instruments for calculating forward to an effect, or backward to a cause.

MILL, J. S.
System of Logic, Bk. 3, chap. 24, sect. 9.

1520. The ordinary mathematical treatment of any applied science substitutes exact axioms for the approximate results of experience, and deduces from these axioms the rigid mathematical conclusions. In applying this method it must not be forgotten that the mathematical developments transcending the limits of exactness of the science are of no practical value. It follows that a large portion of abstract mathematics remains without finding any practical application, the amount of mathematics that can be usefully employed in any science being in proportion to the degree of accuracy attained in the science. Thus, while the astronomer can put to use a wide range of mathematical theory, the chemist is only just beginning to apply the first derivative, i. e. the rate of change at which certain processes are going on; for second derivatives he does not seem to have found any use as yet.—KLEIN, F.

> Lectures on Mathematics (New York, 1911), p. 47.

1521. The bond of union among the physical sciences is the mathematical spirit and the mathematical method which pervades them. . . . Our knowledge of nature, as it advances, continuously resolves differences of quality into differences of quantity. All exact reasoning—indeed all reasoning—about quantity is mathematical reasoning; and thus as our knowledge increases, that portion of it which becomes mathematical increases at a still more rapid rate.—SMITH, H. J. S.

> Presidential Address British Association for the Advancement of Science, Section A (1873); Nature, Vol. 8, p. 449.

1522. Another way of convincing ourselves how largely this process [of assimilation of mathematics by physics] has gone on would be to try to conceive the effect of some intellectual catastrophe, supposing such a thing possible, whereby all knowledge of mathematics should be swept away from men's minds. Would it not be that the departure of mathematics would be the destruction of physics? Objective physical phenomena would, indeed, remain as they are now, but physical science would cease to exist. We should no doubt see the same colours on looking into a spectroscope or polariscope, vibrating strings would produce the same sounds, electrical machines would give sparks, and galvanometer needles would be deflected; but all these things would have lost their meaning; they would be but as the dry bones—the disjecta membra—of what is now a living and growing science. To follow this conception further, and to try to image to ourselves in some detail what would be the kind of knowledge of physics which would remain possible, supposing all mathematical ideas to be blotted out, would be extremely interesting, but it would lead us directly into a dim and entangled region where the subjective seems to be always passing itself off for the objective, and where I at least could not attempt to lead the way, gladly as I would follow any one who could show where a firm footing is to be found. But without venturing to do more than to look from a safe distance over this puzzling ground, we may see clearly enough that mathematics is the connective tissue of physics, binding what would else be merely a list of detached observations into an organized body of science.—FOSTER, G. C.

Presidential Address British Association for the Advancement of Science, Section A (1877); Nature, Vol. 16, p. 313.

1523. In *Plato's* time mathematics was purely a play of the free intellect; the mathematic-mystical reveries of a Pythagoras foreshadowed a far-reaching significance, but such a significance (except in the case of music) was as yet entirely a matter of fancy; yet even in that time mathematics was the prerequisite to all other studies! But today, when mathematics furnishes the *only* language by means of which we may formulate the most comprehensive laws of nature, laws which the ancients scarcely dreamed of, when moreover mathematics is the *only* means by which these laws may be understood,—how few learn today anything of the real essence of our mathematics! . . . In the schools of today mathematics serves only as a disciplinary study, a mental gymnastic; that it includes the highest ideal value for the comprehension of the universe, one dares scarcely to think of in view of our present day instruction.

LINDEMAN, F.
Lehren und Lernen in der Mathematik (München, 1904), p. 14.

1524. All applications of mathematics consist in extending the empirical knowledge which we possess of a limited number or region of accessible phenomena into the region of the unknown and inaccessible; and much of the progress of pure analysis consists in inventing definite conceptions, marked by symbols, of complicated operations; in ascertaining their properties as independent objects of research; and in extending their meaning

beyond the limits they were originally invented for,—thus opening out new and larger regions of thought.—MERZ, J. T.
History of European Thought in the 19th Century (Edinburgh and London, 1903), Vol. 1, p. 698.

1525. All the effects of nature are only mathematical results of a small number of immutable laws.—LAPLACE.
A Philosophical Essay on Probabilities [Truscott and Emory] (New York, 1902), p. 177; Oeuvres, t. 7, p. 139.

1526. What logarithms are to mathematics that mathematics are to the other sciences.—NOVALIS.
Schriften (Berlin, 1901), Teil 2, p. 222.

1527. Any intelligent man may now, by resolutely applying himself for a few years to mathematics, learn more than the great Newton knew after half a century of study and meditation.
MACAULAY.
Milton; Critical and Miscellaneous Essays (New York, 1879), Vol. 1, p. 13.

1528. In questions of science the authority of a thousand is not worth the humble reasoning of a single individual.
GALILEO.
Quoted in Arago's Eulogy on Laplace; Smithsonian Report, 1874, p. 164.

1529. Behind the artisan is the chemist, behind the chemist a physicist, behind the physicist a mathematician.—WHITE, W. F.
Scrap-book of Elementary Mathematics (Chicago, 1908), p. 217.

1530. The advance in our knowledge of physics is largely due to the application to it of mathematics, and every year it becomes more difficult for an experimenter to make any mark in the subject unless he is also a mathematician.—BALL, W. W. R.
History of Mathematics (London, 1901), p. 503.

1531. In very many cases the most obvious and direct experimental method of investigating a given problem is extremely difficult, or for some reason or other untrustworthy.

In such cases the mathematician can often point out some other problem more accessible to experimental treatment, the solution of which involves the solution of the former one. For example, if we try to deduce from direct experiments the law according to which one pole of a magnet attracts or repels a pole of another magnet, the observed action is so much complicated with the effects of the mutual induction of the magnets and of the forces due to the second pole of each magnet, that it is next to impossible to obtain results of any great accuracy. Gauss, however, showed how the law which applied in the case mentioned can be deduced from the deflections undergone by a small suspended magnetic needle when it is acted upon by a small fixed magnet placed successively in two determinate positions relatively to the needle; and being an experimentalist as well as a mathematician, he showed likewise how these deflections can be measured very easily and with great precision.

FOSTER, G. C.
Presidential Address British Association for the Advancement of Science, Section A (1877); Nature, Vol. 16, p. 313.

1532. Give me to learn each secret cause;
Let Number's, Figure's, Motion's laws
Reveal'd before me stand;
These to great Nature's scenes apply,
And round the globe, and through the sky,
Disclose her working hand.—AKENSIDE, M.
Hymn to Science.

1533. Now there are several scores, upon which skill in mathematicks may be useful to the experimental philosopher. For there are some general advantages, which mathematicks may bring to the minds of men, to whatever study they apply themselves, and consequently to the student of natural philosophy; namely, that these disciplines are wont to make men accurate, and very attentive to the employment that they are about, keeping their thoughts from wandering, and inuring them to patience in going through with tedious and intricate demonstrations; besides, that they much improve reason, by accustoming the mind to deduce successive consequences, and judge of them without easily acquiescing in anything but demonstration.—BOYLE, ROBERT.

Works (London, 1772), Vol. 3, p. 426.

1534. It is not easy to anatomize the constitution and the operations of a mind [like Newton's] which makes such an advance in knowledge. Yet we may observe that there must exist in it, in an eminent degree, the elements which compose the mathematical talent. It must possess distinctness of intuition, tenacity and facility in tracing logical connection, fertility of invention, and a strong tendency to generalization.

WHEWELL, W.
*History of the Inductive Sciences (New York,
1894), Vol. 1, p. 416.*

1535. The domain of physics is no proper field for mathematical pastimes. The best security would be in giving a geometrical training to physicists, who need not then have recourse to mathematicians, whose tendency is to despise experimental science. By this method will that union between the abstract and the concrete be effected which will perfect the uses of mathematical, while extending the positive value of physical science. Meantime, the uses of analysis in physics is clear enough. Without it we should have no precision, and no co-ordination; and what account could we give of our study of heat, weight, light, etc.? We should have merely series of unconnected facts, in which we could foresee nothing but by constant recourse to experiment; whereas, they now have a character of rationality which fits them for purposes of prevision.—COMTE, A.

Positive Philosophy [Martineau] Bk. 3, chap. 1.

1536. It must ever be remembered that the true positive spirit first came forth from the pure sources of mathematical science; and it is only the mind that has imbibed it there, and which has been face to face with the lucid truths of geometry and mechanics, that can bring into full action its natural positivity, and apply it in bringing the most complex studies into the reality of demonstration. No other discipline can fitly prepare the intellectual organ.—COMTE, A.

Positive Philosophy, [Martineau] Bk. 3, chap. 1.

1537. During the last two centuries and a half, physical knowledge has been gradually made to rest upon a basis which it had not before. It has become *mathematical*. The question now is, not whether this or that hypothesis is better or worse to the pure thought, but whether it accords with observed phenomena in those consequences which can be shown necessarily to follow from it, if it be true. Even in those sciences which are not yet under the dominion of mathematics, and perhaps never will be, a working copy of the mathematical process has been made. This is not known to the followers of those sciences who are not themselves mathematicians, and who very often exalt their horns against the mathematics in consequence. They might as well be squaring the circle, for any sense they show in this particular.—DE MORGAN, A.

A Budget of Paradoxes (London, 1872), p. 2.

1538. Among the mere talkers so far as mathematics are concerned, are to be ranked three out of four of those who apply mathematics to physics, who, wanting a tool only, are very impatient of everything which is not of direct aid to the actual methods which are in their hands.—DE MORGAN, A.

Graves' Life of Sir William Rowan Hamilton (New York, 1882–1889), Vol. 3, p. 348.

1539. Something has been said about the use of mathematics in physical science, the mathematics being regarded as a weapon forged by others, and the study of the weapon being completely set aside. I can only say that there is danger of obtaining untrustworthy results in physical science, if only the results of mathematics are used; for the person so using the weapon can remain unacquainted with the conditions under which it can be rightly applied. . . . The results are often correct, sometimes are incorrect; the consequence of the latter class of cases is to throw doubt upon all the applications of such a worker until a result has been otherwise tested. Moreover, such a practice in the use of mathematics leads a worker to a mere repetition in the use of familiar weapons; he is unable to adapt them with any confidence when some new set of conditions arise with a demand for a new method: for want of adequate instruction in the

forging of the weapon, he may find himself, sooner or later in the
progress of his subject, without any weapon worth having.

FORSYTH, A. R.
Perry's Teaching of Mathematics (London,
1902), p. 36.

1540. If in the range of human endeavor after sound knowledge there is one subject that needs to be practical, it surely is
Medicine. Yet in the field of Medicine it has been found that
branches such as biology and pathology must be studied for
themselves and be developed by themselves with the single aim
of increasing knowledge; and it is then that they can be best
applied to the conduct of living processes. So also in the pursuit of mathematics, the path of practical utility is too narrow
and irregular, not always leading far. The witness of history
shows that, in the field of natural philosophy, mathematics will
furnish the more effective assistance if, in its systematic development, its course can freely pass beyond the ever-shifting domain
of use and application.—FORSYTH, A. R.

Presidential Address British Association for
the Advancement of Science, Section A; Nature,
Vol. 56 (1897), p. 377.

1541. If the Greeks had not cultivated Conic Sections,
Kepler could not have superseded Ptolemy; if the Greeks had
cultivated Dynamics, Kepler might have anticipated Newton.

WHEWELL, W.
History of the Inductive Science (New York,
1894), Vol. 1, p. 311.

1542. If we may use the great names of Kepler and Newton to
signify stages in the progress of human discovery, it is not too
much to say that without the treatises of the Greek geometers on
the conic sections there could have been no Kepler, without
Kepler no Newton, and without Newton no science in the
modern sense of the term, or at least no such conception of
nature as now lies at the basis of all our science, of nature as
subject in the smallest as well as in its greatest phenomena, to
exact quantitative relations, and to definite numerical laws.

SMITH, H. J. S.
Presidential Address British Association for
the Advancement of Science, Section A; Nature,
Vol. 8 (1873), p. 450.

1543. The silent work of the great Regiomontanus in his chamber at Nuremberg computed the Ephemerides which made possible the discovery of America by Columbus.—RUDIO, F.

Quoted in Max Simon's Geschichte der Mathematik im Altertum (Berlin, 1909), Einleitung, p. xi.

1544. The calculation of the eclipses of Jupiter's satellites, many a man might have been disposed, originally, to regard as a most unprofitable study. But the utility of it to navigation (in the determination of longitudes) is now well known.

WHATELY, R.

Annotations to Bacon's Essays (Boston, 1783), p. 492.

1545. Who could have imagined, when Galvani observed the twitching of the frog muscles as he brought various metals in contact with them, that eighty years later Europe would be overspun with wires which transmit messages from Madrid to St. Petersburg with the rapidity of lightning, by means of the same principle whose first manifestations this anatomist then observed ! . . .

He who seeks for immediate practical use in the pursuit of science, may be reasonably sure, that he will seek in vain. Complete knowledge and complete understanding of the action of forces of nature and of the mind, is the only thing that science can aim at. The individual investigator must find his reward in the joy of new discoveries, as new victories of thought over resisting matter, in the esthetic beauty which a well-ordered domain of knowledge affords, where all parts are intellectually related, where one thing evolves from another, and all show the marks of the mind's supremacy; he must find his reward in the consciousness of having contributed to the growing capital of knowledge on which depends the supremacy of man over the forces hostile to the spirit.—HELMHOLTZ, H.

Vorträge und Reden (Braunschweig, 1884), Bd. 1, p. 142.

1546. When the time comes that knowledge will not be sought for its own sake, and men will not press forward simply in a desire of achievement, without hope of gain, to extend the limits of human knowledge and information, then, indeed, will the race enter upon its decadence.—HUGHES, C. E.

> Quoted in D. E. Smith's Teaching of Geometry (Boston, 1911), p. 9.

1547. [In the Opus Majus of Roger Bacon] there is a chapter, in which it is proved by reason, that all sciences require mathematics. And the arguments which are used to establish this doctrine, show a most just appreciation of the office of mathematics in science. They are such as follows: That other sciences use examples taken from mathematics as the most evident:— That mathematical knowledge is, as it were, innate to us, on which point he refers to the well-known dialogue of Plato, as quoted by Cicero:—That this science, being the easiest, offers the best introduction to the more difficult:—That in mathematics, things as known to us are identical with things as known to nature:—That we can here entirely avoid doubt and error, and obtain certainty and truth:—That mathematics is prior to other sciences in nature, because it takes cognizance of quantity, which is apprehended by intuition (*intuitu intellectus*). "Moreover," he adds, "there have been found famous men, as Robert, bishop of Lincoln, and Brother Adam Marshman (de Marisco), and many others, who by the power of mathematics have been able to explain the causes of things; as may be seen in the writings of these men, for instance, concerning the Rainbow and Comets, and the generation of heat, and climates, and the celestial bodies."—WHEWELL, W.

> History of the Inductive Sciences (New York, 1894), Vol. 1, p. 519. Bacon, Roger: Opus Majus, Part 4, Distinctia Prima, cap. 3.

1548. The analysis which is based upon the conception of function discloses to the astronomer and physicist not merely the formulae for the computation of whatever desired distances, times, velocities, physical constants; it moreover gives him insight into the laws of the processes of motion, teaches him to predict future occurrences from past experiences and supplies him with means to a scientific knowledge of nature, i. e. it enables him to trace back whole groups of various, sometimes extremely heterogeneous, phenomena to a minimum of simple fundamental laws.—PRINGSHEIM, A.

> *Jahresbericht der Deutschen Mathematiker Vereinigung, Bd. 13, p. 366.*

1549. " As is known, scientific physics dates its existence from the discovery of the differential calculus. Only when it was learned how to follow continuously the course of natural events, attempts, to construct by means of abstract conceptions the connection between phenomena, met with success. To do this two things are necessary: First, simple fundamental concepts with which to construct; second, some method by which to deduce, from the simple fundamental laws of the construction which relate to instants of time and points in space, laws for finite intervals and distances, which alone are accessible to observation (can be compared with experience)." [Riemann.]

The first of the two problems here indicated by Riemann consists in setting up the differential equation, based upon physical facts and hypotheses. The second is the integration of this differential equation and its application to each separate concrete case, this is the task of mathematics.—WEBER, HEINRICH.

> *Die partiellen Differentialgleichungen der mathematischen Physik (Braunschweig, 1882), Bd. 1, Vorrede.*

1550. Mathematics is the most powerful instrument which we possess for this purpose [to trace into their farthest results those general laws which an inductive philosophy has supplied]: in many sciences a profound knowledge of mathematics is indispensable for a successful investigation. In the most delicate researches into the theories of light, heat, and sound it is the only instrument; they have properties which no other language can express; and their argumentative processes are beyond the reach of other symbols.—PRICE, B.

> *Treatise on Infinitesimal Calculus (Oxford, 1858), Vol. 3, p. 5.*

1551. Notwithstanding the eminent difficulties of the mathematical theory of sonorous vibrations, we owe to it such progress as has yet been made in acoustics. The formation of the

differential equations proper to the phenomena is, independent
of their integration, a very important acquisition, on account of
the approximations which mathematical analysis allows between
questions, otherwise heterogeneous, which lead to similar
equations. This fundamental property, whose value we have so
often to recognize, applies remarkably in the present case; and
especially since the creation of mathematical thermology, whose
principal equations are strongly analogous to those of vibratory
motion.—This means of investigation is all the more valuable
on account'of the difficulties in the way of direct inquiry into
the phenomena of sound. We may decide the necessity of the
atmospheric medium for the transmission of sonorous vibrations; and we may conceive of the possibility of determining by
experiment the duration of the propagation, in the air, and then
through other media; but the general laws of the vibrations of
sonorous bodies escape immediate observation. We should
know almost nothing of the whole case if the mathematical
theory did not come in to connect the different phenomena of
sound, enabling us to substitute for direct observation an
equivalent examination of more favorable cases subjected to the
same law. For instance, when the analysis of the problem of
vibrating chords has shown us that, other things being equal,
the number of oscillations is in inverse proportion to the length
of the chord, we see that the most rapid vibrations of a very
short chord may be counted, since the law enables us to direct
our attention to very slow vibrations. The same substitution
is at our command in many cases in which it is less direct.

COMTE, A.

Positive Philosophy [*Martineau*], *Bk. 3,
chap. 4.*

1552. Problems relative to the uniform propagation, or
to the varied movements of heat in the interior of solids, are
reduced . . . to problems of pure analysis, and the progress of
this part of physics will depend in consequence upon the advance
which may be made in the art of analysis. The differential
equations . . . contain the chief results of the theory; they
express, in the most general and concise manner, the necessary
relations of numerical analysis to a very extensive class of

phenomena; and they connect forever with mathematical science one of the most important branches of natural philosophy.—FOURIER, J.
Theory of Heat [Freeman], (Cambridge, 1878), Chap. 3, p. 131.

1553. The effects of heat are subject to constant laws which cannot be discovered without the aid of mathematical analysis. The object of the theory is to demonstrate these laws; it reduces all physical researches on the propagation of heat, to problems of the integral calculus, whose elements are given by experiment. No subject has more extensive relations with the progress of industry and the natural sciences; for the action of heat is always present, it influences the processes of the arts, and occurs in all the phenomena of the universe.—FOURIER, J.
Theory of Heat [Freeman], (Cambridge, 1878), Chap. 1, p. 12.

1554. Dealing with any and every amount of static electricity, the mathematical mind has balanced and adjusted them with wonderful advantage, and has foretold results which the experimentalist can do no more than verify. . . . So in respect of the force of gravitation, it has calculated the results of the power in such a wonderful manner as to trace the known planets through their courses and perturbations, and in so doing has *discovered* a planet before unknown.—FARADAY.
Some Thoughts on the Conservation of Force.

1555. Certain branches of natural philosophy (such as physical astronomy and optics), . . . are, in a great measure, inaccessible to those who have not received a regular mathematical education . . .—STEWART, DUGALD.
Philosophy of the Human Mind, Part 3, chap. 1, sect. 3.

1556. So intimate is the union between mathematics and physics that probably by far the larger part of the accessions to our mathematical knowledge have been obtained by the efforts of mathematicians to solve the problems set to them by experiment, and to create "for each successive class of phenomena, a new calculus or a new geometry, as the case might be, which

might prove not wholly inadequate to the subtlety of nature."
Sometimes, indeed, the mathematician has been before the
physicist, and it has happened that when some great and new
question has occurred to the experimentalist or the observer,
he has found in the armoury of the mathematician the weapons
which he has needed ready made to his hand. But, much
oftener, the questions proposed by the physicist have transcended the utmost powers of the mathematics of the time, and a
fresh mathematical creation has been needed to supply the
logical instrument requisite to interpret the new enigma.

SMITH, H. J. S.
*Presidential Address British Association for
the Advancement of Science, Section A; Nature,
Vol. 8 (1873), p. 450.*

1557. Of all the great subjects which belong to the province of
his section, take that which at first sight is the least within the
domain of mathematics—I mean meteorology. Yet the part
which mathematics plays in meteorology increases every year,
and seems destined to increase. Not only is the theory of the
simplest instruments essentially mathematical, but the discussions of the observations—upon which, be it remembered,
depend the hopes which are already entertained with increasing
confidence, of reducing the most variable and complex of all
known phenomena to exact laws—is a problem which not only
belongs wholly to mathematics, but which taxes to the utmost
the resources of the mathematics which we now possess.

SMITH, H. J. S.
*Presidential Address British Association for
the Advancement of Science, Section A; Nature,
Vol. 8 (1873), p. 449.*

1558. You know that if you make a dot on a piece of paper,
and then hold a piece of Iceland spar over it, you will see not one
dot but two. A mineralogist, by measuring the angles of a
crystal, can tell you whether or no it possesses this property
without looking through it. He requires no scientific thought to
do that. But Sir William Roman Hamilton . . . knowing
these facts and also the explanation of them which Fresnel had

given, thought about the subject, and he predicted that by looking through certain crystals in a particular direction we should see not two dots but a continuous circle. Mr. Lloyd made the experiment, and saw the circle, a result which had never been even suspected. This has always been considered one of the most signal instances of scientific thought in the domain of physics.—CLIFFORD, W. K.

> Lectures and Essays (New York, 1901), Vol. 1, p. 144.

1559. The discovery of this planet [Neptune] is justly reckoned as the greatest triumph of mathematical astronomy. Uranus failed to move precisely in the path which the computers predicted for it, and was misguided by some unknown influence to an extent which a keen eye might almost see without telescopic aid. . . . These minute discrepancies constituted the data which were found sufficient for calculating the position of a hitherto unknown planet, and bringing it to light. Leverrier wrote to Galle, in substance: *"Direct your telescope to a point on the ecliptic in the constellation of Aquarius, in longitude 326°, and you will find within a degree of that place a new planet, looking like a star of about the ninth magnitude, and having a perceptible disc."* The planet was found at Berlin on the night of Sept. 26, 1846, in exact accordance with this prediction, within half an hour after the astronomers began looking for it, and only about 52′ distant from the precise point that Leverrier had indicated.

> YOUNG, C. A.
> General Astronomy (Boston, 1891), Art. 653.

1560. I am convinced that the future progress of chemistry as an exact science depends very much indeed upon the alliance with mathematics.—FRANKLAND, A.

> American Journal of Mathematics, Vol. 1, p. 349.

1561. It is almost impossible to follow the later developments of physical or general chemistry without a working knowledge of higher mathematics.—MELLOR, J. W.

> Higher Mathematics (New York, 1902), Preface.

1562. . . . Mount where science guides;
Go measure earth, weigh air, and state the tides;
Instruct the planets in what orb to run,
Correct old time, and regulate the sun.—THOMSON, W.
On the Figure of the Earth, Title page.

1563. Admission to its sanctuary [referring to astronomy] and to the privileges and feelings of a votary, is only to be gained by one means,—*sound and sufficient knowledge of mathematics, the great instrument of all exact inquiry, without which no man can ever make such advances in this or any other of the higher departments of science as can entitle him to form an independent opinion on any subject of discussion within their range.*—HERSCHEL, J.
Outlines of Astronomy, Introduction, sect. 7.

1564. The long series of connected truths which compose the science of astronomy, have been evolved from the appearances and observations by calculation, and a process of reasoning entirely geometrical. It was not without reason that Plato called geometry and arithmetic the wings of astronomy; for it is only by means of these two sciences that we can give a rational account of any of the appearances, or connect any fact with theory, or even render a single observation available to the most common astronomical purpose. It is by geometry that we are enabled to reason our way up through the apparent motions to the real orbits of the planets, and to assign their positions, magnitudes and eccentricities. And it is by application of geometry—a sublime geometry, indeed, invented for the purpose—to the general laws of mechanics, that we demonstrate the law of gravitation, trace it through its remotest effects on the different planets, and, comparing these effects with what we observe, determine the densities and weights of the minutest bodies belonging to the system. The whole science of astronomy is in fact a tissue of geometrical reasoning, applied to the data of observation; and it is from this circumstance that it derives its peculiar character of precision and certainty. To disconnect it from geometry, therefore, and to substitute familiar illustrations and vague description for close and logical reasoning, is to deprive it of its principal advantages, and to reduce it to the condition of an ordinary province of natural history.

Edinburgh Review, Vol. 58 (1833–1834), p. 168.

1565. But geometry is not only the instrument of astronomical investigation, and the bond by which the truths are enchained together,—it is also the instrument of explanation, affording, by the peculiar brevity and perspicuity of its technical processes, not only aid to the learner, but also such facilities to the teacher as he will find it very difficult to supply, if he voluntarily undertakes to forego its assistance. Few undertakings, indeed, are attended with greater difficulty than that of attempting to exhibit the connecting links of a chain of mathematical reasoning, when we lay aside the technical symbols and notation which relieve the memory, and speak at once to the eyes and the understanding: . . .

Edinburgh Review, Vol. 58 (1833–1834), p. 169.

1566. With an ordinary acquaintance of trigonometry, and the simplest elements of algebra, one may take up any well-written treatise on plane astronomy, and work his way through it, from beginning to end, with perfect ease; and he will acquire, in the course of his progress, from the mere examples put before him, an infinitely more correct and precise idea of astronomical methods and theories, than he could obtain in a lifetime from the most eloquent general descriptions that ever were written. At the same time he will be strengthening himself for farther advances, and accustoming his mind to habits of close comparison and rigid demonstration, which are of infinitely more importance than the acquisition of stores of undigested facts.

Edinburgh Review, Vol. 58 (1833–1834), p. 170.

1567. While the telescope serves as a means of penetrating space, and of bringing its remotest regions nearer us, mathematics, by inductive reasoning, have led us onwards to the remotest regions of heaven, and brought a portion of them within the range of our possibilities; nay, in our own times—so propitious to the extension of knowledge—the application of all the elements yielded by the present conditions of astronomy has even revealed to the intellectual eyes a heavenly body, and assigned to it its place, orbit, mass, before a single telescope has been directed towards it.—HUMBOLDT, A.

Cosmos [Otte], Vol. 2, part 2, sect. 3.

1568. Mighty are numbers, joined with art resistless.

EURIPIDES.
Hecuba, Line 884.

1569. No single instrument of youthful education has such mighty power, both as regards domestic economy and politics, and in the arts, as the study of arithmetic. Above all, arithmetic stirs up him who is by nature sleepy and dull, and makes him quick to learn, retentive, shrewd, and aided by art divine he makes progress quite beyond his natural powers.—PLATO.

Laws [Jowett,] Bk. 5, p. 747.

1570. For all the higher arts of construction some acquaintance with mathematics is indispensable. The village carpenter, who, lacking rational instruction, lays out his work by empirical rules learned in his apprenticeship, equally with the builder of a Britannia Bridge, makes hourly reference to the laws of quantitative relations. The surveyor on whose survey the land is purchased; the architect in designing a mansion to be built on it; the builder in preparing his estimates; his foreman in laying out the foundations; the masons in cutting the stones; and the various artisans who put up the fittings; are all guided by geometrical truths. Railway-making is regulated from beginning to end by mathematics: alike in the preparation of plans and sections; in staking out the lines; in the mensuration of cuttings and embankments; in the designing, estimating, and building of bridges, culverts, viaducts, tunnels, stations. And similarly with the harbors, docks, piers, and various engineering and architectural works that fringe the coasts and overspread the face of the country, as well as the mines that run underneath it. Out of geometry, too, as applied to astronomy, the art of navigation has grown; and so, by this science, has been made possible that enormous foreign commerce which supports a large part of our population, and supplies us with many necessaries and most of our luxuries. And nowadays even the farmer, for the correct laying out of his drains, has recourse to the level—that is, to geometrical principles.

SPENCER, HERBERT.
Education, chap. 1.

1571. [Arithmetic] is another of the great master-keys of life. With it the astronomer opens the depths of the heavens; the engineer, the gates of the mountains; the navigator, the pathways of the deep. The skillful arrangement, the rapid handling of figures, is a perfect magician's wand. The mighty commerce of the United States, foreign and domestic, passes through the books kept by some thousands of diligent and faithful clerks. Eight hundred bookkeepers, in the Bank of England, strike the monetary balance of half the civilized world. Their skill and accuracy in applying the common rules of arithmetic are as important as the enterprise and capital of the merchant, or the industry and courage of the navigator. I look upon a well-kept ledger with something of the pleasure with which I gaze on a picture or a statue. It is a beautiful work of art.—EVERETT, EDWARD.

Orations and Speeches (Boston, 1870), Vol. 3, p. 47.

1572. [Mathematics] is the fruitful Parent of, I had almost said all, Arts, the unshaken Foundation of Sciences, and the plentiful Fountain of Advantage to Human Affairs. In which last Respect, we may be said to receive from the *Mathematics*, the principal Delights of Life, Securities of Health, Increase of Fortune, and Conveniences of Labour: That we dwell elegantly and commodiously, build decent Houses for ourselves, erect stately Temples to God, and leave wonderful Monuments to Posterity: That we are protected by those Rampires from the Incursions of the Enemy; rightly use Arms, skillfully range an Army, and manage War by Art, and not by the Madness of wild Beasts: That we have safe Traffick through the deceitful Billows, pass in a direct Road through the tractless Ways of the Sea, and come to the designed Ports by the uncertain Impulse of the Winds: That we rightly cast up our Accounts, do Business expeditiously, dispose, tabulate, and calculate scattered Ranks of Numbers, and easily compute them, though expressive of huge Heaps of Sand, nay immense Hills of Atoms: That we make pacifick Separations of the Bounds of Lands, examine the Moments of Weights in an equal Balance, and distribute every one his own by a just Measure: That with a light Touch we thrust forward vast Bodies which way we will, and stop a huge Resistance with a very small Force: That we accurately delineate the Face of this Earthly Orb, and subject the Oeconomy of the Universe to our Sight: That we aptly digest the flowing Series of Time, distinguish what is acted by due Intervals, rightly account and discern the various Returns of the Seasons, the stated Periods of Years and Months, the alternate Increments of Days and Nights, the doubtful Limits of Light and Shadow, and the exact Differences of Hours and Minutes: That we derive the subtle Virtue of the Solar Rays to our Uses, infinitely extend the Sphere of Sight, enlarge the near Appearances of Things, bring to Hand Things remote, discover Things hidden, search Nature out of her Concealments, and unfold her dark Mysteries: That we delight our Eyes with beautiful Images, cunningly imitate the Devices and portray the Works of Nature; imitate did I say? nay excel, while we form to ourselves Things not in being, exhibit Things absent, and represent Things past: That we recreate our Minds and delight our Ears with melodious Sounds, attemperate the inconstant Undulations of the Air to musical Tunes, add a pleasant Voice to a sapless Log and draw a sweet Eloquence from a rigid Metal; celebrate our Maker with an harmonious Praise, and not unaptly imitate the blessed Choirs of Heaven: That we approach and examine the inaccessible Seats of the Clouds, the distant Tracts of Land, unfrequented Paths of the Sea; lofty Tops of the Mountains, low Bottoms of the Valleys, and deep Gulphs of the Ocean: That in Heart we advance to the Saints themselves above, yea draw them to us, scale the etherial Towers, freely range through the celestial Fields, measure the Magnitudes, and determine the Interstices of the Stars, pre- scribe inviolable Laws to the Heavens themselves, and confine the wandering Circuits of the Stars within fixed Bounds: Lastly, that we comprehend the vast Fabrick of the Universe, admire and contemplate the wonderful Beauty of the Divine

Workmanship, and to learn the incredible Force and Sagacity of our own Minds, by certain Experiments, and to acknowledge the Blessings of Heaven with pious Affection.

BARROW, ISAAC.
Mathematical Lectures (London, 1734), pp. 27–30.

1573. Analytical and graphical treatment of statistics is employed by the economist, the philanthropist, the business expert, the actuary, and even the physician, with the most surprisingly valuable results; while symbolic language involving mathematical methods has become a part of wellnigh every large business. The handling of pig-iron does not seem to offer any opportunity for mathematical application. Yet graphical and analytical treatment of the data from long-continued experiments with this material at Bethlehem, Pennsylvania, resulted in the discovery of the law that fatigue varied in proportion to a certain relation between the load and the periods of rest. Practical application of this law increased the amount handled by each man from twelve and a half to forty-seven tons per day. Such study would have been impossible without preliminary acquaintance with the simple invariable elements of mathematics.—KARPINSKY, L.

High School Education (New York, 1912), chap. 6, p. 134.

1574. They [computation and arithmetic] belong then, it seems, to the branches of learning which we are now investigating;—for a military man must necessarily learn them with a view to the marshalling of his troops, and so must a philosopher with the view of understanding real being, after having emerged from the unstable condition of becoming, or else he can never become an apt reasoner.

That is the fact he replied.

But the guardian of ours happens to be both a military man and a philosopher.

Unquestionably so.

It would be proper then, Glaucon, to lay down laws for this branch of science and persuade those about to engage in the most important state-matters to apply themselves to computation, and study it, not in the common vulgar fashion, but with the view of arriving at the contemplation of the nature of numbers by the intellect itself,—not for the sake of buying and selling as anxious merchants and retailers, but for war also, and that the soul may acquire a facility in turning itself from what is in the course of generation to truth and real being.—PLATO.

Republic [Davis], Bk. 7, p. 525.

1575. The scientific part of Arithmetic and Geometry would be of more use for regulating the thoughts and opinions of men than all the great advantage which Society receives from the general application of them: and this use cannot be spread through the Society by the practice; for the Practitioners, however dextrous, have no more knowledge of the Science than the very instruments with which they work. They have taken up the Rules as they found them delivered down to them by scientific men, without the least inquiry after the Principles from which they are derived: and the more accurate the Rules, the less occasion there is for inquiring after the Principles, and consequently, the more difficult it is to make them turn their attention to the First Principles; and, therefore, a Nation ought to have both Scientific and Practical Mathematicians.

WILLIAMSON, JAMES.
Elements of Euclid with Dissertations (Oxford, 1781).

1576. *Where there is nothing to measure there is nothing to calculate,* hence it is impossible to employ mathematics in psychological investigations. Thus runs the syllogism compounded of an adherence to usage and an apparent truth. As to the latter, it is wholly untrue that we may calculate only where we have measured. Exactly the opposite is true. Every hypothetically assumed law of quantitative combination, even such as is recognized as invalid, is subject to calculation; and in case of deeply hidden but important matters it is imperative to try on hypotheses and to subject the consequences which flow from them to precise computation until it is found which one of the various hypotheses coincides with experience. Thus the ancient astronomers *tried* eccentric circles, and Kepler *tried* the ellipse to account for the motion of the planets, the latter also compared the squares of the times of revolution with the cubes of the mean distances before he discovered their agreement. In like manner Newton *tried* whether a gravitation, varying inversely as the square of the distance, sufficed to keep the moon in its orbit about the earth; if this supposition had failed him, he would have tried some other power of the distance, as the fourth or fifth, and deduced the corresponding consequences to compare them with the observations. Just this is the greatest benefit of mathematics, that it enables us to survey the possibilities whose range includes the actual, long before we have adequate definite experience; this makes it possible to employ very incomplete indications of experience to avoid at least the crudest errors. Long before the transit of Venus was employed in the determination of the sun's parallax, it was attempted to determine the instant at which the sun illumines exactly one-half of the moon's disk, in order to compute the sun's distance from the known distance of the moon from the earth. This was not possible, for, owing to psychological reasons, our method of measuring time is too crude to give us the desired instant with sufficient accuracy; yet the attempt gave us the knowledge that the sun's distance from us is at least several hundred times as great as that of the moon. This illustration shows clearly that even a very imperfect estimate of a magnitude in a case where no precise observation is possible, may become very instructive, if we know how to exploit it. Was it necessary to know the scale of our solar system in order to learn of its order in general? Or, taking an illustration from another field, was it impossible to investigate the laws of motion until it was known exactly how far a body falls in a second at some definite place? Not at all. Such determinations of *fundamental measures* are in themselves exceedingly difficult, but fortunately, such investigations form a class of their own; our knowledge of *fundamental laws* does not need to wait on these. To be sure, computation invites measurement, and every easily observed regularity of certain magnitudes is an incentive to mathematical investigation.—HERBART, J. F.

> *Werke [Kehrbach], (Langensalza, 1890), Bd. 5, p. 97.*

1577. Those who pass for naturalists, have, for the most part, been very little, or not at all, versed in mathematicks, if not also jealous of them.—BOYLE, ROBERT.

Works (London, 1772), Vol. 3, p. 426.

1578. However hurtful may have been the incursions of the geometers, direct and indirect, into a domain which it is not for them to cultivate, the physiologists are not the less wrong in turning away from mathematics altogether. It is not only that without mathematics they could not receive their due preliminary training in the intervening sciences: it is further necessary for them to have geometrical and mechanical knowledge, to understand the structure and the play of the complex apparatus of the living, and especially the animal organism. Animal mechanics, statical and dynamical, must be unintelligible to those who are ignorant of the general laws of rational mechanics. The laws of equilibrium and motion are . . . absolutely universal in their action, depending wholly on the energy, and not at all on the nature of the forces considered: and the only difficulty is in their numerical application in cases of complexity. Thus, discarding all idea of a numerical application in biology, we perceive that the general theorems of statics and dynamics must be steadily verified in the mechanism of living bodies, on the rational study of which they cast an indispensable light. The highest orders of animals act in repose and motion, like any other mechanical apparatus of a similar complexity, with the one difference of the mover, which has no power to alter the laws of motion and equilibrium. The participation of rational mechanics in positive biology is thus evident. Mechanics cannot dispense with geometry; and beside, we see how anatomical and physiological speculations involve considerations of form and position, and require a familiar knowledge of the principal geometrical laws which may cast light upon these complex relations.—COMTE, A.

Positive Philosophy [Martineau], Bk. 5, chap. 1.

1579. In mathematics we find the primitive source of rationality; and to mathematics must the biologists resort for means to carry on their researches.—COMTE, A.

Positive Philosophy [Martineau], Bk. 5, chap. 1.

1580. In this school [of mathematics] must they [biologists] learn familiarly the real characters and conditions of scientific evidence, in order to transfer it afterwards to the province of their own theories. The study of it here, in the most simple and perfect cases, is the only sound preparation for its recognition in the most complex.

The study is equally necessary for the formation of intellectual habits; for obtaining an aptitude in forming and sustaining positive abstractions, without which the comparative method cannot be used in either anatomy or physiology. The abstraction which is to be the standard of comparison must be first clearly formed, and then steadily maintained in its integrity, or the analysis becomes abortive: and this is so completely in the spirit of mathematical combinations, that practice in them is the best preparation for it. A student who cannot accomplish the process in the more simple case may be assured that he is not qualified for the higher order of biological researches, and must be satisfied with the humbler office of collecting materials for the use of minds of another order. Hence arises another use of mathematical training;—that of testing and classifying minds, as well as preparing and guiding them. Probably as much good would be done by excluding the students who only encumber the science by aimless and desultory inquiries, as by fitly instituting those who can better fulfill its conditions.—COMTE, A.

> *Positive Philosophy* [*Martineau*], *Bk. 5, chap. 1.*

1581. There seems no sufficient reason why the use of scientific fictions, so common in the hands of geometers, should not be introduced into biology, if systematically employed, and adopted with sufficient sobriety. In mathematical studies, great advantages have arisen from imagining a series of hypothetical cases, the consideration of which, though artificial, may aid the clearing up of the real subject, or its fundamental elaboration. This art is usually confounded with that of hypotheses; but it is entirely different; inasmuch as in the latter case the solution alone is imaginary; whereas in the former, the problem itself is radically ideal. Its use can never be in biology comparable to what it is in mathematics: but it seems to me that the abstract character of the higher conceptions of comparative biology renders them susceptible of such treatment. The process will be to intercalate, among different known organisms, certain purely fictitious organisms, so imagined as to facilitate their comparison, by rendering the biological series more homogeneous and continuous: and it might be that several might hereafter meet with more or less ot a realization among organisms hitherto unexplored. It may be possible, in the present state of our knowledge of living bodies, to conceive of a new organism capable of fulfilling certain given conditions of existence. However that may be, the collocation of real cases with well-imagined ones, after the manner of geometers, will doubtless be practised hereafter, to complete the general laws of comparative anatomy and physiology, and possibly to anticipate occasionally the direct exploration. Even now, the rational use of such an artifice might greatly simplify and clear up the ordinary system of biological instruction. But it is only the highest order of investigators who can be trusted with it. Whenever it is adopted, it will constitute another ground of relation between biology and mathematics.—Comte, A.

> Positive Philosophy [Martineau], Bk. 5, chap. 1.

1582. I think it may safely enough be affirmed, that he, that is not so much as indifferently skilled in mathematicks, can hardly be more than indifferently skilled in the fundamental principles of physiology.—Boyle, Robert.

> Works (London, 1772), Vol. 3, p. 430.

1583. It is not only possible but necessary that mathematics be applied to psychology; the reason for this necessity lies briefly in this: that by no other means can be reached that which is the ultimate aim of all speculation, namely conviction.

> Herbart, J. F.
>
> Werke [Kehrbach], (Langensalza, 1890), Bd. 5, p. 104.

1584. All more definite knowledge must start with computation; and this is of most important consequences not only for the theory of memory, of imagination, of understanding, but as well for the doctrine of sensations, of desires, and affections.—HERBART, J. F.

> Werke [Kehrbach], (Langensalza, 1890), Bd. 5, p. 103.

1585. In the near future mathematics will play an important part in medicine: already there are increasing indications that physiology, descriptive anatomy, pathology and therapeutics cannot escape mathematical legitimation.—DESSOIR, MAX.

> Westermann's Monatsberichte, Bd. 77, p. 380; Ahrens: Scherz und Ernst in der Mathematik (Leipzig, 1904), p. 395.

1586. The social sciences mathematically developed are to be the controlling factors in civilization.—WHITE, W. F.

> A Scrap-book of Elementary Mathematics (Chicago, 1908), p. 208.

1587. It is clear that this education [referring to education preparatory to the science of sociology] must rest on a basis of mathematical philosophy, even apart from the necessity of mathematics to the study of inorganic philosophy. It is only in the region of mathematics that sociologists, or anybody else, can obtain a true sense of scientific evidence, and form the habit of rational and decisive argumentation; can, in short, learn to fulfill the logical conditions of all positive speculation, by studying universal positivism at its source. This training, obtained and employed with the more care on account of the eminent difficulty of social science, is what sociologists have to seek in mathematics.—COMTE, A.

> Positive Philosophy [Martineau], Bk. 6, chap. 4.

1588. It is clear that the individual as a social unit and the state as a social aggregate require a certain modicum of mathematics, some arithmetic and algebra, to conduct their affairs. Under this head would fall the theory of interest, simple and compound, matters of discount and amortization, and, if lotteries hold a prominent place in raising moneys, as in some states, questions of probability must be added. As the state becomes more highly organized and more interested in the scientific analysis of its life, there appears an urgent necessity for various statistical information, and this can be properly obtained, reduced, correlated, and interpreted only when the guiding spirit in the work have the necessary mathematical training in the theory of statistics. (Figures may not lie, but statistics compiled unscientifically and analyzed incompetently are almost sure to be misleading, and when this condition is unnecessarily chronic the so-called statisticians may well be called liars.) The dependence of insurance of various kinds on statistical information and the very great place which insurance occupies in the modern state, albeit often controlled by private corporations instead of by the government, makes the theories of paramount importance to our social life.—WILSON, E. B.

> *Bulletin American Mathematical Society,*
> *Vol. 18 (1912), p. 463.*

1589. The theory of probabilities and the theory of errors now constitute a formidable body of knowledge of great mathematical interest and of great practical importance. Though developed largely through the applications to the more precise sciences of astronomy, geodesy, and physics, their range of applicability extends to all the sciences; and they are plainly destined to play an increasingly important rôle in the development and in the applications of the sciences of the future. Hence their study is not only a commendable element in a liberal education, but some knowledge of them is essential to a correct understanding of daily events.—WOODWARD, R. S.

> *Probability and Theory of Errors (New York,*
> *1906), Preface.*

1590. It was not to be anticipated that a new science [the science of probabilities] which took its rise in games of chance, and which had long to encounter an obloquy, hardly yet extinct, due to the prevailing idea that its only end was to facilitate and encourage the calculations of gamblers, could ever have attained its present status—that its aid should be called for in every department of natural science, both to assist in discovery, which it has repeatedly done (even in pure mathematics), to minimize the unavoidable errors of observation, and to detect the presence of causes as revealed by observed events. Nor are commercial and other practical interests of life less indebted to it: wherever the future has to be forecasted, risk to be provided against, or the true lessons to be deduced from statistics, it corrects for us the rough conjectures of common sense, and decides which course is really, according to the lights of which we are in possession, the wisest for us to pursue.—CROFTON, M. W.

Encyclopedia Britannica, 9th Edition; Article " Probability."

1591. The calculus of probabilities, when confined within just limits, ought to interest, in an equal degree, the mathematician, the experimentalist, and the statesman. From the time when Pascal and Fermat established its first principles, it has rendered, and continues daily to render, services of the most eminent kind. It is the calculus of probabilities, which, after having suggested the best arrangements of the tables of population and mortality, teaches us to deduce from those numbers, in general so erroneously interpreted, conclusions of a precise and useful character; it is the calculus of probabilities which alone can regulate justly the premiums to be paid for assurances; the reserve funds for the disbursements of pensions, annuities, discounts, etc. It is under its influence that lotteries and other shameful snares cunningly laid for avarice and ignorance have definitely disappeared.—ARAGO.

Eulogy on Laplace [Baden-Powell], Smithsonian Report, 1874, p. 164.

1592. Men were surprised to hear that not only births, deaths, and marriages, but the decisions of tribunals, the results of popular elections, the influence of punishments in checking crime, the comparative values of medical remedies, the probable limits of error in numerical results in every department of physical inquiry, the detection of causes, physical, social, and moral, nay, even the weight of evidence and the validity of logical argument, might come to be surveyed with the lynx-eyed scrutiny of a dispassionate analysis.—HERSCHEL, J.

Quoted in Encyclopedia Britannica, 9th Edition; Article " Probability."

1593. If economists expect of the application of the mathematical method any extensive concrete numerical results, and it is to be feared that like other non-mathematicians all too many of them think of mathematics as merely an arithmetical science, they are bound to be disappointed and to find a paucity of results in the works of the few of their colleagues who use that method. But they should rather learn, as the mathematicians among them know full well, that mathematics is much broader, that it has an abstract quantitative (or even qualitative) side, that it deals with relations as well as numbers, . . .

WILSON, E. B.
*Bulletin American Mathematical Society,
Vol. 18 (1912), p. 464.*

1594. The effort of the economist is to *see*, to picture the inter-play of economic elements. The more clearly cut these elements appear in his vision, the better; the more elements he can grasp and hold in his mind at once, the better. The economic world is a misty region. The first explorers used unaided vision. Mathematics is the lantern by which what before was dimly visible now looms up in firm, bold outlines. The old phantasmagoria disappear. We see better. We also see further.

FISHER, IRVING.
*Transactions of Connecticut Academy, Vol. 9
(1892), p. 119.*

1595. In the great inquiries of the moral and social sciences . . . mathematics (I always mean Applied Mathematics) affords the only sufficient type of deductive art. Up to this time, I may venture to say that no one ever knew what deduction is, as a means of investigating the laws of nature, who had not learned it from mathematics, nor can any one hope to understand it thoroughly, who has not, at some time in his life, known enough of mathematics to be familiar with the instrument at work.—MILL, J. S.
*An Examination of Sir William Hamilton's
Philosophy (London, 1878), p. 622.*

1596. Let me pass on to say a word or two about the teaching of mathematics as an academic training for general professional life. It has immense capabilities in that respect. If you consider how much of the effectiveness of an administrator depends upon the capacity for co-ordinating appropriately a number of different ideas, precise accuracy of definition, rigidity of proof, and sustained reasoning, strict in every step, and when you consider what substitutes for these things nine men out of every ten without special training have to put up with, it is clear that a man with a mathematical training has incalculable advantages.—Shaw, W. H.

Perry's Teaching of Mathematics (London, 1902), p. 73.

1597. Before you enter on the study of law a sufficient ground work must be laid. . . . Mathematics and natural philosophy are so useful in the most familiar occurrences of life and are so peculiarly engaging and delightful as would induce everyone to wish an acquaintance with them. Besides this, the faculties of the mind, like the members of a body, are strengthened and improved by exercise. Mathematical reasoning and deductions are, therefore, a fine preparation for investigating the abstruse speculations of the law.

Jefferson, Thomas.
Quoted in Cajori's Teaching and History of Mathematics in the U. S. (Washington, 1890), p. 35.

1598. It has been observed in England of the study of law,—though the acquisition of the most difficult parts of its learning, the interpretation of laws, the comparison of authorities, and the construction of instruments, would seem to require philological and critical training; though the weighing of evidence and the investigation of probable truth belong to the province of the moral sciences, and the peculiar duties of the advocate require rhetorical skill,—yet that a large proportion of the most distinguished members of the profession has proceeded from the university (that of Cambridge) most celebrated for the cultivation of mathematical studies.

Everett, Edward.
Orations and Speeches (Boston, 1870), Vol. 2, p. 511.

1599. All historic science tends to become mathematical. Mathematical power is classifying power.—NOVALIS.

Schriften (Berlin, 1901), Teil 2, p. 192.

1599a. History has never regarded itself as a science of statistics. It was the Science of Vital Energy in relation with time; and of late this radiating centre of its life has been steadily tending,—together with every form of physical and mechanical energy,—toward mathematical expression.—ADAM, HENRY.

A Letter to American Teachers of History (Washington, 1910), p. 115.

1599b. Mathematics can be shown to sustain a certain relation to rhetoric and may aid in determining its laws.

SHERMAN L. A.

University [of Nebraska] Studies, Vol. 1, p. 130.

CHAPTER XVI

ARITHMETIC

1601. There is no problem in all mathematics that cannot be solved by direct counting. But with the present implements of mathematics many operations can be performed in a few minutes which without mathematical methods would take a lifetime.—MACH, ERNST.
> *Popular Scientific Lectures* [*McCormack*] *(Chicago, 1898), p. 197.*

1602. There is no inquiry which is not finally reducible to a question of Numbers; for there is none which may not be conceived of as consisting in the determination of quantities by each other, according to certain relations.—COMTE, A
> *Positive Philosophy* [*Martineau*], *Bk. 1, chap. 1.*

1603. Pythagoras says that number is the origin of all things, and certainly the law of number is the key that unlocks the secrets of the universe. But the law of number possesses an immanent order, which is at first sight mystifying, but on a more intimate acquaintance we easily understand it to be intrinsically necessary; and this law of number explains the wondrous consistency of the laws of nature.—CARUS, PAUL.
> *Reflections on Magic Squares; Monist, Vol. 16 (1906), p. 139.*

1604. An ancient writer said that arithmetic and geometry are the *wings of mathematics;* I believe one can say without speaking metaphorically that these two sciences are the foundation and essence of all the sciences which deal with quantity. Not only are they the foundation, they are also, as it were, the capstones; for, whenever a result has been arrived at, in order to use that result, it is necessary to translate it into numbers or into lines; to translate it into numbers requires the aid of arithmetic, to translate it into lines necessitates the use of geometry.
> LAGRANGE.
> *Leçons Elémentaires sur les Mathématiques, Leçon seconde.*

1605. It is number which regulates everything and it is measure which establishes universal order. . . . A quiet peace, an inviolable order, an inflexible security amidst all change and turmoil characterize the world which mathematics discloses and whose depths it unlocks.—DILLMANN, E.

Die Mathematik die Fackelträgerin einer neuen Zeit (Stuttgart, 1889), p. 12.

1606. Number, the inducer of philosophies,
The synthesis of letters, . . .—AESCHYLUS.

Quoted in, Thomson, J. A., Introduction to Science, chap. 1 (London).

1607. Amongst all the ideas we have, as there is none suggested to the mind by more ways, so there is none more simple, than that of *unity*, or one: it has no shadow of variety or composition in it; every object our senses are employed about; every idea in our understanding; every thought of our minds, brings this idea along with it. And therefore it is the most intimate to our thoughts, as well as it is, in its agreement to all other things, *the most universal idea we have.*—LOCKE, JOHN.

An Essay concerning Human Understanding, Bk. 2, chap. 16, sect. 1.

1608. The *simple modes* of *number* are of all other the most distinct; every the least variation, which is an unit, making each combination as clearly different from that which approacheth nearest to it, as the most remote; two being as distinct from one, as two hundred; and the idea of two as distinct from the idea of three, as the magnitude of the whole earth is from that of a mite.—LOCKE, JOHN.

An Essay concerning Human Understanding, Bk. 2, chap. 16, sect. 3.

1609. The number of a class is the class of all classes similar to the given class.—RUSSELL, BERTRAND.

Principles of Mathematics (Cambridge, 1903), p. 115.

1610. Number is that property of a group of distinct things which remains unchanged during any change to which the group may be subjected which does not destroy the distinctness of the individual things.—FINE, H. B.

Number-system of Algebra (Boston and New York, 1890), p. 3.

1611. The science of arithmetic may be called the science of exact limitation of matter and things in space, force, and time.

PARKER, F. W.

Talks on Pedagogics (New York, 1894), p. 64.

1612. Arithmetic is the science of the Evaluation of Functions,

Algebra is the science of the Transformation of Functions.—HOWISON, G. H.

Journal of Speculative Philosophy, Vol. 5, p. 175.

1613. That *arithmetic* rests on pure intuition of *time* is not so obvious as that geometry is based on pure intuition of space, but it may be readily proved as follows. All counting consists in the repeated positing of unity; only in order to know how often it has been posited, we mark it each time with a different word: these are the numerals. Now repetition is possible only through succession: but succession rests on the immediate intuition of *time*, it is intelligible only by means of this latter concept: hence counting is possible only by means of time.—This dependence of counting on *time* is evidenced by the fact that in all languages multiplication is expressed by "times" [mal], that is, by a concept of time; sexies, ἑξάκις, six fois, six times.

SCHOPENHAUER, A.

Die Welt als Vorstellung und Wille; Werke (Frauenstaedt) (Leipzig, 1877), Bd. 3, p. 39.

1614. The miraculous powers of modern calculation are due to three inventions: the Arabic Notation, Decimal Fractions and Logarithms.—CAJORI, F.

History of Mathematics (New York, 1897), p. 161.

1615. The grandest achievement of the Hindoos and the one which, of all mathematical investigations, has contributed most

to the general progress of intelligence, is the invention of the principle of position in writing numbers.—CAJORI, F.
History of Mathematics (New York, 1897), p. 87.

1616. The invention of logarithms and the calculation of the earlier tables form a very striking episode in the history of exact science, and, with the exception of the *Principia* of Newton, there is no mathematical work published in the country which has produced such important consequences, or to which so much interest attaches as to Napier's Descriptio.
GLAISHER, J. W. L.
Encyclopedia Britannica, 9th Edition; Article "Logarithms."

1617. All minds are equally capable of attaining the science of numbers: yet we find a prodigious difference in the powers of different men, in that respect, after they have grown up, because their minds have been more or less exercised in it.
JOHNSON, SAMUEL.
Boswell's Life of Johnson, Harper's Edition (1871), Vol. 2, p. 33.

1618. The method of arithmetical teaching is perhaps the best understood of any of the methods concerned with elementary studies.—BAIN, ALEXANDER.
Education as a Science (New York, 1898), p. 288.

1619. What a benefite that onely thyng is, to haue the witte whetted and sharpened, I neade not trauell to declare, sith all men confesse it to be as greate as maie be. Excepte any witlesse persone thinke he maie bee to wise. But he that most feareth that, is leaste in daunger of it. Wherefore to conclude, I see moare menne to acknowledge the benefite of nomber, than I can espie willying to studie, to attaine the benefites of it. Many praise it, but fewe dooe greatly practise it: onlesse it bee for the vulgare practice, concernying Merchaundes trade. Wherein the desire and hope of gain, maketh many willying to sustaine some trauell. For aide of whom, I did sette forth the first parte of *Arithmetike*. But if thei knewe how faree this seconde parte, doeeth excell the firste parte, thei would not accoumpte any tyme loste, that were emploied in it. Yea thei would not thinke any tyme well bestowed till thei had gotten soche habilitie by it, that it might be their aide in al other studies.

RECORDE, ROBERT.
Whetstone of Witte (London, 1557).

1620. You see then, my friend, I observed, that our real need of this branch of science [arithmetic] is probably because it seems to compel the soul to use our intelligence in the search after pure truth.

Aye, remarked he, it does this to a remarkable extent.

Have you ever noticed that those who have a turn for arithmetic are, with scarcely an exception, naturally quick in all sciences; and that men of slow intellect, if they be trained and exercised in this study . . . become invariably quicker than they were before?

Exactly so, he replied.

And, moreover, I think you will not easily find that many things give the learner and student more trouble than this.

Of course not.

On all these accounts, then, we must not omit this branch of science, but those with the best of talents should be instructed therein.—PLATO.

Republic [Davis], Bk. 7, chap. 8.

1621. Arithmetic has a very great and elevating effect, compelling the soul to reason about abstract number, and if visible or tangible objects are obtruding upon the argument, refusing to be satisfied.—PLATO.

Republic [Jowett], Bk. 7, p. 525.

1622. Good arithmetic contributes powerfully to purposive effort, to concentration, to tenacity of purpose, to generalship, to faith in right, and to the joy of achievement, which are the elements that make up efficient citizenship. . . . Good arithmetic exalts thinking, furnishes intellectual pleasure, adds appreciably to love of right, and subordinates pure memory.

MYERS, GEORGE.
Monograph on Arithmetic in Public Education (Chicago), p. 21.

1623. On the one side we may say that the purpose of number work is to put a child in possession of the machinery of calculation; on the other side it is to give him a better mastery of the world through a clear (mathematical) insight into the varied physical objects and activities. The whole world, from one point of view, can be definitely interpreted and appreciated by mathematical measurements and estimates. Arithmetic in the common school should give a child this point of view, the ability to see and estimate things with a mathematical eye.

McMURRAY, C. A.
Special Method in Arithmetic (New York, 1906), p. 18.

1624. We are so accustomed to hear arithmetic spoken of as one of the three fundamental ingredients in all schemes of instruction, that it seems like inquiring too curiously to ask why this should be. Reading, Writing, and Arithmetic—these three are assumed to be of co-ordinate rank. Are they indeed co-ordinate, and if so on what grounds?

In this modern "trivium" the art of reading is put first. Well, there is no doubt as to its right to the foremost place. For reading is the instrument of all our acquisition. It is indispensable. There is not an hour in our lives in which it does not make a great difference to us whether we can read or not. And the art of Writing, too; that is the instrument of all communication, and it becomes, in one form or other, useful to us every day. But Counting—doing sums,—how often in life does this accomplishment come into exercise? Beyond the simplest additions, and the power to check the items of a bill, the arithmetical knowledge required of any well-informed person in private life is very limited. For all practical purposes, whatever I may have learned at school of fractions, or proportion, or decimals, is, unless I happen to be in business, far less available to me in life than a knowledge, say, of history of my own country, or the elementary truths of physics. The truth is, that regarded as practical *arts*, reading, writing, and arithmetic have no right to be classed together as co-ordinate elements of education; for the last of these is considerably less useful to the average man or woman not only than the other two, but than many others that might be named. But reading, writing, and such mathematical or logical exercise as may be gained in connection with the manifestation of numbers, *have* a right to constitute the primary elements of instruction. And I believe that arithmetic, if it deserves the high place that it conventionally holds in our educational system, deserves it mainly on the ground that it is to be treated as a logical exercise. It is the only branch of mathematics which has found its way into primary and early education; other departments of pure science being reserved for what is called higher or university instruction. But all the arguments in favor of teaching algebra and trigonometry to advanced students, apply equally to the teaching of the principles or theory of arithmetic to schoolboys. It is calculated to do for them exactly the same kind of service, to educate one side of their minds, to bring into play one set of faculties which cannot be so severely or properly exercised in any other department of learning. In short, relatively to the needs of a beginner, Arithmetic, as a science, is just as valuable—it is certainly quite as intelligible—as the higher mathematics to a university student.—FITCH, J. G.

Lectures on Teaching (New York, 1906), pp. 267–268.

1625. What mathematics, therefore are expected to do for the advanced student at the university, Arithmetic, if taught demonstratively, is capable of doing for the children even of the humblest school. It furnishes training in reasoning, and particularly in deductive reasoning. It is a discipline in closeness and continuity of thought. It reveals the nature of fallacies, and refuses to avail itself of unverified assumptions. It is the one department of school-study in which the sceptical and inquisitive spirit has the most legitimate scope; in which authority goes for nothing. In other departments of instruction you have a right to ask for the scholar's confidence, and to expect many things to be received on your testimony with the understanding that they will be explained and verified afterwards. But here you are justified in saying to your pupil "Believe nothing which you cannot understand. Take nothing for granted." In short, the proper office of arithmetic is to serve as elementary training in logic. All through your work as teachers you will bear in mind the fundamental difference between knowing and thinking; and will feel how much more important relatively to the health of the intellectual life the habit of thinking is than the power of knowing, or even facility of achieving visible results. But here this principle has special significance. It is by Arithmetic more than by any other subject in the school course that the art of thinking—consecutively, closely, logically—can be effectually taught.—FITCH, J. G.

> Lectures on Teaching (New York, 1906), pp. 292-293.

1626. Arithmetic and geometry, those wings on which the astronomer soars as high as heaven.—BOYLE, ROBERT.

> Usefulness of Mathematics to Natural Philosophy; Works (London, 1772), Vol. 3, p. 429.

1627. Arithmetical symbols are written diagrams and geometrical figures are graphic formulas.—HILBERT, D.

> Mathematical Problems; Bulletin American Mathematical Society, Vol. 8 (1902), p. 443.

1628. Arithmetic and geometry are much more certain than the other sciences, because the objects of them are in themselves so simple and so clear that they need not suppose anything which experience can call in question, and both proceed by a chain of consequences which reason deduces one from another. They are also the easiest and clearest of all the sciences, and their object is such as we desire; for, except for want of attention, it is hardly supposable that a man should go astray in them. We must not be surprised, however, that many minds apply themselves by preference to other studies, or to philosophy. Indeed everyone allows himself more freely the right to make his guess if the matter be dark than if it be clear, and it is much easier to have on any question some vague ideas than to arrive at the truth itself on the simplest of all.—DESCARTES.

> Rules for the Direction of the Mind; Torrey's Philosophy of Descartes (New York, 1892), p. 63.

1629. Why are *wise* few, *fools* numerous in the excesse?
'Cause, wanting *number*, they are *numberlesse*.

LOVELACE.

Noah Bridges: Vulgar Arithmetike (London, 1659), p. 127.

1630. The clearness and distinctness of each mode of number from all others, even those that approach nearest, makes me apt to think that demonstrations in numbers, if they are not more evident and exact than in extension, yet they are more general in their use, and more determinate in their application. Because the ideas of numbers are more precise and distinguishable than in extension; where every equality and excess are not so easy to be observed or measured; because our thoughts cannot in space arrive at any determined smallness beyond which it cannot go, as an unit; and therefore the quantity or proportion of any the least excess cannot be discovered.—LOCKE, JOHN.

An Essay concerning Human Understanding, Bk. 2, chap. 16, sect. 4.

1631. Battalions of figures are like battalions of men, not always as strong as is supposed.—SAGE, M.

Mrs. Piper and the Society for Psychical Research [Robertson] (New York, 1909), p. 151.

1632. Number was born in superstition and reared in mystery, . . . numbers were once made the foundation of religion and philosophy, and the tricks of figures have had a marvellous effect on a credulous people.—PARKER, F. W.

Talks on Pedagogics (New York, 1894), p. 64.

1633. A rule to trick th' arithmetic.—KIPLING, R.

To the True Romance.

1634. God made integers, all else is the work of man.

KRONECKER, L.

Jahresberichte der Deutschen Mathematiker Vereinigung, Bd. 2, p. 19.

1635. Plato said "ἀεὶ ὁ θεὸς γεωμέτρει." Jacobi changed this to "ἀεὶ ὁ θεὸς ἀριθμητίζει." Then came Kronecker

and created the memorable expression "Die ganzen Zahlen hat Gott gemacht, alles andere ist Menschenwerk."—Klein, F.
> Jahresbericht der Deutschen Mathematiker Vereinigung, Bd. 6, p. 136.

1636. Integral numbers are the fountainhead of all mathematics.—Minkowski, H.
> Diophantische Approximationen (Leipzig, 1907), Vorrede.

1637. The "Disquisitiones Arithmeticae" that great book with seven seals.—Merz, J. T.
> A History of European Thought in the Nineteenth Century (Edinburgh and London, 1903), p. 721.

1638. It may fairly be said that the germs of the modern algebra of linear substitutions and concomitants are to be found in the fifth section of the Disquisitiones Arithmeticae; and inversely, every advance in the algebraic theory of forms is an acquisition to the arithmetical theory.—Mathews, G. B.
> Theory of Numbers (Cambridge, 1892), Part 1, sect. 48.

1639. Strictly speaking, the theory of numbers has nothing to do with negative, or fractional, or irrational quantities, as such. No theorem which cannot be expressed without reference to these notions is purely arithmetical: and no proof of an arithmetical theorem, can be considered finally satisfactory if it intrinsically depends upon extraneous analytical theories.

> Mathews, G. B.
> Theory of Numbers (Cambridge, 1892), Part 1, sect. 1.

1640. Many of the greatest masters of the mathematical sciences were first attracted to mathematical inquiry by problems relating to numbers, and no one can glance at the periodicals of the present day which contain questions for solution without noticing how singular a charm such problems still continue to exert. The interest in numbers seems implanted in the human mind, and it is a pity that it should not have freer scope in this country. The methods of the theory of numbers are peculiar to itself, and are not readily acquired by a student whose mind has for years been familiarized with the very different treatment which is appropriate to the theory of continuous magnitude; it is therefore extremely desirable that some portion of the theory should be included in the ordinary course of mathematical instruction at our University. From the moment that Gauss, in his wonderful treatise of 1801, laid down the true lines of the theory, it entered upon a new day, and no one is likely to be able to do useful work in any part of the subject who is unacquainted with the principles and conceptions with which he endowed it.—GLAISHER, J. W. L.

> *Presidential Address British Association for the Advancement of Science (1890); Nature, Vol. 42, p. 467.*

1641. Let us look for a moment at the general significance of the fact that calculating machines actually exist, which relieve mathematicians of the purely mechanical part of numerical computations, and which accomplish the work more quickly and with a greater degree of accuracy; for the machine is not subject to the slips of the human calculator. The existence of such a machine proves that computation is not concerned with the significance of numbers, but that it is concerned essentially only with the formal laws of operation; for it is only these that the machine can obey—having been thus constructed—an intuitive perception of the significance of numbers being out of the question.—KLEIN, F.

> *Elementarmathematik vom höheren Standpunkte aus. (Leipzig, 1908), Bd. 1, p. 53.*

1642. Mathematics is the queen of the sciences and arithmetic the queen of mathematics. She often condescends to render service to astronomy and other natural sciences, but in all relations she is entitled to the first rank.—GAUSS.

> *Sartorius von Waltershausen: Gauss zum Gedächtniss. (Leipzig, 1856), p. 79.*

1643. Zu Archimedes kam ein wissbegieriger Jüngling,
  Weihe mich, sprach er zu ihm, ein in die göttliche Kunst,

Die so herrliche Dienste der Sternenkunde geleistet,
Hinter dem Uranos noch einen Planeten entdeckt.
Göttlich nennst Du die Kunst, sie ist's, versetzte der
    Weise,
Aber sie war es, bevor noch sie den Kosmos erforscht,
Ehe sie herrliche Dienste der Sternenkunde geleistet,
Hinter dem Uranos noch einen Planeten entdeckt.
Was Du im Kosmos erblickst, ist nur der Göttlichen
    Abglanz,
In der Olympier Schaar thronet die ewige Zahl.

                            JACOBI, C. G. J.
                Journal für Mathematik, Bd. 101 (1887), p.
                338.

To Archimedes came a youth intent upon knowledge,
Quoth he, "Initiate me into the science divine
Which to astronomy, lo! such excellent service has
    rendered,
And beyond Uranus' orb a hidden planet revealed."
"Call'st thou the science divine? So it is," the wise
    man responded,
"But so it was long before its light on the Cosmos it
    shed,
Ere in astronomy's realm such excellent service it
    rendered,
And beyond Uranus' orb a hidden planet revealed.
Only reflection divine is that which Cosmos dis-
    closes,
Number herself sits enthroned among Olympia's hosts.

1644. The higher arithmetic presents us with an inexhaustible store of interesting truths,—of truths too, which are not isolated, but stand in a close internal connexion, and between which, as our knowledge increases, we are continually discovering new and sometimes wholly unexpected ties. A great part of its theories derives an additional charm from the peculiarity that important propositions, with the impress of simplicity upon them, are often easily discoverable by induction, and yet are of so profound a character that we cannot find their demonstration till after many vain attempts; and even then, when we do succeed, it is often by some tedious and artificial process, while the simpler methods may long remain concealed.

GAUSS, C. F.

Preface to Eisenstein's Mathematische Abhandlungen (Berlin, 1847), [H. J. S. Smith].

1645. The Theory of Numbers has acquired a great and increasing claim to the attention of mathematicians. It is equally remarkable for the number and importance of its results, for the precision and rigorousness of its demonstrations, for the variety of its methods, for the intimate relations between truths apparently isolated which it sometimes discloses, and for the numerous applications of which it is susceptible in other parts of analysis.—SMITH, H. J. S.

Report on the Theory of Numbers, British Association, 1859; Collected Mathematical Papers, Vol. 1, p. 38.

1646. The invention of the symbol $\equiv$ by Gauss affords a striking example of the advantage which may be derived from an appropriate notation, and marks an epoch in the development of the science of arithmetic.—MATHEWS, G. B.

Theory of Numbers (Cambridge, 1892), Part 1, sect. 29.

1647. As Gauss first pointed out, the problem of cyclotomy, or division of the circle into a number of equal parts, depends in a very remarkable way upon arithmetical considerations. We have here the earliest and simplest example of those relations of the theory of numbers to transcendental analysis, and even to pure geometry, which so often unexpectedly present themselves, and which, at first sight, are so mysterious.

MATHEWS, G. B.

Theory of Numbers (Cambridge, 1892), Part 1, sect. 167.

1648. I have sometimes thought that the profound mystery which envelops our conceptions relative to prime numbers depends upon the limitations of our faculties in regard to time, which like space may be in its essence poly-dimensional, and that this and such sort of truths would become self-evident to a being whose mode of perception is according to *superficially* as distinguished from our own limitation to *linearly* extended time.—SYLVESTER, J. J.

> *Collected Mathematical Papers, Vol. 4, p. 600, footnote.*

CHAPTER XVII

1701. The science of algebra, independently of any of its uses, has all the advantages which belong to mathematics in general as an object of study, and which it is not necessary to enumerate. Viewed either as a science of quantity, or as a language of symbols, it may be made of the greatest service to those who are sufficiently acquainted with arithmetic, and who have sufficient power of comprehension to enter fairly upon its difficulties.—DE MORGAN, A.

Elements of Algebra (London, 1837), Preface.

1702. Algebra is generous, she often gives more than is asked of her.—D'ALEMBERT.

Quoted in Bulletin American Mathematical Society, Vol. 2 (1905), p. 285.

1703. The operations of symbolic arithmetick seem to me to afford men one of the clearest exercises of reason that I ever yet met with, nothing being there to be performed without strict and watchful ratiocination, and the whole method and progress of that appearing at once upon the paper, when the operation is finished, and affording the analyst a lasting, and, as it were, visible ratiocination.—BOYLE, ROBERT.

Works (London, 1772), Vol. 3, p. 426.

1704. The human mind has never invented a labor-saving machine equal to algebra.—

The Nation, Vol. 33, p. 237.

1705. They that are ignorant of Algebra cannot imagine the wonders in this kind are to be done by it: and what further improvements and helps advantageous to other parts of knowledge the sagacious mind of man may yet find out, it is not easy to determine. This at least I believe, that the *ideas of quantity* are not those alone that are capable of demonstration and knowledge; and that other, and perhaps more useful, parts of contemplation, would afford us certainty, if vices, passions, and domineering interest did not oppose and menace such endeavours.—LOCKE, JOHN.

An Essay concerning Human Understanding,
Bk. 4, chap. 3, sect. 18.

1706. Algebra is but written geometry and geometry is but figured algebra.—GERMAIN, SOPHIE.

Mémoire sur la surfaces élastiques.

1707. So long as algebra and geometry proceeded separately their progress was slow and their application limited, but when these two sciences were united, they mutually strengthened each other, and marched together at a rapid pace toward perfection.

LAGRANGE.

Leçons élémentaires sur les Mathématiques,
Leçon Cinquième.

1708. The laws of algebra, though suggested by arithmetic, do not depend on it. They depend entirely on the conventions by which it is stated that certain modes of grouping the symbols are to be considered as identical. This assigns certain properties to the marks which form the symbols of algebra. The laws regulating the manipulation of algebraic symbols are identical with those of arithmetic. It follows that no algebraic theorem can ever contradict any result which could be arrived at by arithmetic; for the reasoning in both cases merely applies the same general laws to different classes of things. If an algebraic theorem can be interpreted in arithmetic, the corresponding arithmetical theorem is therefore true.

WHITEHEAD, A. N.

Universal Algebra (Cambridge, 1898), p. 2.

1709. That a formal science like algebra, the creation of our abstract thought, should thus, in a sense, dictate the laws of its own being, is very remarkable. It has required the experience of centuries for us to realize the full force of this appeal.

MATHEWS, G. B.

F. Spencer: Chapters on Aims and Practice of
Teaching (London, 1899), p. 184.

1710. The rules of algebra may be investigated by its own principles, without any aid from geometry; and although in many cases the two sciences may serve to illustrate each other, there is not now the least necessity in the more elementary parts to call in the aid of the latter in expounding the former.

CHRYSTAL, GEORGE.
Encyclopedia Britannica, 9th Edition; Article "Algebra."

1711. Algebra, as an art, can be of no use to any one in the business of life; certainly not as taught in the schools. I appeal to every man who has been through the school routine whether this be not the case. Taught as an art it is of little use in the higher mathematics, as those are made to feel who attempt to study the differential calculus without knowing more of the principles than is contained in books of rules.

DE MORGAN, A.
Elements of Algebra (London, 1837), Preface.

1712. We may always depend upon it that algebra, which cannot be translated into good English and sound common sense, is bad algebra —CLIFFORD, W. K.
Common Sense in the Exact Sciences (London, 1885), chap. 1, sect. 7.

1713. The best review of arithmetic consists in the study of algebra.—CAJORI, F.
Teaching and History of Mathematics in U. S. (Washington, 1896), p. 110.

1714. [Algebra] has for its object the resolution of equations; taking this expression in its full logical meaning, which signifies the transformation of implicit functions into equivalent explicit ones. In the same way arithmetic may be defined as destined to the determination of the values of functions. . . . We will briefly say that *Algebra is the Calculus of Functions*, and *Arithmetic the Calculus of Values.*—COMTE, A.
Philosophy of Mathematics [Gillespie] (New York, 1851), p. 55.

1715. . . . the subject matter of algebraic science is the abstract notion of time; divested of, or not yet clothed with, any actual knowledge which we may possess of the real Events of History, or any conception which we may frame of Cause and Effect in Nature; but involving, what indeed it *cannot* be divested of, the thought of *possible* Succession, or of pure, *ideal* Progression.—HAMILTON, W. R.

> *Graves' Life of Hamilton (New York, 1882–*
> *1889), Vol. 3, p. 633.*

1716. . . . instead of seeking to attain consistency and uniformity of system, as some modern writers have attempted, by banishing this thought of time from the *higher* Algebra, I seek to attain the same object, by systematically introducing it into the *lower* or earlier parts of the science —HAMILTON, W. R.

> *Graves' Life of Hamilton (New York, 1882–*
> *1889), Vol. 3, p. 634.*

1717. The circumstances that algebra has its origin in arithmetic, however widely it may in the end differ from that science, led Sir Isaac Newton to designate it "Universal Arithmetic," a designation which, vague as it is, indicates its character better than any other by which it has been attempted to express its functions—better certainly, to ordinary minds, than the designation which has been applied to it by Sir William Rowan Hamilton, one of the greatest mathematicians the world has seen since the days of Newton—"the Science of Pure Time;" or even than the title by which De Morgan would paraphrase Hamilton's words—"the Calculus of Succession."

> CHRYSTAL, GEOR E.
> *Encyclopedia Britannica, 9th Edition; Article*
> *"Algebra."*

1718. Time is said to have only *one dimension*, and space to have *three dimensions*. . . . The mathematical *quaternion* partakes of *both* these elements; in technical language it may be said to be "time plus space," or "space plus time:" and in this sense it has, or at least involves a reference to, *four dimensions*. . . .

And how the One of Time, of Space the Three,
Might in the Chain of Symbols girdled be.

HAMILTON, W. R.

Graves' Life of Hamilton (New York, 1882–
1889), Vol. 3, p. 635.

1719. It is confidently predicted, by those best qualified to
judge, that in the coming centuries Hamilton's Quaternions will
stand out as the great discovery of our nineteenth century.
Yet how silently has the book taken its place upon the shelves of
the mathematician's library! Perhaps not fifty men on this
side of the Atlantic have seen it, certainly not five have read it.

HILL, THOMAS.

North American Review, Vol. 85, p. 223.

1720. I think the time may come when double algebra will
be the beginner's tool; and quaternions will be where double
algebra is now. The Lord only knows what will come above the
quaternions.—DE MORGAN, A.

Graves' Life of Hamilton (New York, 1882–
1889), Vol. 3, p. 493.

1721. Quaternions came from Hamilton after his really good
work had been done; and though beautifully ingenious, have
been an unmixed evil to those who have touched them in any
way, including Clerk Maxwell.—THOMSON, WILLIAM.

Thompson, S. P.: Life of Lord Kelvin (London,
1910), p. 1138.

1722. The whole affair [quaternions] has in respect to mathematics a value not inferior to that of "Volapuk" in respect to
language.—THOMSON, WILLIAM.

Thompson, S. P.: Life of Lord Kelvin (London,
1910), p. 1138.

1723. A quaternion of maladies! Do send me some formula
by help of which I may so doctor them that they may all become
imaginary or positively equal to nothing.—SEDGWICK.

Graves' Life of Hamilton (New York, 1882–
1889), Vol. 3, p. 2.

1724. If nothing more could be said of Quaternions than that they enable us to exhibit in a singularly compact and elegant form, whose meaning is obvious at a glance on account of the utter inartificiality of the method, results which in the ordinary Cartesian co-ordinates are of the utmost complexity, a very powerful argument for their use would be furnished. But it would be unjust to Quaternions to be content with such a statement; for we are fully entitled to say that in *all* cases, even in those to which the Cartesian methods seem specially adapted, they give as simple an expression as any other method; while in the great majority of cases they give a vastly simpler one. In the common methods a judicious choice of co-ordinates is often of immense importance in simplifying an investigation; in Quaternions there is usually *no choice*, for (except when they degrade to mere scalars) they are in general utterly independent of any particular directions in space, and select of themselves the most natural reference lines for each particular problem.

TAIT, P. G

Presidential Address British Association for the Advancement of Science (1871); Nature, Vol. 4, p. 270.

1725. Comparing a Quaternion investigation, no matter in what department, with the equivalent Cartesian one, even when the latter has availed itself to the utmost of the improvements suggested by Higher Algebra, one can hardly help making the remark that they contrast even more strongly than the decimal notation with the binary scale, or with the old Greek arithmetic—or than the well-ordered subdivisions of the metrical system with the preposterous no-systems of Great Britain, a mere fragment of which (in the form of Table of Weights and Measures) form, perhaps the most effective, if not the most ingenious, of the many instruments of torture employed in our elementary teaching.—TAIT, P. G.

Presidential Address British Association for the Advancement of Science (1871); Nature, Vol. 4, p. 271.

1726. It is true that, in the eyes of the pure mathematician, Quaternions have one grand and fatal defect. They cannot be applied to space of n dimensions, they are contented to deal with those poor three dimensions in which mere mortals are doomed to dwell, but which cannot bound the limitless aspirations of a Cayley or a Sylvester. From the physical point of view this, instead of a defect, is to be regarded as the greatest possible recommendation. It shows, in fact, Quaternions to be the special instrument so constructed for application to the *Actual* as to have thrown overboard everything which is not absolutely necessary, without the slightest consideration whether or no it was thereby being rendered useless for application to the *Inconceivable.*—TAIT, P. G.

> *Presidential Address British Association for the Advancement of Science (1871); Nature, Vol. 4, p. 271.*

1727. There is an old epigram which assigns the empire of the sea to the English, of the land to the French, and of the clouds to the Germans. Surely it was from the clouds that the Germans fetched + and − ; the ideas which these symbols have generated are much too important to the welfare of humanity to have come from the sea or from the land.—WHITEHEAD, A. N.

> *An Introduction to Mathematics (New York, 1911), p. 86.*

1728. Now as to what pertains to these Surd numbers (which, as it were by way of reproach and calumny, having no merit of their own are also styled Irrational, Irregular, and Inexplicable) they are by many denied to be numbers properly speaking, and are wont to be banished from arithmetic to another Science, (which yet is no science) viz. algebra.—BARROW, ISAAC.

> *Mathematical Lectures (London, 1734), p. 44.*

1729. If it is true as Whewell says, that the essence of the triumphs of science and its progress consists in that it enables us to consider evident and necessary, views which our ancestors held to be unintelligible and were unable to comprehend, then the extension of the number concept to include the irrational, and we will at once add, the imaginary, is the greatest forward step which pure mathematics has ever taken.

> HANKEL, HERMANN.
> *Theorie der Complexen Zahlen (Leipzig, 1867), p. 60.*

1730. That this subject [of imaginary magnitudes] has hitherto been considered from the wrong point of view and surrounded by a mysterious obscurity, is to be attributed largely to an ill-adapted notation. If for instance, $+1$, -1, $\sqrt{-1}$ had been called direct, inverse, and lateral units, instead of positive, negative, and imaginary (or even impossible) such an obscurity would have been out of question.—GAUSS, C. F.

Theoria residiorum biquadraticorum, Commentatio secunda; Werke, Bd. 2 (Goettingen, 1863), p. 177.

1731. . . . the imaginary, this bosom-child of complex mysticism.—DÜHRING, EUGEN.

Kritische Geschichte der allgemeinen Principien der Mechanik (Leipzig, 1877), p. 517.

1732. Judged by the only standards which are admissible in a pure doctrine of numbers i is imaginary in the same sense as the negative, the fraction, and the irrational, but in no other sense; all are alike mere symbols devised for the sake of representing the results of operations even when these results are not numbers (positive integers).—FINE, H. B.

The Number-System of Algebra (Boston, 1890), p. 36.

1733. This symbol $[\sqrt{-1}]$ is restricted to a precise signification as the representative of perpendicularity in quaternions, and this wonderful algebra of space is intimately dependent upon the special use of the symbol for its symmetry, elegance, and power. The immortal author of quaternions has shown that there are other significations which may attach to the symbol in other cases. But the strongest use of the symbol is to be found in its magical power of doubling the actual universe, and placing by its side an ideal universe, its exact counterpart, with which it can be compared and contrasted, and, by means of curiously connecting fibres, form with it an organic whole, from which modern analysis has developed her surpassing geometry.—PEIRCE, BENJAMIN.

On the Uses and Transformations of Linear Algebras; American Journal of Mathematics, Vol. 4 (1881), p. 216.

1734. The conception of the inconceivable [imaginary], this measurement of what not only does not, but cannot exist, is one of the finest achievements of the human intellect. No one can deny that such imaginings are indeed imaginary. But they lead to results grander than any which flow from the imagination of the poet. The imaginary calculus is one of the masterkeys to physical science. These realms of the inconceivable afford in many places our only mode of passage to the domains of positive knowledge. Light itself lay in darkness until this imaginary calculus threw light upon light. And in all modern researches into electricity, magnetism, and heat, and other subtile physical inquiries, these are the most powerful instruments.—HILL, THOMAS.

North American Review, Vol. 85, p. 235.

1735. All the fruitful uses of imaginaries, in Geometry, are those which begin and end with real quantities, and use imaginaries only for the intermediate steps. Now in all such cases, we have a real spatial interpretation at the beginning and end of our argument, where alone the spatial interpretation is important; in the intermediate links, we are dealing in purely algebraic manner with purely algebraic quantities, and may perform any operations which are algebraically permissible. If the quantities with which we end are capable of spatial interpretation, then, and only then, our results may be regarded as geometrical. To use geometrical language, in any other case, is only a convenient help to the imagination. To speak, for example, of projective properties which refer to the circular points, is a mere *memoria technica* for purely algebraical properties; the circular points are not to be found in space, but only in the auxiliary quantities by which geometrical equations are transformed. That no contradictions arise from the geometrical interpretation of imaginaries is not wonderful; for they are interpreted solely by the rules of Algebra, which we may admit as valid in their interpretation to imaginaries. The perception of space being wholly absent, Algebra rules supreme, and no inconsistency can arise.—RUSSELL, BERTRAND.

Foundations of Geometry (Cambridge, 1897), p. 45.

1736. Indeed, if one understands by algebra the application of arithmetic operations to composite magnitudes of all kinds, whether they be rational or irrational number or space magnitudes, then the learned Brahmins of Hindostan are the true inventors of algebra.—HANKEL, HERMANN.

> Geschichte der Mathematik im Altertum und Mittelalter (Leipzig, 1874), p. 195.

1737. It is remarkable to what extent Indian mathematics enters into the science of our time. Both the form and the spirit of the arithmetic and algebra of modern times are essentially Indian and not Grecian.—CAJORI, F.

> History of Mathematics (New York, 1897), p. 100.

1738. There are many questions in this science [algebra] which learned men have to this time in vain attempted to solve; and they have stated some of these questions in their writings, to prove that this science contains difficulties, to silence those who pretend they find nothing in it above their ability, to warn mathematicians against undertaking to answer every question that may be proposed, and to excite men of genius to attempt their solution. Of these I have selected seven.

1. To divide 10 into two parts, such, that when each part is added to its square-root and the sums multiplied together, the product is equal to the supposed number.

2. What square is that, which being increased or diminished by 10, the sum and remainder are both square numbers?

3. A person said he owed to Zaid 10 all but the square-root of what he owed to Amir, and that he owed Amir 5 all but the square-root of what he owed Zaid.

4. To divide a cube number into two cube numbers.

5. To divide 10 into two parts such, that if each is divided by the other, and the two quotients are added together, the sum is equal to one of the parts.

6. There are three square numbers in continued geometric proportion, such, that the sum of the three is a square number.

7. There is a square, such, that when it is increased and

diminished by its root and 2, the sum and the difference are squares.—KHULASAT–AL–HISAB.

Algebra; quoted in Hutton: A Philosophical and Mathematical Dictionary (London, 1815), Vol. 1, p. 70.

1739. The solution of such questions as these [referring to the solution of cubic equations] depends on correct judgment, aided by the assistance of God.—BIJA GANITA.

Quoted in Hutton: A Philosophical and Mathematical Dictionary (London, 1815), Vol. 1, p. 65.

1740. For what is the theory of determinants? It is an algebra upon algebra; a calculus which enables us to combine and foretell the results of algebraical operations, in the same way as algebra itself enables us to dispense with the performance of the special operations of arithmetic. All analysis must ultimately clothe itself under this form.—SYLVESTER, J. J.

Philosophical Magazine, Vol. 1, (1851), p. 300; Collected Mathematical Papers, Vol. 1, p. 247.

1741. Fuchs. Fast möcht' ich nun *moderne Algebra* studieren.

Meph. Ich wünschte nicht euch irre zu führen.

Was diese Wissenschaft betrifft,

Es ist so schwer, die leere Form zu meiden,

Und wenn ihr es nicht recht begrifft,

Vermögt die Indices ihr kaum zu unterscheiden.

Am Besten ist's, wenn ihr nur *Einem* traut

Und auf des Meister's Formeln baut.

Im Ganzen—haltet euch an die *Symbole.*

Dann geht ihr zu der Forschung Wohle

Ins sichre Reich der Formeln ein.

Fuchs. Ein Resultat muss beim Symbole sein?

Meph. Schon gut! Nur muss man sich nicht alzu ängstlich quälen.

Denn eben, wo die Resultate fehlen,

Stellt ein Symbol zur rechten Zeit sich ein.

Symbolisch lässt sich alles schreiben,

Müsst nur im Allgemeinen bleiben.

Wenn man der Gleichung Lösung nicht er-
    kannte,
Schreibt man sie als Determinante.
Schreib' was du willst, nur rechne *nie* was aus.
Symbole lassen trefflich sich traktieren,
Mit einem Strich ist alles auszuführen,
Und mit Symbolen kommt man immer aus.

LASSWITZ, KURD.

Der Faust-Tragödie (–n)ter Teil; Zeitschrift für
mathematischen und naturwissenschaftlichen
Unterricht, Bd. 14, p. 317.

Fuchs. To study *modern algebra* I'm most persuaded.
Meph. 'Twas not my wish to lead thee astray.
    But as concerns this science, truly
    'Tis difficult to avoid the empty form,
    And should'st thou lack clear comprehension,
    Scarcely the indices thou'll know apart.
    'Tis safest far to trust but *one*
    And built upon your master's formulas.
    On the whole—cling closely to your *symbols*.
    Then, for the weal of research you may gain
    An entrance to the formula's sure domain.
Fuchs. The symbol, it must lead to some result?
Meph. Granted. But never worry about results,
    For, mind you, just where the results are
        wanting
    A symbol at the nick of time appears.
    To symbolic treatment all things yield,
    Provided we stay in the general field.
    Should a solution prove elusive,
    Write the equation in determinant form.
    Write what you please, but *never* calculate.
    Symbols are patient and long suffering,
    A single stroke completes the whole affair.
    Symbols for every purpose do suffice.

1742. As all roads are said to lead to Rome, so I find, in my
own case at least, that all algebraic inquiries sooner or later end

at the Capitol of Modern Algebra over whose shining portal is inscribed "Theory of Invariants."—SYLVESTER, J. J.

> On Newton's Rule for the Discovery of Imaginary Roots; Collected Mathematical Papers, Vol. 2, p. 380.

1743. If we consider the beauty of the theorem [Sylvester's Theorem on Newton's Rule for the Discovery of Imaginary Roots] which has now been expounded, the interest which belongs to the rule associated with the great name of Newton, and the long lapse of years during which the reason and extent of that rule remained undiscovered by mathematicians, among whom Maclaurin, Waring and Euler are explicitly included, we must regard Professor Sylvester's investigations made to the Theory of Equations in modern times, justly to be ranked with those of Fourier, Sturm and Cauchy.—TODHUNTER, I.

> Theory of Equations (London, 1904), p. 250.

1744. Considering the remarkable elegance, generality, and simplicity of the method [Horner's Method of finding the numerical values of the roots of an equation], it is not a little surprising that it has not taken a more prominent place in current mathematical textbooks. . . . As a matter of fact, its spirit is purely arithmetical; and its beauty, which can only be appreciated after one has used it in particular cases, is of that indescribably simple kind, which distinguishes the use of position in the decimal notation and the arrangement of the simple rules of arithmetic. It is, in short, one of those things whose invention was the creation of a commonplace.

> CHRYSTAL, GEORGE.
> Algebra (London and Edinburgh, 1893), Vol. 1, chap. 15, sect. 25.

1745. *To a missing member of a family group of terms in an algebraical formula.*

Lone and discarded one! divorced by fate,
Far from thy wished-for fellows—whither art flown?
Where lingerest thou in thy bereaved estate,
Like some lost star, or buried meteor stone?

Thou mindst me much of that presumptuous one
Who loth, aught less than greatest, to be great,
From Heaven's immensity fell headlong down
To live forlorn, self-centred, desolate:
Or who, like Heraclid, hard exile bore,
Now buoyed by hope, now stretched on rack of fear,
Till throned Astæa, wafting to his ear
Words of dim portent through the Atlantic roar,
Bade him "the sanctuary of the Muse revere
And strew with flame the dust of Isis' shore."

SYLVESTER, J. J.
*Inaugural Lecture, Oxford, 1885; Nature,
Vol. 33, p. 228.*

1746. In every subject of inquiry there are certain entities, the mutual relations of which, under various conditions, it is desirable to ascertain. A certain combination of these entities are submitted to certain processes or are made the subjects of certain operations. The theory of invariants in its widest scientific meaning determines these combinations, elucidates their properties, and expresses results when possible in terms of them. Many of the general principles of political science and economics can be represented by means of invariantive relations connecting the factors which enter as entities into the special problems. The great principle of chemical science which asserts that when elementary or compound bodies combine with one another the total weight of the materials is unchanged, is another case in point. Again, in physics, a given mass of gas under the operation of varying pressure and temperature has the well-known invariant, pressure multiplied by volume and divided by absolute temperature. . . . In mathematics the entities under examination may be arithmetical, algebraical, or geometrical; the processes to which they are subjected may be any of those which are met with in mathematical work. . . . It is the *principle* which is so valuable. It is the *idea* of invariance that pervades today all branches of mathematics.

MACMAHON, P. A.
*Presidential Address British Association for
the Advancement of Science (1901); Nature,
Vol. 64, p. 481.*

1747. [The theory of invariants] has invaded the domain of geometry, and has almost re-created the analytical theory; but it has done more than this for the investigations of Cayley have required a full reconsideration of the very foundations of geometry. It has exercised a profound influence upon the theory of algebraic equations; it has made its way into the theory of differential equations; and the generalisation of its ideas is opening out new regions of most advanced and profound functional analysis. And so far from its course being completed, its questions fully answered, or its interest extinct, there is no reason to suppose that a term can be assigned to its growth and its influence.—FORSYTH, A. R.

Presidential Address British Association for the Advancement of Science (1897); Nature, Vol. 56, p. 378.

1748. . . . the doctrine of Invariants, a theory filling the heavens like a light-bearing ether, penetrating all the branches of geometry and analysis, revealing everywhere abiding configurations in the midst of change, everywhere disclosing the eternal reign of the law of form.—KEYSER, C. J.

Lectures on Science, Philosophy and Art (New York, 1908), p. 28.

1749. It is in the mathematical doctrine of Invariance, the realm wherein are sought and found configurations and types of being that, amidst the swirl and stress of countless hosts of transformations remain immutable, and the spirit dwells in contemplation of the serene and eternal reign of the subtile laws of Form, it is there that Theology may find, if she will, the clearest conceptions, the noblest symbols, the most inspiring intimations, the most illuminating illustrations, and the surest guarantees of the object of her teaching and her quest, an Eternal Being, unchanging in the midst of the universal flux.

KEYSER, C. J.

Lectures on Science, Philosophy and Art (New York, 1908), p. 42.

1750. I think that young chemists desirous of raising their science to its proper rank would act wisely in making themselves master betimes of the theory of algebraic forms. What mechan-

ics is to physics, that I think is algebraic morphology, founded
at option on the theory of partitions or ideal elements, or both,
is destined to be to the chemistry of the future. . . . invariants
and isomerism are sister theories.—SYLVESTER, J. J.
> American Journal of Mathematics, Vol. 1
> (1878), p. 126.

1751. The great notion of Group, . . . though it had barely
merged into consciousness a hundred years ago, has meanwhile
become a concept of fundamental importance and prodigious
fertility, not only affording the basis of an imposing doctrine—
the Theory of Groups—but therewith serving also as a bond of
union, a kind of connective tissue, or rather as an immense
cerebro-spinal system, uniting together a large number of widely
dissimilar doctrines as organs of a single body.—KEYSER, C. J.
> Lectures on Science, Philosophy and Art (New
> York, 1908), p. 12.

1752. In recent times the view becomes more and more
prevalent that many branches of mathematics are nothing but
the theory of invariants of special groups.—LIE, SOPHUS.
> Continuierliche Gruppen—Scheffers (Leipzig,
> 1893), p. 665.

1753. Universal Algebra has been looked on with some
suspicion by many mathematicians, as being without intrinsic
mathematical interest and as being comparatively useless as an
engine of investigation. . . But it may be shown that Universal
Algebra has the same claim to be a serious subject of mathematical study as any other branch of mathematics.
> WHITEHEAD, A. N.
> Universal Algebra (Cambridge, 1898), Preface,
> p. vi.

1754. [Function] theory was, in effect, founded by Cauchy;
but, outside his own investigations, it at first made slow and
hesitating progress. At the present day, its fundamental ideas
may be said almost to govern most departments of the analysis
of continuous quantity. On many of them, it has shed a completely new light; it has educed relations between them before
unknown. It may be doubted whether any subject is at the

present day so richly endowed with variety of method and fertility of resource; its activity is prodigious, and no less remarkable than its activity is its freshness.—FORSYTH, A. R.
Presidential Address British Association for the Advancement of Science (1897); Nature, Vol. 56, p. 378.

1755. Let me mention one other contribution which this theory [Theory of functions of a complex variable] has made to knowledge lying somewhat outside our track. During the rigorous revision to which the foundations of the theory have been subjected in its re-establishment by Weierstrass, new ideas as regards number and continuity have been introduced. With him and with others influenced by him, there has thence sprung a new theory of higher arithmetic; and with its growth, much has concurrently been effected in the elucidation of the general notions of number and quantity. . . . It thus appears to be the fact that, as with Plato, or Descartes, or Leibnitz, or Kant, the activity of pure mathematics is again lending some assistance to the better comprehension of those notions of time, space, number, quantity, which underlie a philosophical conception of the universe.—FORSYTH, A. R.
Presidential Address British Association for the Advancement of Science (1897); Nature, Vol. 56, p. 378.

CHAPTER XVIII

1801. The science of figures is most glorious and beautiful. But how inaptly it has received the name geometry!

FRISCHLINUS, N.
Dialog 1.

1802. Plato said that God geometrizes continually.

PLUTARCH.
Convivialium disputationum, liber 8, 2.

1803. μηδεὶς ἀγεωμέτρητος εἰσίτω μοῦ τὴν στέγην.
[Let no one ignorant of geometry enter my door.]

PLATO.
Tzetzes, Chiliad, 8, 972.

1804. All the authorities agree that he [Plato] made a study of geometry or some exact science an indispensable preliminary to that of philosophy. The inscription over the entrance to his school ran "Let none ignorant of geometry enter my door," and on one occasion an applicant who knew no geometry is said to have been refused admission as a student.—BALL, W. W. R.
History of Mathematics (London, 1901), p. 45.

1805. Form and size constitute the foundation of all search for truth.—PARKER, F. W.
Talks on Pedagogics (New York, 1894), p. 72.

1806. At present the science [of geometry] is in flat contradiction to the language which geometricians use, as will hardly be denied by those who have any acquaintance with the study: for they speak of finding the side of a square, and applying and adding, and so on, as if they were engaged in some business, and as if all their propositions had a practical end in view: whereas in reality the science is pursued wholly for the sake of knowledge.

Certainly, he said.

Then must not a further admission be made?

What admission?

The admission that this knowledge at which geometry aims is of the eternal, and not of the perishing and transient.

That may be easily allowed. Geometry, no doubt, is the knowledge of what eternally exists.

Then, my noble friend, geometry will draw the soul towards truth, and create the mind of philosophy, and raise up that which is now unhappily allowed to fall down.—PLATO.

Republic [Jowett-Davies], Bk. 7, p. 527.

1807. Among them [the Greeks] geometry was held in highest honor: nothing was more glorious than mathematics. But we have limited the usefulness of this art to measuring and calculating.—CICERO.

Tusculanae Disputationes, 1, 2, 5.

1808.   Geometria,
      Through which a man hath the sleight
      Of length, and brede, of depth, of height.

GOWER, JOHN.

Confessio Amantis, Bk. 7.

1809. Geometrical truths are in a way asymptotes to physical truths, that is to say, the latter approach the former indefinitely near without ever reaching them exactly.—D'ALEMBERT.

Quoted in Rebière: Mathématiques et Mathématiciens (Paris, 1898), p. 10.

1810. Geometry exhibits the most perfect example of logical stratagem.—BUCKLE, H. T.

History of Civilization in England (New York, 1891), Vol. 2, p. 342.

1811. It is the glory of geometry that from so few principles, fetched from without, it is able to accomplish so much.

NEWTON.

Philosophiae Naturalis Principia Mathematica, Praefat.

1812. Geometry is the application of strict logic to those properties of space and figure which are self-evident, and which therefore cannot be disputed. But the rigor of this science is carried one step further; for no property, however evident it may be, is allowed to pass without demonstration, if that can be given. The question is therefore to demonstrate all geometrical truths with the smallest possible number of assumptions.

DE MORGAN, A.
On the Study and Difficulties of Mathematics
(Chicago, 1902), p. 231.

1813. Geometry is a true natural science:—only more simple, and therefore more perfect than any other. We must not suppose that, because it admits the application of mathematical analysis, it is therefore a purely logical science, independent of observation. Every body studied by geometers presents some primitive phenomena which, not being discoverable by reasoning, must be due to observation alone.—COMTE, A.

Positive Philosophy [Martineau], Bk. 1, chap. 3.

1814. Geometry in every proposition speaks a language which experience never dares to utter; and indeed of which she but half comprehends the meaning. Experience sees that the assertions are true, but she sees not how profound and absolute is their truth. She unhesitatingly assents to the laws which geometry delivers, but she does not pretend to see the origin of their obligation. She is always ready to acknowledge the sway of pure scientific principles as a matter of fact, but she does not dream of offering her opinion on their authority as a matter of right; still less can she justly claim to herself the source of that authority.—WHEWELL, WILLIAM.

The Philosophy of the Inductive Sciences,
Part 1, Bk. 1, chap. 6, sect. 1 (London, 1858).

1815. Geometry is the science created to give understanding and mastery of the external relations of things; to make easy the explanation and description of such relations and the transmission of this mastery.—HALSTED, G. B.

Proceedings of the American Association for
the Advancement of Science (1904), p. 359.

1816. A mathematical point is the most indivisible and unique thing which art can present.—DONNE, JOHN.

Letters, 21.

1817. It is certain that from its completeness, uniformity and faultlessness, from its arrangement and progressive character, and from the universal adoption of the completest and best line of argument, Euclid's " Elements " stand preëminently at the head of all human productions. In no science, in no department of knowledge, has anything appeared like this work: for upward of 2000 years it has commanded the admiration of mankind, and that period has suggested little toward its improvement.

KELLAND, P.
Lectures on the Principles of Demonstrative Mathematics (London, 1843), p. 17.

1818. In comparing the performance in Euclid with that in Arithmetic and Algebra there could be no doubt that Euclid had made the deepest and most beneficial impression: in fact it might be asserted that this constituted by far the most valuable part of the whole training to which such persons [students, the majority of which were not distinguished for mathematical taste and power] were subjected.

TODHUNTER, I.
Essay on Elementary Geometry; Conflict of Studies and other Essays (London, 1873), p. 167.

1819. In England the geometry studied is that of Euclid, and I hope it never will be any other; for this reason, that so much has been written on Euclid, and all the difficulties of geometry have so uniformly been considered with reference to the form in which they appear in Euclid, that the study of that author is a better key to a great quantity of useful reading than any other.

DE MORGAN, A.
Elements of Algebra (London, 1837), Introduction.

1820. This book [Euclid] has been for nearly twenty-two centuries the encouragement and guide of that scientific thought which is one thing with the progress of man from a worse to a better state. The encouragement; for it contained a body of knowledge that was really known and could be relied on, and that moreover was growing in extent and application. For even at the time this book was written—shortly after the foundation of the Alexandrian Museum—Mathematics was no longer the merely ideal science of the Platonic school, but had started on her career of conquest over the whole world of Phenomena. The guide; for the aim of every scientific student of every subject was to bring his knowledge of that subject into a form as perfect as that which geometry had attained. Far up on the great mountain of Truth, which all the sciences hope to scale, the foremost of that sacred sisterhood was seen, beckoning for the rest to follow her. And hence she was called, in the dialect of the Phythagoreans, "the purifier of the reasonable soul."—CLIFFORD, W. K.

> Lectures and Essays (London, 1901), Vol. 1, p. 354.

1821. [Euclid] at once the inspiration and aspiration of scientific thought.—CLIFFORD, W. K.

> Lectures and Essays (London, 1901), Vol 1, p. 355.

1822. The "elements" of the Great Alexandrian remain for all time the first, and one may venture to assert, the *only* perfect model of logical exactness of principles, and of rigorous development of theorems. If one would see how a science can be constructed and developed to its minutest details from a very small number of intuitively perceived axioms, postulates, and plain definitions, by means of rigorous, one would almost say chaste, syllogism, which nowhere makes use of surreptitious or foreign aids, if one would see how a science may thus be constructed one must turn to the elements of Euclid.—HANKEL, H.

> Die Entwickelung der Mathematik in den letzten Jahrhunderten (Tübingen, 1884), p. 7.

1823. If we consider him [Euclid] as meaning to be what his commentators have taken him to be, a model of the most unscrupulous formal rigour, we can deny that he has altogether succeeded, though we admit that he made the nearest approach.

DE MORGAN, A.
Smith's Dictionary of Greek and Roman Biography and Mythology (London, 1902); Article "Eucleides."

1824. The Elements of Euclid is as small a part of mathematics as the Iliad is of literature; or as the sculpture of Phidias is of the world's total art.—KEYSER, C. J.
Lectures on Science, Philosophy and Art (New York, 1908), p. 8.

1825. I should rejoice to see . . . Euclid honourably shelved or buried " deeper than did ever plummet sound " out of the schoolboys' reach; morphology introduced into the elements of algebra; projection, correlation, and motion accepted as aids to geometry; the mind of the student quickened and elevated and his faith awakened by early initiation into the ruling ideas of polarity, continuity, infinity, and familiarization with the doctrines of the imaginary and inconceivable.

SYLVESTER, J. J.
A Plea for the Mathematician; Nature, Vol. 1, p. 261.

1826. The early study of Euclid made me a hater of geometry, . . . and yet, in spite of this repugnance, which had become a second nature in me, whenever I went far enough into any mathematical question, I found I touched, at last, a geometrical bottom.—SYLVESTER, J. J.
A Plea for the Mathematician; Nature, Vol. 1, p. 262.

1827. Newton had so remarkable a talent for mathematics that Euclid's Geometry seemed to him "a trifling book," and he wondered that any man should have taken the trouble to demonstrate propositions, the truth of which was so obvious to him at the first glance. But, on attempting to read the more abstruse geometry of Descartes, without having mastered the elements of the science, he was baffled, and was glad to come back again to his Euclid.—PARTON, JAMES.
Sir Isaac Newton.

1828. As to the need of improvement there can be no question whilst the reign of Euclid continues. My own idea of a useful course is to begin with arithmetic, and then not Euclid but algebra. Next, not Euclid, but practical geometry, solid as well as plane; not demonstration, but to make acquaintance. Then not Euclid, but elementary vectors, conjoined with algebra, and applied to geometry. Addition first; then the scalar product. Elementary calculus should go on simultaneously, and come into the vector algebraic geometry after a bit. Euclid might be an extra course for learned men, like Homer. But Euclid for children is barbarous.—HEAVISIDE, OLIVER.

> *Electro-Magnetic Theory (London, 1893),*
> *Vol. 1, p. 148.*

1829. Geometry is nothing if it be not rigorous, and the whole educational value of the study is lost, if strictness of demonstration be trifled with. The methods of Euclid are, by almost universal consent, unexceptionable in point of rigour.

> SMITH, H. J. S.
> *Nature, Vol. 8, p. 450.*

1830. To seek for proof of geometrical propositions by an appeal to observation proves nothing in reality, except that the person who has recourse to such grounds has no due apprehension of the nature of geometrical demonstration. We have heard of persons who convince themselves by measurement that the geometrical rule respecting the squares on the sides of a right-angles triangle was true: but these were persons whose minds had been engrossed by practical habits, and in whom speculative development of the idea of space had been stifled by other employments.—WHEWELL, WILLIAM.

> *The Philosophy of the Inductive Sciences,*
> *(London, 1858), Part 1, Bk. 2, chap. 1, sect. 4.*

1831. No one has ever given so easy and natural a chain of geometrical consequences [as Euclid]. There is a never-erring truth in the results.—DE MORGAN, A.

> *Smith's Dictionary of Greek and Roman Biog-*
> *raphy and Mythology (London, 1902); Article*
> *"Eucleides."*

1832. Beyond question, Egyptian geometry, such as it was, was eagerly studied by the early Greek philosophers, and was the germ from which in their hands grew that magnificent science to which every Englishman is indebted for his first lessons in right seeing and thinking.—Gow, JAMES.

> *A Short History of Greek Mathematics (Cambridge, 1884), p. 131.*

1833. A figure and a step onward:
Not a figure and a florin.

> MOTTO OF THE PYTHAGOREAN BROTHERHOOD.
>
> *W. B. Frankland: Story of Euclid (London, 1902), p. 33.*

1834. The doctrine of proportion, as laid down in the fifth book of Euclid, is, probably, still unsurpassed as a masterpiece of exact reasoning; although the cumbrousness of the forms of expression which were adopted in the old geometry has led to the total exclusion of this part of the elements from the ordinary course of geometrical education. A zealous defender of Euclid might add with truth that the gap thus created in the elementary teaching of mathematics has never been adequately supplied.—SMITH, H. J. S.

> *Presidential Address British Association for the Advancement of Science (1873); Nature, Vol. 8, p. 451.*

1835. The Definition in the Elements, according to Clavius, is this: Magnitudes are said to be in the same Reason [ratio], a first to a second, and a third to a fourth, when the Equimultiples of the first and third according to any Multiplication whatsoever are both together either short of, equal to, or exceed the Equimultiples of the second and fourth, if those be taken, which answer one another. . . . Such is Euclid's Definition of Proportions; that *scare*-Crow at which the over modest or slothful Dispositions of Men are generally affrighted: they are modest, who distrust their own Ability, as soon as a Difficulty appears, but they are slothful that will not give some Attention for the learning of Sciences; as if while we are involved in Obscurity we could clear ourselves without Labour. Both of

which Sorts of Persons are to be admonished, that the former be not discouraged, nor the latter refuse a little Care and Diligence when a Thing requires some Study.—BARROW, ISAAC.
Mathematical Lectures (London, 1734), p. 388.

1836. Of all branches of human knowledge, there is none which, like it [geometry] has sprung a completely armed Minerva from the head of Jupiter; none before whose death-dealing Aegis doubt and inconsistency have so little dared to raise their eyes. It escapes the tedious and troublesome task of collecting experimental facts, which is the province of the natural sciences in the strict sense of the word: the sole form of its scientific method is deduction. Conclusion is deduced from conclusion, and yet no one of common sense doubts but that these geometrical principles must find their practical application in the real world about us. Land surveying, as well as architecture, the construction of machinery no less than mathematical physics, are continually calculating relations of space of the most varied kinds by geometrical principles; they expect that the success of their constructions and experiments shall agree with their calculations; and no case is known in which this expectation has been falsified, provided the calculations were made correctly and with sufficient data.—HELMHOLTZ, H.
The Origin and Significance of Geometrical Axioms; Popular Scientific Lectures [Atkinson], Second Series (New York, 1881), p. 27.

1837. The amazing triumphs of this branch of mathematics [geometry] show how powerful a weapon that form of deduction is which proceeds by an artificial separation of facts, in themselves inseparable.—BUCKLE, H. T.
History of Civilization in England (New York, 1891), Vol. 2, p. 343.

1838. Every theorem in geometry is a law of external nature, and might have been ascertained by generalizing from observation and experiment, which in this case resolve themselves into comparisons and measurements. But it was found practicable, and being practicable was desirable, to deduce these truths by ratiocination from a small number of general laws of nature, the certainty and universality of which was obvious to the most careless observer, and which compose the first principles and ultimate premises of the science.—MILL, J. S.

System of Logic, Bk. 3, chap. 24, sect. 7.

1839. All such reasonings [natural philosophy, chemistry, agriculture, political economy, etc.] are, in comparison with mathematics, very complex; requiring so much *more* than that does, beyond the process of merely deducing the conclusion logically from the premises: so that it is no wonder that the longest mathematical demonstration should be much more easily constructed and understood, than a much shorter train of just reasoning concerning real facts. The former has been aptly compared to a long and steep, but even and regular, flight of steps, which tries the breath, and the strength, and the perseverance only; while the latter resembles a short, but rugged and uneven, ascent up a precipice, which requires a quick eye, agile limbs, and a firm step; and in which we have to tread now on this side, now on that—ever considering as we proceed, whether this or that projection will afford room for our foot, or whether some loose stone may not slide from under us. There are probably as many steps of pure reasoning in one of the longer of Euclid's demonstrations, as in the whole of an argumentative treatise on some other subject, occupying perhaps a considerable volume.—WHATELY, R.

Elements of Logic, Bk. 4, chap. 2, sect. 5.

1840. [Geometry] that held acquaintance with the stars,
And wedded soul to soul in purest bond
Of reason, undisturbed by space or time.

WORDSWORTH.
The Prelude, Bk. 5.

1841. The statement that a given individual has received a sound geometrical training implies that he has segregated from the whole of his sense impressions a certain set of these impressions, that he has eliminated from their consideration all irrelevant impressions (in other words, acquired a subjective command of these impressions), that he has developed on the basis of these impressions an ordered and continuous system of logical deduction, and finally that he is capable of expressing the

nature of these impressions and his deductions therefrom in terms simple and free from ambiguity. Now the slightest consideration will convince any one not already conversant with the idea, that the same sequence of mental processes underlies the whole career of any individual in any walk of life if only he is not concerned entirely with manual labor; consequently a full training in the performance of such sequences must be regarded as forming an essential part of any education worthy of the name. Moreover the full appreciation of such processes has a higher value than is contained in the mental training involved, great though this be, for it induces an appreciation of intellectual unity and beauty which plays for the mind that part which the appreciation of schemes of shape and color plays for the artistic faculties; or, again, that part which the appreciation of a body of religious doctrine plays for the ethical aspirations. Now geometry is not the sole possible basis for inculcating this appreciation. Logic is an alternative for adults, provided that the individual is possessed of sufficient wide, though rough, experience on which to base his reasoning. Geometry is, however, highly desirable in that the objective bases are so simple and precise that they can be grasped at an early age, that the amount of training for the imagination is very large, that the deductive processes are not beyond the scope of ordinary boys, and finally that it affords a better basis for exercise in the art of simple and exact expression than any other possible subject of a school course.—CARSON, G. W. L.
> The Functions of Geometry as a Subject of Education (Tonbridge, 1910), p. 3.

1842. It seems to me that the thing that is wanting in the education of women is not the acquaintance with any facts, but accurate and scientific habits of thought, and the courage to think that true which appears unlikely. And for supplying this want there is a special advantage in geometry, namely that it does not require study of a physically laborious kind, but rather that rapid intuition which women certainly possess; so that it is fit to become a scientific pursuit for them.—CLIFFORD, W. K.
> Quoted by Pollock in Clifford's Lectures and Essays (London, 1901), Vol. 1, Introduction, p. 43.

1843. On the lecture slate
The circle rounded under female hands
With flawless demonstration.—TENNYSON.
The Princess, II, l. 493.

1844. It is plain that that part of geometry which bears upon strategy does concern us. For in pitching camps, or in occupying positions, or in closing or extending the lines of an army, and in all the other manœuvres of an army whether in battle or on the march, it will make a great difference to a general, whether he is a geometrician or not.—PLATO.
Republic, Bk. 7, p. 526.

1845. Then nothing should be more effectually enacted, than that the inhabitants of your fair city should learn geometry. Moreover the science has indirect effects, which are not small.
Of what kind are they? he said.
There are the military advantages of which you spoke, I said; and in all departments of study, as experience proves, any one who has studied geometry is infinitely quicker of apprehension.—PLATO.
Republic [Jowett], Bk. 7, p. 527.

1846. It is doubtful if we have any other subject that does so much to bring to the front the danger of carelessness, of slovenly reasoning, of inaccuracy, and of forgetfulness as this science of geometry, which has been so polished and perfected as the centuries have gone on.—SMITH, D. E.
The Teaching of Geometry (Boston, 1911), p. 12.

1847. The culture of the geometric imagination, tending to produce precision in remembrance and invention of visible forms will, therefore, tend directly to increase the appreciation of works of belles-lettres.—HILL, THOMAS.
The Uses of Mathesis; Bibliotheca Sacra, Vol. 32, p. 504.

1848. Yet may we not entirely overlook
The pleasures gathered from the rudiments
Of geometric science. Though advanced
In these inquiries, with regret I speak,

No farther than the threshold, there I found
Both elevation and composed delight:
With Indian awe and wonder, ignorance pleased
With its own struggles, did I meditate
On the relations those abstractions bear
To Nature's laws.

．　　．　　．　　．　　．　　．　　．　　．

More frequently from the same source I drew
A pleasure quiet and profound, a sense
Of permanent and universal sway,
And paramount belief; there, recognized
A type, for finite natures, of the one
Supreme Existence, the surpassing life
Which to the boundaries of space and time,
Of melancholy space and doleful time,
Superior and incapable of change,
Nor touched by welterings of passion—is,
And hath the name of God.　Transcendent peace
And silence did wait upon these thoughts
That were a frequent comfort to my youth.

．　　．　　．　　．　　．　　．　　．　　．

　　　　　Mighty is the charm
Of those abstractions to a mind beset
With images and haunted by himself,
And specially delightful unto me
Was that clear synthesis built up aloft
So gracefully; even then when it appeared
Not more than a mere plaything, or a toy
To sense embodied: not the thing it is
In verity, an independent world,
Created　out　of　pure　intelligence.—WORDSWORTH.
　　　　　　　　　　　　The Prelude, Bk. 6.

1849. 'Tis told by one whom stormy waters threw,
With fellow-sufferers by the shipwreck spared,
Upon a desert coast, that having brought
To land a single volume, saved by chance,
A treatise of Geometry, he wont,

Although of food and clothing destitute,
And beyond common wretchedness depressed,
To part from company, and take this book
(Then first a self taught pupil in its truths)
To spots remote, and draw his diagrams
With a long staff upon the sand, and thus
Did oft beguile his sorrow, and almost
Forget his feeling:—WORDSWORTH.

The Prelude, Bk. 6.

1850. We study art because we receive pleasure from the great works of the masters, and probably we appreciate them the more because we have dabbled a little in pigments or in clay. We do not expect to be composers, or poets, or sculptors, but we wish to appreciate music and letters and the fine arts, and to derive pleasure from them and be uplifted by them. . . .

So it is with geometry. We study it because we derive pleasure from contact with a great and ancient body of learning that has occupied the attention of master minds during the thousands of years in which it has been perfected, and we are uplifted by it. To deny that our pupils derive this pleasure from the study is to confess ourselves poor teachers, for most pupils do have positive enjoyment in the pursuit of geometry, in spite of the tradition that leads them to proclaim a general dislike for all study. This enjoyment is partly that of the game,—the playing of a game that can always be won, but that cannot be won too easily. It is partly that of the æsthetic, the pleasure of symmetry of form, the delight of fitting things together. But probably it lies chiefly in the mental uplift that geometry brings, the contact with absolute truth, and the approach that one makes to the Infinite. We are not quite sure of any one thing in biology; our knowledge of geology is relatively very slight, and the economic laws of society are uncertain to every one except some individual who attempts to set them forth; but before the world was fashioned the square on the hypotenuse was equal to the sum of the squares on the other two sides of a right triangle, and it will be so after this world is dead; and the inhabitant of Mars, if he exists, probably knows its truth as we know it. The uplift of this contact with absolute truth, with truth eternal, gives pleasure to humanity to a greater or less degree, depending upon the mental equipment of the particular individual; but it probably gives an appreciable amount of pleasure to every student of geometry who has a teacher worthy of the name.

SMITH, D. E.
The Teaching of Geometry (Boston, 1911), p. 16.

1851. No other person can judge better of either [the merits of a writer and the merits of his works] than himself; for none have had access to a closer or more deliberate examination of them. It is for this reason, that in proportion that the value of a work is intrinsic, and independent of opinion, the less eagerness will the author feel to conciliate the suffrages of the public. Hence that inward satisfaction, so pure and so complete, which the study of geometry yields. The progress which an individual makes in this science, the degree of eminence which he attains in it, all this may be measured with the same rigorous accuracy as the methods about which his thoughts are employed. It is only when we entertain some doubts about the justness of our own standard, that we become anxious to relieve ourselves from our uncertainty, by comparing it with the standard of another. Now, in all matters which fall under the cognizance of taste, this standard is necessarily somewhat variable; depending on a sort of gross estimate, always a little arbitrary, either in whole or in part; and liable to continual alteration in its dimensions, from negligence, temper, or caprice. In consequence of these circumstances I have no doubt, that if men lived separate from each other, and could in such a situation occupy themselves about anything but self-preservation, they would prefer the study of the exact sciences to the cultivation of the agreeable arts. It is chiefly on account of others, that a man aims at excellence in the latter, it is on his own account that he devotes himself to the former. In a desert island, accordingly, I should think that a poet could scarcely be vain; whereas a geometrician might still enjoy the pride of discovery.—D'ALEMBERT.

Essai sur les Gens Lettres; Melages (Amsterdam 1764), t. 1, p. 334.

1852. If it were required to determine inclined planes of varying inclinations of such lengths that a free rolling body would descend on them in equal times, any one who understands the mechanical laws involved would admit that this would necessitate sundry preparations. But in the circle the proper arrangement takes place of its own accord for an infinite variety of positions yet with the greatest accuracy in each individual case. For all chords which meet the vertical diameter whether at its highest or lowest point, and whatever their inclinations, have this in common: that the free descent along them takes place in equal times. I remember, one bright pupil, who, after I had stated and demonstrated this theorem to him, and he had caught the full import of it, was moved as by a miracle. And, indeed, there is just cause for astonishment and wonder when one beholds such a strange union of manifold things in accordance with such fruitful rules in so plain and simple an object as the circle. Moreover, there is no miracle in nature, which because of its pervading beauty or order, gives greater cause for astonishment, unless it be, for the reason that its causes are not so clearly comprehended, marvel being a daughter of ignorance.—KANT.

Der einzig mögliche Beweisgrund zu einer Demonstration des Daseins Gottes; Werke (Hartenstein), Bd. 2, p. 137.

1853. These examples [taken from the geometry of the circle] indicate what a countless number of other such harmonic relations obtain in the properties of space, many of which are manifested in the relations of the various classes of curves in higher geometry, all of which, besides exercising the understanding through intellectual insight, affect the emotion in a similar or even greater degree than the occasional beauties of nature.

KANT.

Der einzig mögliche Beweisgrund zu einer Demonstration des Daseins Gottes; Werke (Hartenstein), Bd. 2, p. 138.

1854. But neither thirty years, nor thirty centuries, affect the clearness, or the charm, of Geometrical truths. Such a theorem as " the square of the hypotenuse of a right-angled triangle is equal to the sum of the squares of the sides " is as dazzlingly beautiful now as it was in the day when Pythagoras first discovered it, and celebrated its advent, it is said, by sacrificing a hecatomb of oxen—a method of doing honor to Science that has always seemed to me *slightly* exaggerated and uncalled-for. One can imagine oneself, even in these degenerate days, marking the epoch of some brilliant scientific discovery by inviting a convivial friend or two, to join one in a beefsteak and a bottle of wine. But a *hecatomb* of oxen! It would produce a quite inconvenient supply of beef.—DODGSON, C. L.

> *A New Theory of Parallels (London, 1895),*
> *Introduction, p. 16.*

1855. After Pythagoras discovered his fundamental theorem he sacrificed a hecatomb of oxen. Since that time all dunces * [Ochsen] tremble whenever a new truth is discovered.—BOERNE.

> *Quoted in Moszkowski: Die unsterbliche Kiste*
> *(Berlin, 1908), p. 18.*

1856.   *Vom Pythagorieschen Lehrsatz.*

Die Wahrheit, sie besteht in Ewigkeit,
Wenn erst die blöde Welt ihr Licht erkannt:
Der Lehrsatz, nach Pythagoras benannt,
Gilt heute, wie er galt in seiner Zeit.

Ein Opfer hat Pythagoras geweiht
Den Göttern, die den Lichtstrahl ihm gesandt;
Es thaten kund, geschlachtet und verbrannt,
Ein hundert Ochsen seine Dankbarkeit.

Die Ochsen seit den Tage, wenn sie wittern,
Dass eine neue Wahrheit sich enthülle,
Erheben ein unmenschliches Gebrülle;

Pythagoras erfüllt sie mit Entsetzen;
Und machtlos, sich dem Licht zu wiedersetzen,
Verschiessen sie die Augen und erzittern.

> CHAMISSO, ADELBERT VON.
> *Gedichte, 1835 (Haushenbusch), (Berlin, 1889),*
> *p. 302.*

* In the German vernacular a dunce or blockhead is called an ox.

Truth lasts throughout eternity,
When once the stupid world its light discerns:
The theorem, coupled with Pythagoras' name,
Holds true today, as't did in olden times.

A splendid sacrifice Pythagoras brought
The gods, who blessed him with this ray divine;
A great burnt offering of a hundred kine,
Proclaimed afar the sage's gratitude.

Now since that day, all cattle [blockheads] when they
    scent
New truth about to see the light of day,
In frightful bellowings manifest their dismay;

Pythagoras fills them all with terror;
And powerless to shut out light by error,
In sheer despair they shut their eyes and tremble.

1857. To the question "Which is the signally most beautiful
of geometrical truths?" Frankland replies: "One star excels
another in brightness, but the very sun will be, by common consent, a property of the circle [Euclid, Book 3, Proposition 31]
selected for particular mention by Dante, that greatest of all
exponents of the beautiful."—FRANKLAND, W. B.
    The Story of Euclid (London, 1902), p. 70.

1858.   As one
Who vers'd in geometric lore, would fain
Measure the circle; and, though pondering long
And deeply, that beginning, which he needs,
Finds not; e'en such was I, intent to scan
The novel wonder, and trace out the form,
How to the circle fitted, and therein
How plac'd: but the flight was not for my wing;
                                        DANTE.
    Paradise [Carey] Canto 33, lines 122–129.

1859. If geometry were as much opposed to our passions and
present interests as is ethics, we should contest it and violate it

but little less, notwithstanding all the demonstrations of Euclid and of Archimedes, which you would call dreams and believe full of paralogisms; and Joseph Scaliger, Hobbes, and others, who have written against Euclid and Archimedes, would not find themselves in such a small company as at present.

LEIBNITZ.
New Essays concerning Human Understanding [Langley], Bk. 1, chap. 2, sect. 12.

1860. I have no fault to find with those who teach geometry. That science is the only one which has not produced sects; it is founded on analysis and on synthesis and on the calculus; it does not occupy itself with probable truth; moreover it has the same method in every country.—FREDERICK THE GREAT.
Oeuvres (Decker), t. 7, p. 100.

1861. There are, undoubtedly, the most ample reasons for stating both the principles and theorems [of geometry] in their general form, . . . But, that an unpractised learner, even in making use of one theorem to demonstrate another, reasons rather from particular to particular than from the general proposition, is manifest from the difficulty he finds in applying a theorem to a case in which the configuration of the diagram is extremely unlike that of the diagram by which the original theorem was demonstrated. A difficulty which, except in cases of unusual mental powers, long practice can alone remove, and removes chiefly by rendering us familiar with all the configurations consistent with the general conditions of the theorem.

MILL, J. S.
System of Logic, Bk. 2, chap. 3, sect. 3.

1862. The reason why I impute any defect to geometry, is, because its original and fundamental principles are deriv'd merely from appearances; and it may perhaps be imagin'd, that this defect must always attend it, and keep it from ever reaching a greater exactness in the comparison of objects or ideas, than what our eye or imagination alone is able to attain. I own that this defect so far attends it, as to keep it from ever aspiring to a full certainty. But since these fundamental principles depend on the easiest and least deceitful appearances, they bestow on

their consequences a degree of exactness, of which these consequences are singly incapable.—HUME, D.

A Treatise of Human Nature, Part 3, sect. 1.

1863. I have already observed, that geometry, or the art, by
which we fix the proportions of figures, tho' it much excels both
in universality and exactness, the loose judgments of the senses
and imagination; yet never attains a perfect precision and
exactness. Its first principles are still drawn from the general
appearance of the objects; and that appearance can never
afford us any security, when we examine the prodigious minute-
ness of which nature is susceptible. . . .

There remain, therefore, algebra and arithmetic as the only
sciences, in which we can carry on a chain of reasoning to any
degree of intricacy, and yet preserve a perfect exactness and
certainty.—HUME, D.

A Treatise of Human Nature, Part 3, sect. 1.

1864. All geometrical reasoning is, in the last resort, circular:
if we start by assuming points, they can only be defined by the
lines or planes which relate them; and if we start by assuming
lines or planes, they can only be defined by the points through
which they pass.—RUSSELL, BERTRAND.

Foundations of Geometry (Cambridge, 1897),
p. 120.

1865. The description of right lines and circles, upon which
Geometry is founded, belongs to Mechanics. Geometry does
not teach us to draw these lines, but requires them to be
drawn. . . . it requires that the learner should first be taught
to describe these accurately, before he enters upon Geometry;
then it shows how by these operations problems may be solved.
To describe right lines and circles are problems, but not geometrical problems. The solution of these problems is required
from Mechanics; by Geometry the use of them, when solved, is
shown. . . . Therefore Geometry is founded in mechanical
practice, and is nothing but that part of universal Mechanics
which accurately proposes and demonstrates the art of measuring. But since the manual arts are chiefly conversant in the

moving of bodies, it comes to pass that Geometry is commonly referred to their magnitudes, and Mechanics to their motion.

NEWTON.

Philosophiae Naturalis Principia Mathematica, Praefat.

1866. We must, then, admit . . . that there is an independent science of geometry just as there is an independent science of physics, and that either of these may be treated by mathematical methods. Thus geometry becomes the simplest of the natural sciences, and its axioms are of the nature of physical laws, to be tested by experience and to be regarded as true only within the limits of error of observation —BÔCHER, MAXIME.

Bulletin American Mathematical Society, Vol. 2 (1904), p. 124.

1867. Geometry is not an experimental science; experience forms merely the occasion for our reflecting upon the geometrical ideas which pre-exist in us. But the occasion is necessary, if it did not exist we should not reflect, and if our experiences were different, doubtless our reflections would also be different. Space is not a form of sensibility; it is an instrument which serves us not to represent things to ourselves, but to reason upon things.—POINCARÉ, H.

On the Foundations of Geometry; Monist, Vol. 9 (1898–1899), p. 41.

1868. It has been said that geometry is an instrument. The comparison may be admitted, provided it is granted at the same time that this instrument, like Proteus in the fable, ought constantly to change its form.—ARAGO.

Oeuvres, t. 2 (1854), p. 694.

1869. It is essential that the treatment [of geometry] should be rid of everything superfluous, for the superfluous is an obstacle to the acquisition of knowledge; it should select everything that embraces the subject and brings it to a focus, for this is of the highest service to science; it must have great regard both to clearness and to conciseness, for their opposites trouble our understanding; it must aim to generalize its theorems, for the division of knowledge into small elements renders it difficult of comprehension.—PROCLUS.

Quoted in D. E. Smith: The Teaching of Geometry (Boston, 1911), p. 71.

1870. Many are acquainted with mathematics, but mathesis few know. For it is one thing to know a number of propositions and to make some obvious deductions from them, by accident rather than by any sure method of procedure, another thing to know clearly the nature and character of the science itself, to penetrate into its inmost recesses, and to be instructed by its universal principles, by which facility in working out countless problems and their proofs is secured. For as the majority of artists, by copying the same model again and again, gain certain technical skill in painting, but no other knowledge of the art of painting than what their eyes suggest, so many, having read the books of Euclid and other geometricians, are wont to devise, in imitation of them and to prove some propositions, but the most profound method of solving more difficult demonstrations and problems they are utterly ignorant of.—LaFAILLE, J. C.

Theoremata de Centro Gravitatis (Anvers, 1632), Praefat.

1871. The elements of plane geometry should precede algebra for every reason known to sound educational theory. It is more fundamental, more concrete, and it deals with things and their relations rather than with symbols.—BUTLER, N. M.

The Meaning of Education etc. (New York, 1905), p. 171.

1872. The reason why geometry is not so difficult as algebra, is to be found in the less general nature of the symbols employed. In algebra a general proposition respecting numbers is to be proved. Letters are taken which may represent any of the numbers in question, and the course of the demonstration, far from making use of a particular case, does not even allow that any reasoning, however general in its nature, is conclusive, unless the symbols are as general as the arguments. . . . In geometry on the contrary, at least in the elementary parts, any proposition may be safely demonstrated on reasonings on any one particular example. . . . It also affords some facility that the results of elementary geometry are in many cases sufficiently evident of themselves to the eye; for instance, that two sides of a triangle are greater than the third, whereas in algebra many rudimentary propositions derive no evidence from the senses; for example, that $a^3 - b^3$ is always divisible without a remainder by $a - b$.—DE MORGAN, A.

> On the Study and Difficulties of Mathematics (Chicago, 1902), chap. 13.

1873. The principal characteristics of the ancient geometry are:—

(1) A wonderful clearness and definiteness of its concepts and an almost perfect logical rigour of its conclusions.

(2) A complete want of general principles and methods. . . . In the demonstration of a theorem, there were, for the ancient geometers, as many different cases requiring separate proof as there were different positions of the lines. The greatest geometers considered it necessary to treat all possible cases independently of each other, and to prove each with equal fulness. To devise methods by which all the various cases could all be disposed of with one stroke, was beyond the power of the ancients.—CAJORI, F.

> History of Mathematics (New York, 1897), p. 62.

1874. It has been observed that the ancient geometers made use of a kind of anaylsis, which they employed in the solution of problems, although they begrudged to posterity the knowledge of it.—DESCARTES.

> Rules for the Direction of the Mind; The Philosophy of Descartes [Torrey] (New York, 1892), p. 68.

1875. The ancients studied geometry with reference to the *bodies* under notice, or specially: the moderns study it with reference to the *phenomena* to be considered, or generally. The ancients extracted all they could out of one line or surface, before passing to another; and each inquiry gave little or no assistance in the next. The moderns, since Descartes, employ themselves on questions which relate to any figure whatever. They abstract, to treat by itself, every question relating to the same geometrical phenomenon, in whatever bodies it may be considered. Geometers can thus rise to the study of new geometrical conceptions, which, applied to the curves investigated by the ancients, have brought out new properties never suspected by them.—COMTE.

Positive Philosophy [Martineau] Bk. 1, chap. 3.

1876. It is astonishing that this subject [projective geometry] should be so generally ignored, for mathematics offers nothing more attractive. It possesses the concreteness of the ancient geometry without the tedious particularity, and the power of the analytical geometry without the reckoning, and by the beauty of its ideas and methods illustrates the esthetic generality which is the charm of higher mathematics, but which the elementary mathematics generally lacks.

Report of the Committee of Ten on Secondary School Studies (Chicago, 1894), p. 116.

1877. There exist a small number of very simple fundamental relations which contain the scheme, according to which the remaining mass of theorems [in projective geometry] permit of orderly and easy development.

By a proper appropriation of a few fundamental relations one becomes master of the whole subject; order takes the place of chaos, one beholds how all parts fit naturally into each other, and arrange themselves serially in the most beautiful order, and how related parts combine into well-defined groups. In this manner one arrives, as it were, at the elements, which nature herself employs in order to endow figures with numberless properties with the utmost economy and simplicity.

STEINER, J.

Werke, Bd. 1 (1881), p. 233.

1878. Euclid once said to his king Ptolemy, who, as is easily understood, found the painstaking study of the "Elements" repellant, "There exists no royal road to mathematics." But we may add: Modern geometry is a royal road. It has disclosed "the organism, by means of which the most heterogeneous phenomena in the world of space are united one with another"

(Steiner), and has, as we may say without exaggeration, almost attained to the scientific ideal.—HANKEL, H.
> Die Entwickelung der Mathematik in den letzten Jahrhunderten (Tübingen, 1869).

1879. The two mathematically fundamental things in projective geometry are anharmonic ratio, and the quadrilateral construction. Everything else follows mathematically from these two.—RUSSELL, BERTRAND.
> Foundations of Geometry (Cambridge, 1897), p. 122.

1880. . . . Projective Geometry: a boundless domain of countless fields where reals and imaginaries, finites and infinites, enter on equal terms, where the spirit delights in the artistic balance and symmetric interplay of a kind of conceptual and logical counterpoint,—an enchanted realm where thought is double and flows throughout in parallel streams.
> KEYSER, C. J.
> Lectures on Science, Philosophy and Arts (New York, 1908), p. 2.

1881. The ancients, in the early days of the science, made great use of the graphic method, even in the form of construction; as when Aristarchus of Samos estimated the distance of the sun and moon from the earth on a triangle constructed as nearly as possible in resemblance to the right-angled triangle formed by the three bodies at the instant when the moon is in quadrature, and when therefore an observation of the angle at the earth would define the triangle. Archimedes himself, though he was the first to introduce calculated determinations into geometry, frequently used the same means. The introduction of trigonometry lessened the practice; but did not abolish it. The Greeks and Arabians employed it still for a great number of investigations for which we now consider the use of the Calculus indispensable.—COMTE, A.
> Positive Philosophy [Martineau], Bk. 1, chap. 3.

1882. A mathematical problem may usually be attacked by what is termed in military parlance the method of "systematic approach;" that is to say, its solution may be gradually felt for, even though the successive steps leading to that solution cannot be clearly foreseen. But a Descriptive Geometry problem must be seen through and through before it can be attempted. The entire scope of its conditions, as well as each step toward its solution, must be grasped by the imagination. It must be "taken by assault."—CLARKE, G. S.

> Quoted in W. S. Hall: Descriptive Geometry
> (New York, 1902), chap. 1.

1883. The grand use [of Descriptive Geometry] is in its application to the industrial arts;—its few abstract problems, capable of invariable solution, relating essentially to the contacts and intersections of surfaces; so that all the geometrical questions which may arise in any of the various arts of construction,—as stone-cutting, carpentry, perspective, dialing, fortification, etc.,—can always be treated as simple individual cases of a single theory, the solution being certainly obtainable through the particular circumstances of each case. This creation must be very important in the eyes of philosophers who think that all human achievement, thus far, is only a first step toward a philosophical renovation of the labours of mankind; towards that precision and logical character which can alone ensure the future progression of all arts. . . . Of Descriptive Geometry, it may further be said that it usefully exercises the student's faculty of Imagination,—of conceiving of complicated geometrical combinations in space; and that, while it belongs to the geometry of the ancients by the character of its solutions, it approaches to the geometry of the moderns by the nature of the questions which compose it.—COMTE, A.

> Positive Philosophy [Martineau] Bk. 1, chap. 3.

1884. There is perhaps nothing which so occupies, as it were, the middle position of mathematics, as trigonometry.

> HERBART, J. F.
> Idee eines A B C der Anschauung; Werke
> (Kehrbach) (Langensalza, 1890), Bd. 1, p. 174.

1885. Trigonometry contains the science of continually undulating magnitude: meaning magnitude which becomes alternately greater and less, without any termination to succession of increase and decrease. . . . All trigonometric functions are not undulating: but it may be stated that in common algebra nothing but infinite series undulate: in trigonometry nothing but infinite series do not undulate.—DE MORGAN, A.

> *Trigonometry and Double Algebra (London, 1849), Bk. 1, chap. 1.*

1886. Sin²ϕ is odious to me, even though Laplace made use of it; should it be feared that sinϕ^2 might become ambiguous, which would perhaps never occur, or at most very rarely when speaking of sin (ϕ^2), well then, let us write (sinϕ)², but not sin²ϕ, which by analogy should signify sin (sinϕ).—GAUSS.

> *Gauss-Schumacher Briefwechsel, Bd. 3, p. 292; Bd. 4, p. 63.*

1887. Perhaps to the student there is no part of elementary mathematics so repulsive as is spherical trigonometry.

> TAIT, P. G.
>
> *Encyclopedia Britannica, 9th Edition; Article "Quaternions."*

1888. "Napier's Rule of circular parts" is perhaps the happiest example of artificial memory that is known.—CAJORI, F.

> *History of Mathematics (New York, 1897), p. 165.*

1889. The analytical equations, unknown to the ancients, which Descartes first introduced into the study of curves and surfaces, are not restricted to the properties of figures, and to those properties which are the object of rational mechanics; they apply to all phenomena in general. There cannot be a language more universal and more simple, more free from errors and obscurities, that is to say, better adapted to express the invariable relations of nature.—FOURIER.

> *Théorie Analytique de la Chaleur, Discours Préliminaire.*

1890. It is impossible not to feel stirred at the thought of the emotions of men at certain historic moments of adventure and discovery—Columbus when he first saw the Western shore, Pizarro when he stared at the Pacific Ocean, Franklin when the electric spark came from the string of his kite, Galileo when he first turned his telescope to the heavens. Such moments are also granted to students in the abstract regions of thought, and high among them must be placed the morning when Descartes lay in bed and invented the method of co-ordinate geometry.

WHITEHEAD, A. N.
An Introduction to Mathematics (New York, 1911), p. 122.

1891. It is often said that an equation contains only what has been put into it. It is easy to reply that the new form under which things are found often constitutes by itself an important discovery. But there is something more: analysis, by the simple play of its symbols, may suggest generalizations far beyond the original limits.—PICARD, E.

Bulletin American Mathematical Society, Vol. 2 (1905), p. 409.

1892. It is not the Simplicity of the Equation, but the Easiness of the Description, which is to determine the Choice of our Lines for the Constructions of Problems. For the Equation that expresses a Parabola is more simple than that that expresses the Circle, and yet the Circle, by its more simple Construction, is admitted before it.—NEWTON.

The Linear Constructions of Equations; Universal Arithmetic (London, 1769), Vol. 2, p. 468.

1893. The pursuit of mathematics unfolds its formative power completely only with the transition from the elementary subjects to analytical geometry. Unquestionably the simplest geometry and algebra already accustom the mind to sharp quantitative thinking, as also to assume as true only axioms and what has been proven. But the representation of functions by curves or surfaces reveals a new world of concepts and teaches the use of one of the most fruitful methods, which the human mind ever employed to increase its own effectiveness. What the discovery of this method by Vieta and Descartes brought to humanity, that it brings today to every one who is in any measure endowed for such things: a life-epoch-making beam of light [Lichtblick]. This method has its roots in the farthest depths of human cognition and so has an entirely different significance, than the most ingenious artifice which serves a special purpose.—BOIS-REYMOND, EMIL DU.

Reden, Bd. 1 (Leipzig, 1885), p. 287.

1894. *Song of the Screw.*

A moving form or rigid mass,
　　Under whate'er conditions
Along successive screws must pass
　　Between each two positions.
It turns around and slides along—
This is the burden of my song.

The pitch of screw, if multiplied
　　By angle of rotation,
Will give the distance it must glide
　　In motion of translation.
Infinite pitch means pure translation,
And zero pitch means pure rotation.

Two motions on two given screws,
　　With amplitudes at pleasure,
Into a third screw-motion fuse,
　　Whose amplitude we measure
By parallelogram construction
(A very obvious deduction).

Its axis cuts the nodal line
　　Which to both screws is normal,
And generates a form divine,
　　Whose name, in language formal,
Is "surface-ruled of third degree."
Cylindroid is the name for me.

Rotation round a given line
　　Is like a force along,
If to say couple you decline,
　　You're clearly in the wrong;—
'Tis obvious, upon reflection,
A line is not a mere direction.

So couples with translations too
 In all respects agree;
And thus there centres in the screw
 A wondrous harmony
Of Kinematics and of Statics,—
The sweetest thing in mathematics.

The forces on one given screw,
 With motion on a second,
In general some work will do,
 Whose magnitude is reckoned
By angle, force, and what we call
The coefficient virtual.

Rotation now to force convert,
 And force into rotation;
Unchanged the work, we can assert,
 In spite of transformation.
And if two screws no work can claim,
Reciprocal will be their name.

Five numbers will a screw define,
 A screwing motion, six;
For four will give the axial line,
 One more the pitch will fix;
And hence we always can contrive
One screw reciprocal to five.

Screws—two, three, four or five, combined
 (No question here of six),
Yield other screws which are confined
 Within one screw complex.
Thus we obtain the clearest notion
Of freedom and constraint of motion.

In complex III, three several screws
 At every point you find,
Or if you one direction choose,
 One screw is to your mind;

And complexes of order III.
Their own reciprocals may be.

In IV, wherever you arrive,
    You find of screws a cone,
On every line of complex V.
    There is precisely one;
At each point of this complex rich,
A plane of screws have given pitch.

But time would fail me to discourse
    Of Order and Degree;
Of Impulse, Energy and Force,
    And Reciprocity.
All these and more, for motions small,
Have been discussed by Dr. Ball.

ANONYMOUS.

CHAPTER XIX

THE CALCULUS AND ALLIED TOPICS

1901. It may be said that the conceptions of differential quotient and integral, which in their origin certainly go back to Archimedes, were introduced into science by the investigations of Kepler, Descartes, Cavalieri, Fermat and Wallis. . . . The capital discovery that differentiation and integration are *inverse* operations belongs to Newton and Leibnitz.

LIE, SOPHUS.
Leipziger Berichte, 47 (1895), Math.–phys. Classe, p. 53.

1902. It appears that Fermat, the true inventor of the differential calculus, considered that calculus as derived from the calculus of finite differences by neglecting infinitesimals of higher orders as compared with those of a lower order. . . . Newton, through his method of fluxions, has since rendered the calculus more analytical, he also simplified and generalized the method by the invention of his binomial theorem. Leibnitz has enriched the differential calculus by a very happy notation.

LAPLACE.
Lés Intégrales Définies, etc.; Oeuvres, t. 12 (Paris, 1898), p. 359.

1903. Professor Peacock's Algebra, and Mr. Whewell's Doctrine of Limits should be studied by every one who desires to comprehend the evidence of mathematical truths, and the meaning of the obscure processes of the calculus; while, even after mastering these treatises, the student will have much to learn on the subject from M. Comte, of whose admirable work one of the most admirable portions is that in which he may truly be said to have created the philosophy of the higher mathematics.—MILL, J. S.

System of Logic, Bk. 3, chap. 24, sect. 6.

1904. If we must confine ourselves to one system of notation then there can be no doubt that that which was invented by Leibnitz is better fitted for most of the purposes to which the infinitesimal calculus is applied than that of fluxions, and for some (such as the calculus of variations) it is indeed almost essential.—BALL, W. W. R.

*History of Mathematics (London, 1901),
p. 371.*

1905. The difference between the method of infinitesimals and that of limits (when exclusively adopted) is, that in the latter it is usual to retain evanescent quantities of higher orders until the *end* of the calculation and then neglect them. On the other hand, such quantities are neglected from the commencement in the infinitesimal method, from the conviction that they cannot affect the final result, as they must disappear when we proceed to the limit.—WILLIAMSON, B.

*Encyclopedia Britannica, 9th Edition; Article
"Infinitesimal Calculus," sect. 14.*

1906. When we have grasped the spirit of the infinitesimal method, and have verified the exactness of its results either by the geometrical method of prime and ultimate ratios, or by the analytical method of derived functions, we may employ infinitely small quantities as a sure and valuable means of shortening and simplifying our proofs.—LAGRANGE.

*Méchanique Analytique, Preface; Oeuvres,
t. 2 (Paris, 1888), p. 14.*

1907. The essential merit, the sublimity, of the infinitesimal method lies in the fact that it is as easily performed as the simplest method of approximation, and that it is as accurate as the results of an ordinary calculation. This advantage would be lost, or at least greatly impaired, if, under the pretense of securing greater accuracy throughout the whole process, we were to substitute for the simpler method given by Leibnitz, one less convenient and less in harmony with the probable course of natural events. . . .

The objections which have been raised against the infinitesimal method are based on the false supposition that the errors due to neglecting infinitely small quantities during the actual calculation will continue to exist in the result of the calculation.

CARNOT, L.
Réflections sur la Métaphysique du Calcul Infinitésimal (Paris, 1813), p. 215.

1908. A limiting ratio is neither more nor less difficult to define than an infinitely small quantity.—CARNOT, L.
Réflections sur la Métaphysique du Calcul Infinitésimal (Paris, 1813), p. 210.

1909. A limit is a peculiar and fundamental conception, the use of which in proving the propositions of Higher Geometry cannot be superseded by any combination of other hypotheses and definitions. The axiom just noted that what is true up to the limit is true at the limit, is involved in the very conception of a limit: and this principle, with its consequences, leads to all the results which form the subject of the higher mathematics, whether proved by the consideration of evanescent triangles, by the processes of the Differential Calculus, or in any other way.—WHEWELL, W.
The Philosophy of the Inductive Sciences, Part 1, bk. 2, chap. 12, sect. 1, (London, 1858).

1910. The differential calculus has all the exactitude of other algebraic operations.—LAPLACE.
Théorie Analytique des Probabilités, Introduction; Oeuvres, t. 7 (Paris, 1886), p. 37.

1911. The method of fluxions is probably one of the greatest, most subtle, and sublime discoveries of any age: it opens a new world to our view, and extends our knowledge, as it were, to infinity; carrying us beyond the bounds that seemed to have been prescribed to the human mind, at least infinitely beyond those to which the ancient geometry was confined.

HUTTON, CHARLES.
A Philosophical and Mathematical Dictionary (London, 1815), Vol. 1, p. 525.

1912. The states and conditions of matter, as they occur in nature, are in a state of perpetual flux, and these qualities may be effectively studied by the Newtonian method (Methodus fluxionem) whenever they can be referred to number or subjected to measurement (real or imaginary). By the aid of Newton's calculus the mode of action of natural changes from moment to moment can be portrayed as faithfully as these words represent the thoughts at present in my mind. From this, the law which controls the whole process can be determined with unmistakable certainty by pure calculation.

MELLOR, J. W.
Higher Mathematics for Students of Chemistry and Physics (London, 1902), Prologue.

1913. The calculus is the greatest aid we have to the appreciation of physical truth in the broadest sense of the word.

OSGOOD, W. F.
Bulletin American Mathematical Society, Vol. 13 (1907), p. 467.

1914. [Infinitesimal] analysis is the most powerful weapon of thought yet devised by the wit of man.—SMITH, W. B.
Infinitesimal Analysis (New York, 1898), Preface, p. vii.

1915. The method of Fluxions is the general key by help whereof the modern mathematicians unlock the secrets of Geometry, and consequently of Nature. And, as it is that which hath enabled them so remarkably to outgo the ancients in discovering theorems and solving problems, the exercise and application thereof is become the main if not sole employment of all those who in this age pass for profound geometers.

BERKELEY, GEORGE.
The Analyst, sect. 3.

1916. I have at last become fully satisfied that the language and idea of infinitesimals should be used in the most elementary instruction—under all safeguards of course.—DE MORGAN, A.
Graves' Life of W. R. Hamilton (New York, 1882–1889), Vol. 3, p. 479.

1917. Pupils should be taught how to differentiate and how to integrate simple algebraic expressions before we attempt to teach them geometry and these other complicated things. The dreadful fear of the symbols is entirely broken down in those cases where at the beginning the teaching of the calculus is adopted. Then after the pupil has mastered those symbols you may begin geometry or anything you please. I would also abolish out of the school that thing called geometrical conics. There is a great deal of superstition about conic sections. The student should be taught the symbols of the calculus and the simplest use of these symbols at the earliest age, instead of these being left over until he has gone to the College or University.—THOMPSON, S. P.

Perry's Teaching of Mathematics (London, 1902), p. 49.

1918. Every one versed in the matter will agree that even the elements of a scientific study of nature can be understood only by those who have a knowledge of at least the elements of the differential and integral calculus, as well as of analytical geometry—i. e. the so-called lower part of the higher mathematics. . . . We should raise the question, whether sufficient time could not be reserved in the curricula of at least the science high schools [Realanstalten] to make room for these subjects. . . .

The first consideration would be to entirely relieve from the mathematical requirements of the university [Hochschule] certain classes of students who can get along without extended mathematical knowledge, or to make the necessary mathematical knowledge accessible to them in a manner which, for various reasons, has not yet been adopted by the university. Among such students I would count architects, also the chemists and in general the students of the so-called descriptive natural sciences. I am moreover of the opinion—and this has been for long a favorite idea of mine—, that it would be very useful to medical students to acquire such mathematical knowledge as is indicated by the above described modest limits; for it seems impossible to understand far-reaching physiological investigations, if one is terrified as soon as a differential or integration symbol appears.—KLEIN, F.

Jahresbericht der Deutschen Mathematiker Vereinigung, Bd. 2 (1902), p. 131.

1919. Common integration is only the *memory of differentiation* . . . the different artifices by which integration is effected, are changes, not from the known to the unknown, but from forms in which memory will not serve us to those in which it will.

DE MORGAN, A.

*Transactions Cambridge Philosophical Society,
Vol. 8 (1844), p. 188.*

1920. Given for one instant an intelligence which could comprehend all the forces by which nature is animated and the respective positions of the beings which compose it, if moreover this intelligence were vast enough to submit these data to analysis, it would embrace in the same formula both the movements of the largest bodies in the universe and those of the lightest atom: to it nothing would be uncertain, and the future as the past would be present to its eyes. The human mind offers a feeble outline of that intelligence, in the perfection which it has given to astronomy. Its discoveries in mechanics and in geometry, joined to that of universal gravity, have enabled it to comprehend in the same analytical expressions the past and future states of the world system.—LAPLACE.

Théorie Analytique des Probabilités, Introduction; Oeuvres, t. 7 (Paris, 1886), p. 6.

1921. There is perhaps the same relation between the action of natural selection during one generation and the accumulated result of a hundred thousand generations, that there exists between differential and integral. How seldom are we able to follow completely this latter relation although we subject it to calculation. Do we on that account doubt the correctness of our integrations?—BOIS-REYMOND, EMIL DU.

Reden, Bd. 1 (Leipzig, 1885), p. 228.

1922. It seems to be expected of every pilgrim up the slopes of the mathematical Parnassus, that he will at some point or other of his journey sit down and invent a definite integral or two towards the increase of the common stock.

SYLVESTER, J. J.

*Notes to the Meditation on Poncelet's Theorem;
Mathematical Papers, Vol. 2, p. 214.*

1923. The experimental verification of a theory concerning any natural phenomenon generally rests on the result of an integration.—MELLOR, J. W.

> *Higher Mathematics for Students of Chemistry and Physics (New York, 1902), p. 150.*

1924. Among all the mathematical disciplines the theory of differential equations is the most important. . . . It furnishes the explanation of all those elementary manifestations of nature which involve time. . . .—LIE, SOPHUS.

> *Leipziger Berichte, 47 (1895); Math.–phys. Classe, p. 262.*

1925. If the mathematical expression of our ideas leads to equations which cannot be integrated, the working hypothesis will either have to be verified some other way, or else relegated to the great repository of unverified speculations.

> MELLOR, J. W.
> *Higher Mathematics for Students of Chemistry and Physics (New York, 1902), p. 157.*

1926. It is well known that the central problem of the whole of modern mathematics is the study of the transcendental functions defined by differential equations.—KLEIN, F.

> *Lectures on Mathematics (New York, 1911), p. 8.*

1927. Every one knows what a curve is, until he has studied enough mathematics to become confused through the countless number of possible exceptions. . . . A curve is the totality of points, whose co-ordinates are functions of a parameter which may be differentiated as often as may be required.—KLEIN, F.

> *Elementar Mathematik vom höheren Standpunkte aus. (Leipzig. 1909) Vol. 2, p. 354.*

1928. Fourier's theorem is not only one of the most beautiful results of modern analysis, but it may be said to furnish an indispensable instrument in the treatment of nearly every recondite question in modern physics. To mention only sonorous vibrations, the propagation of electric signals along telegraph wires, and the conduction of heat by the earth's

crust, as subjects in their generality intractable without it, is to give but a feeble idea of its importance.—THOMSON AND TAIT.
Elements of Natural Philosophy, chap. 1.

1929. The principal advantage arising from the use of hyperbolic functions is that they bring to light some curious analogies between the integrals of certain irrational functions.

BYERLY, W. E.
Integral Calculus (Boston, 1890), p. 30.

1930. Hyperbolic functions are extremely useful in every branch of pure physics and in the applications of physics whether to observational and experimental sciences or to technology. Thus whenever an entity (such as light, velocity, electricity, or radio-activity) is subject to gradual absorption or extinction, the decay is represented by some form of hyperbolic functions. Mercator's projection is likewise computed by hyperbolic functions. Whenever mechanical strains are regarded great enough to be measured they are most simply expressed in terms of hyperbolic functions. Hence geological deformations invariably lead to such expressions. . . .—WALCOTT, C. D.
Smithsonian Mathematical Tables, Hyberbolic Functions (Washington, 1909), Advertisement.

1931. Geometry may sometimes appear to take the lead over analysis, but in fact precedes it only as a servant goes before his master to clear the path and light him on the way. The interval between the two is as wide as between empiricism and science, as between the understanding and the reason, or as between the finite and the infinite.—SYLVESTER, J. J.
Philosophic Magazine, Vol. 31 (1866), p. 521.

1932. Nature herself exhibits to us measurable and observable quantities in definite mathematical dependence; the conception of a function is suggested by all the processes of nature where we observe natural phenomena varying according to distance or to time. Nearly all the "known" functions have presented themselves in the attempt to solve geometrical, mechanical, or physical problems.—MERZ, J. T.
A History of European Thought in the Nineteenth Century (Edinburgh and London, 1903), p. 696.

1933. That flower of modern mathematical thought—the notion of a function.—MCCORMACK, THOMAS J.

On the Nature of Scientific Law and Scientific Explanation, Monist, Vol. 10 (1899–1900), p. 555.

1934. Fuchs. Ich bin von alledem so consterniert,
Als würde mir ein Kreis im Kopfe quadriert.

Meph. Nachher vor allen andern Sachen
Müsst ihe euch an die Funktionen-Theorie machen.
Da seht, dass ihr tiefsinnig fasst,
Was sich zu integrieren nicht passt.
An Theoremen wird's euch nicht fehlen,
Müsst nur die Verschwindungspunkte zählen,
Umkehren, abbilden, auf der Eb'ne 'rumfahren
Und mit den Theta-Produkten nicht sparen.

LASSWITZ, KURD.

Der Faust-Tragödie (–n)ter Tiel; Zeitschrift für den math.-natur.Unterricht, Bd. 14 (1883), p. 316.

Fuchs. Your words fill me with an awful dread,
Seems like a circle were squared in my head.

Meph. Next in order you certainly ought
On function-theory bestow your thought,
And penetrate with contemplation
What resists your attempts at integration.
You'll find no dearth of theorems there—
To vanishing-points give proper care—
Enumerate, reciprocate,
Nor forget to delineate,
Traverse the plane from end to end,
And theta-functions freely spend.

1935. The student should avoid *founding results* upon divergent series, as the question of their legitimacy is disputed upon grounds to which no answer commanding anything like general assent has yet been given. But they may be used as means of discovery, provided that their results be verified by other means before they are considered as established.

De Morgan, A.
Trigonometry and Double Algebra (London, 1849), p. 55.

1936. There is nothing now which ever gives me any thought or care in algebra except divergent series, which I cannot follow the French in rejecting.—De Morgan, A.
Graves' Life of W. R. Hamilton (New York, 1882–1889), Vol. 3, p. 249.

1937. It is a strange vicissitude of our science that these [divergent] series which early in the century were supposed to be banished once and for all from rigorous mathematics should at its close be knocking at the door for readmission.—Pierpont, J.
Congress of Arts and Sciences (Boston and New York, 1905), Vol. 1, p. 476.

1938. Zeno was concerned with three problems. . . . These are the problem of the infinitesimal, the infinite, and continuity. . . . From him to our own day, the finest intellects of each generation in turn attacked these problems, but achieved broadly speaking nothing. . . . Weierstrass, Dedekind, and Cantor, . . . have completely solved them. Their solutions . . . are so clear as to leave no longer the slightest doubt of difficulty. This achievement is probably the greatest of which the age can boast. . . . The problem of the infinitesimal was solved by Weierstrass, the solution of the other two was begun by Dedekind and definitely accomplished by Cantor.

Russell, Bertrand.
International Monthly, Vol. 4 (1901), p. 89.

1939. It was not till Leibnitz and Newton, by the discovery of the differential calculus, had dispelled the ancient darkness which enveloped the conception of the infinite, and had clearly established the conception of the continuous and continuous change, that a full and productive application of the newly-found mechanical conceptions made any progress.

Helmholtz, H.
Aim and Progress of Physical Science; Popular Lectures [Flight] (New York, 1900), p. 372.

1940. The idea of an infinitesimal involves no contradiction . . . As a mathematician, I prefer the method of infinitesimals to that of limits, as far easier and less infested with snares.—PIERCE, C. F.

The Law of Mind; Monist, Vol. 2 (1891–1892), pp. 543, 545.

1941. The chief objection against all *abstract* reasonings is derived from the ideas of space and time; ideas, which, in common life and to a careless view, are very clear and intelligible, but when they pass through the scrutiny of the profound sciences (and they are the chief object of these sciences) afford principles, which seem full of obscurity and contradiction. No priestly *dogmas*, invented on purpose to tame and subdue the rebellious reason of mankind, ever shocked common sense more than the doctrine of the infinite divisibility of extension, with its consequences; as they are pompously displayed by all geometricians and metaphysicians, with a kind of triumph and exultation. A real quantity, infinitely less than any finite quantity, containing quantities infinitely less than itself, and so on *in infinitum;* this is an edifice so bold and prodigious, that it is too weighty for any pretended demonstration to support, because it shocks the clearest and most natural principles of human reason. But what renders the matter more extraordinary, is, that these seemingly absurd opinions are supported by a chain of reasoning, the clearest and most natural; nor is it possible for us to allow the premises without admitting the consequences. Nothing can be more convincing and satisfactory than all the conclusions concerning the properties of circles and triangles; and yet, when these are once received, how can we deny, that the angle of contact between a circle and its tangent is infinitely less than any rectilineal angle, that as you may increase the diameter of the circle *in infinitum*, this angle of contact becomes still less, even *in infinitum,* and that the angle of contact between other curves and their tangents may be infinitely less than those between any circle and its tangent, and so on, *in infinitum?* The demonstration of these principles seems as unexceptionable as that which proves the three angles of a triangle to be equal to two right ones, though the latter opinion be natural and easy, and the former big with contradiction and absurdity. Reason here seems to be thrown into a kind of amazement and suspense, which, without the suggestion of any sceptic, gives her a diffidence of herself, and of the ground on which she treads. She sees a full light, which illuminates certain places; but that light borders upon the most profound darkness. And between these she is so dazzled and confounded, that she scarcely can pronounce with certainty and assurance concerning any one object.—HUME, DAVID.

> An Inquiry concerning Human Understanding,
> Sect. 12, part 2.

1942. He who can digest a second or third fluxion, a second or third difference, need not, methinks, be squeamish about any point in Divinity.—BERKELEY, G.

> The Analyst, sect. 7.

1943. And what are these fluxions? The velocities of evanescent increments. And what are these same evanescent increments? They are neither finite quantities, nor quantities infinitely small, nor yet nothing. May we not call them ghosts of departed quantities?—BERKELEY, G.

> The Analyst, sect. 35.

1944. It is said that the minutest errors are not to be neglected in mathematics; that the fluxions are celerities, not proportional to the finite increments, though ever so small; but only to the moments or nascent increments, whereof the proportion alone, and not the magnitude, is considered. And of the aforesaid fluxions there be other fluxions, which fluxions of fluxions are called second fluxions. And the fluxions of these second fluxions are called third fluxions: and so on, fourth, fifth, sixth, etc., ad infinitum. Now, as our Sense is strained and puzzled with the perception of objects extremely minute, even so the Imagination, which faculty derives from sense, is very much strained and puzzled to frame clear ideas of the least particle of time, or the least increment generated therein: and much more to comprehend the moments, or those increments of the flowing quantities in status nascenti, in their first origin or beginning to exist, before they become finite particles. And it seems still more difficult to conceive the abstracted velocities of such nascent imperfect entities. But the velocities of the velocities, the second, third, fourth, and fifth velocities, etc., exceed, if I mistake not, all human understanding. The further the mind analyseth and pursueth these fugitive ideas the more it is lost and bewildered; the objects, at first fleeting and minute, soon vanishing out of sight. Certainly, in any sense, a second or third fluxion seems an obscure Mystery. The incipient celerity of an incipient celerity, the nascent augment of a nascent augment, i. e. of a thing which hath no magnitude; take it in what light you please, the clear conception of it will, if I mistake not, be found impossible; whether it be so or no I appeal to the trial of every thinking reader. And if a second fluxion be inconceivable, what are we to think of third, fourth, fifth fluxions, and so on without end.—BERKELEY, G.

The Analyst, sect. 4.

1945. The *infinite* divisibility of *finite* extension, though it is not expressly laid down either as an axiom or theorem in the elements of that science, yet it is throughout the same everywhere supposed and thought to have so inseparable and essential a connection with the principles and demonstrations in Geometry, that mathematicians never admit it into doubt, or make the least question of it. And, as this notion is the source whence do spring all those amusing geometrical paradoxes which have such a direct repugnancy to the plain common sense of mankind, and are admitted with so much reluctance into a mind not yet debauched by learning; so it is the principal occasion of all that nice and extreme subtility which renders the study of Mathematics so difficult and tedious.—BERKELEY, G.

On the Principles of Human Knowledge,
Sect. 123.

1946. To avoid misconception, it should be borne in mind that infinitesimals are not regarded as being actual quantities in the ordinary acceptation of the words, or as capable of exact representation. They are introduced for the purpose of abridgment and simplification of our reasonings, and are an ultimate phase of magnitude when it is conceived by the mind as capable of diminution below any assigned quantity, however small. . . .

Moreover such quantities are neglected, not, as Leibnitz stated, because they are infinitely small in comparison with those that are retained, which would produce an infinitely small error, but because they must be neglected to obtain a rigorous result; since such result must be definite and determinate, and consequently independent of these *variable indefinitely small quantities*. It may be added that the precise principles of the infinitesimal calculus, like those of any other science, cannot be thoroughly apprehended except by those who have already studied the science, and made some progress in the application of its principles.—WILLIAMSON, B.

Encyclopedia Britannica, 9th Edition; Article
"Infinitesimal Calculus," Sect. 12, 14.

1947. We admit, in geometry, not only infinite magnitudes, that is to say, magnitudes greater than any assignable magnitude, but infinite magnitudes infinitely greater, the one than the other. This astonishes our dimension of brains, which is only about six inches long, five broad, and six in depth, in the largest heads.—VOLTAIRE.

A Philosophical Dictionary; Article "Infinity."
(Boston, 1881).

1948. Infinity is the land of mathematical hocus pocus. There Zero the magician is king. When Zero divides any number he changes it without regard to its magnitude into the infinitely small [great?], and inversely, when divided by any number he begets the infinitely great [small?]. In this domain the circumference of the circle becomes a straight line, and then the circle can be squared. Here all ranks are abolished, for Zero reduces everything to the same level one way or another. Happy is the kingdom where Zero rules!—CARUS, PAUL.

Logical and Mathematical Thought; Monist,
Vol. 20 (1909–1910), p. 69.

1949. Great fleas have little fleas upon their backs to bite 'em,
And little fleas have lesser fleas, and so *ad infinitum*.
And the great fleas themselves, in turn, have greater fleas to go on;
While these again have greater still, and greater still, and so on.—DE MORGAN, A.

Budget of Paradoxes (London, 1872), p. 377.

1950. We have adroitly defined the infinite in arithmetic by a loveknot, in this manner ∞; but we possess not therefore the clearer notion of it.—VOLTAIRE.

> *A Philosophical Dictionary; Article "Infinity."*
> *(Boston, 1881).*

1951. I protest against the use of infinite magnitude as something completed, which in mathematics is never permissible. Infinity is merely a *facon de parler*, the real meaning being a limit which certain ratios approach indefinitely near, while others are permitted to increase without restriction.—GAUSS.

> *Brief an Schumacher (1831); Werke, Bd. 8*
> *p. 216.*

1952. In spite of the essential difference between the conceptions of the *potential* and the *actual* infinite, the former signifying a *variable* finite magnitude increasing beyond all finite limits, while the latter is a *fixed, constant* quantity lying beyond all finite magnitudes, it happens only too often that the one is mistaken for the other. . . . Owing to a justifiable aversion to such *illegitimate* actual infinities and the influence of the modern epicuric-materialistic tendency, a certain *horror infiniti* has grown up in extended scientific circles, which finds its classic expression and support in the letter of Gauss [see 1951], yet it seems to me that the consequent uncritical rejection of the legitimate actual infinite is no lesser violation of the nature of things, which must be taken as they are.—CANTOR, G.

> *Zum Problem des actualen Unendlichen; Natur*
> *und Offenbarung, Bd. 32 (1886), p. 226.*

1953. The Infinite is often confounded with the Indefinite, but the two conceptions are diametrically opposed. Instead of being a quantity with unassigned yet assignable limits, the Infinite is not a quantity at all, since it neither admits of augmentation nor diminution, having no assignable limits; it is the operation of continuously *withdrawing* any limits that may have been assigned: the endless addition of new quantities to the old: the flux of continuity. The Infinite is no more a quantity than Zero is a quantity. If Zero is the sign of a vanished quantity, the

Infinite is a sign of that continuity of Existence which has been ideally divided into discrete parts in the affixing of limits.

LEWES, G. H.
Problems of Life and Mind (Boston, 1875), Vol. 2, p. 384.

1954. A great deal of misunderstanding is avoided if it be remembered that the terms *infinity, infinite, zero, infinitesimal* must be interpreted in connexion with their context, and admit a variety of meanings according to the way in which they are defined.—MATHEWS, G. B.
Theory of Numbers (Cambridge, 1892), Part 1, sect. 104.

1955. This further is observable in number, that it is that which the mind makes use of in measuring all things that by us are measurable, which principally are *expansion* and *duration;* and our idea of infinity, even when applied to those, seems to be nothing but the infinity of number. For what else are our ideas of Eternity and Immensity, but the repeated additions of certain ideas of imagined parts of duration and expansion, with the infinity of number; in which we can come to no end of addition?—LOCKE, JOHN.
An Essay concerning Human Understanding, Bk. 2, chap. 16, sect. 8.

1956. But of all other ideas, it is number, which I think furnishes us with the clearest and most distinct idea of infinity we are capable of.—LOCKE, JOHN.
An Essay concerning Human Understanding, Bk. 2, chap. 17, sect. 9.

1957. Willst du ins Unendliche schreiten?
Geh nur im Endlichen nach allen Seiten!
Willst du dich am Ganzen erquicken,
So musst du das Ganze im Kleinsten erblicken.

GOETHE.
Gott, Gemüt und Welt (1815).

[Would'st thou the infinite essay?
The finite but traverse in every way.
Would'st in the whole delight thy heart?
Learn to discern the whole in its minutest part.]

1958. Ich häufe ungeheure Zahlen,
Gebürge Millionen auf,
Ich setze Zeit auf Zeit und Welt auf Welt zu Hauf,
Und wenn ich von der grausen Höh'
Mit Schwindeln wieder nach dir seh,'
Ist alle Macht der Zahl, vermehrt zu tausendmalen,
Noch nicht ein Theil von dir.
Ich zieh' sie ab, und du liegst ganz vor mir.
                    HALLER, ALBR. VON.
               Quoted in Hegel: Wissenschaft der Logik,
               Buch 1, Abschnitt 2, Kap. 2, C, b.

[Numbers upon numbers pile,
Mountains millions high,
Time on time and world on world amass,
Then, if from the dreadful hight, alas!
Dizzy-brained, I turn thee to behold,
All the power of number, increased thousandfold,
Not yet may match thy part.
Subtract what I will, wholly whole thou art.]

1959. A collection of terms is infinite when it contains as parts other collections which have just as many terms in it as it has. If you can take away some of the terms of a collection, without diminishing the number of terms, then there is an infinite number of terms in the collection —RUSSELL, BERTRAND.
International Monthly, Vol. 4 (1901), p. 93.

1960. An assemblage (ensemble, collection, group, manifold) of elements (things, no matter what) is infinite or finite according as it has or has not a part to which the whole is just *equivalent* in the sense that between the elements composing that part and those composing the whole there subsists a unique and reciprocal (one-to-one) correspondence.—KEYSER, C. J.
          The Axioms of Infinity; Hibbert Journal,
          Vol. 2 (1903–1904), p. 539.

1961. Whereas in former times the Infinite betrayed its presence not indeed to the faculties of Logic but only to the spiritual Imagination and Sensibility, mathematics has shown . . . that

the structure of Transfinite Being is open to exploration by the
organon of Thought.—KEYSER, C. J.

> Lectures on Science, Philosophy and Art (New
> York, 1908), p. 42.

1962. The mathematical theory of probability is a science
which aims at reducing to calculation, where possible, the
amount of credence due to propositions or statements, or to the
occurrence of events, future or past, more especially as contingent
or dependent upon other propositions or events the probability
of which is known.—CROFTON, M. W.

> Encyclopedia Britannica, 9th Edition; Article,
> "Probability."

1963. The theory of probabilities is at bottom nothing but
common sense reduced to calculus; it enables us to appreciate
with exactness that which accurate minds feel with a sort of
instinct for which ofttimes they are unable to account. If we
consider the analytical methods to which this theory has given
birth, the truth of the principles on which it is based, the fine
and delicate logic which their employment in the solution of
problems requires, the public utilities whose establishment rests
upon it, the extension which it has received and which it may
still receive through its application to the most important
problems of natural philosophy and the moral sciences; if
again we observe that, even in matters which cannot be submitted to the calculus, it gives us the surest suggestions for the
guidance of our judgments, and that it teaches us to avoid the
illusions which often mislead us, then we shall see that there is no
science more worthy of our contemplations nor a more useful
one for admission to our system of public education.—LAPLACE.

> Théorie Analytique des Probabilitiés, Introduc-
> tion; Oeuvres, t. 7 (Paris, 1886), p. 153.

1964. It is a truth very certain that, when it is not in our
power to determine what is true, we ought to follow what is
most probable.—DESCARTES.

> Discourse on Method, Part 3.

1965. As *demonstration* is the showing the agreement or
disagreement of two ideas, by the intervention of one or more

proofs, which have a constant, immutable, and visible connexion one with another; so *probability* is nothing but the appearance of such an agreement or disagreement, by the intervention of proofs, whose connexion is not constant and immutable, or at least is not perceived to be so, and it is enough to induce the mind to judge the proposition to be true or false, rather than contrary.—LOCKE, JOHN.

> *An Essay concerning Human Understanding,*
> *Bk. 4, chap. 15, sect. 1.*

1966. The difference between necessary and contingent truths is indeed the same as that between commensurable and incommensurable numbers. For the reduction of commensurable numbers to a common measure is analogous to the demonstration of necessary truths, or their reduction to such as are identical. But as, in the case of surd ratios, the reduction involves an infinite process, and yet approaches a common measure, so that a definite but unending series is obtained, so also contingent truths require an infinite analysis, which God alone can accomplish.—LEIBNITZ.

> *Philosophische Schriften [Gerhardt] Bd. 7*
> *(Berlin, 1890), p. 200.*

1967. The theory in question [theory of probability] affords an excellent illustration of the application of the theory of permutation and combinations which is the fundamental part of the algebra of discrete quantity; it forms in the elementary parts an excellent logical exercise in the accurate use of terms and in the nice discrimination of shades of meaning; and, above all, it enters into the regulation of some of the most important practical concerns of modern life.—CHRYSTAL, GEORGE.

> *Algebra, Vol. 2 (Edinburgh, 1889), chap. 36,*
> *sect. 1.*

1968. There is possibly no branch of mathematics at once so interesting, so bewildering, and of so great practical importance as the theory of probabilities. Its history reveals both the wonders that can be accomplished and the bounds that cannot be transcended by mathematical science. It is the link between rigid deduction and the vast field of inductive science. A complete theory of probabilities would be the complete theory of the formation of belief. It is certainly a pity then, that, to quote M. Bertrand, "one cannot well understand the calculus of probabilities without having read Laplace's work," and that "one cannot read Laplace's work without having prepared oneself for it by the most profound mathematical studies."

DAVIS, E. W.
Bulletin American Mathematical Society,
Vol. 1 (1894–1895), p. 16.

1969. The most important questions of life are, for the most part, really only problems of probability. Strictly speaking one may even say that nearly all our knowledge is problematical; and in the small number of things which we are able to know with certainty, even in the mathematical sciences themselves, induction and analogy, the principal means for discovering truth, are based on probabilities, so that the entire system of human knowledge is connected with this theory.—LAPLACE.
Théorie Analytique des Probabilitiés, Introduc-
tion; Oeuvres, t. 7 (Paris, 1886), p. 5.

1970. There is no more remarkable feature in the mathematical theory of probability than the manner in which it has been found to harmonize with, and justify, the conclusions to which mankind have been led, not by reasoning, but by instinct and experience, both of the individual and of the race. At the same time it has corrected, extended, and invested them with a definiteness and precision of which these crude, though sound, appreciations of common sense were till then devoid.

CROFTON, M. W.
Encyclopedia Britannica, 9th Edition; Article
"Probability."

1971. It is remarkable that a science [probabilities] which began with the consideration of games of chance, should have become the most important object of human knowledge.

LAPLACE.
Théorie Analytique des Probabilités, Introduc-
tion; Oeuvres, t. 7 (Paris, 1886), p. 152.

1972. Not much has been added to the subject [of probability] since the close of Laplace's career. The history of science records more than one parallel to this abatement of activity. When such a genius has departed, the field of his labours seems exhausted for the time, and little left to be gleaned by his successors. It is to be regretted that so little remains to us of the inner workings of such gifted minds, and of the clue by which each of their discoveries was reached. The didactic and synthetic form in which these are presented to the world retains but faint traces of the skilful inductions, the keen and delicate perception of fitness and analogy, and the power of imagination . . . which have doubtless guided such a master as Laplace or Newton in shaping out such great designs—only the minor details of which have remained over, to be supplied by the less cunning hand of commentator and disciple.

CROFTON, M. W.
Encyclopedia Britannica, 9th Edition; Article "Probability."

1973. The theory of errors may be defined as that branch of mathematics which is concerned, first, with the expression of the resultant effect of one or more sources of error to which computed and observed quantities are subject; and, secondly, with the determination of the relation between the magnitude of an error and the probability of its occurrence.—WOODWARD, R. S.
Probability and Theory of Errors (New York, 1906), p. 30.

1974. Of all the applications of the doctrine of probability none is of greater utility than the theory of errors. In astronomy, geodesy, physics, and chemistry, as in every science which attains precision in measuring, weighing, and computing, a knowledge of the theory of errors is indispensable. By the aid of this theory the exact sciences have made great progress during the nineteenth century, not only in the actual determinations of the constants of nature, but also in the fixation of clear ideas as to the possibilities of future conquests in the same direction. Nothing, for example, is more satisfactory and instructive in the history of science than the success with which the unique method of least squares has been applied to the problems presented by the earth and the other members of the solar system. So great, in fact, are the practical value and theoretical importance of least squares, that it is frequently mistaken for the whole theory of errors, and is sometimes regarded as embodying the major part of the doctrine of probability itself.

WOODWARD, R. S.
Probability and Theory of Errors (New York, 1906), pp. 9–10.

1975. Direct and inverse ratios have been applied by an ingenious author to measure human affections, and the moral worth of actions. An eminent Mathematician attempted to ascertain by calculation, the ratio in which the evidence of facts must decrease in the course of time, and fixed the period when the evidence of the facts on which Christianity is founded shall become evanescent, and when in consequence no faith shall be found on the earth.—REID, THOMAS.

Essays on the Powers of the Human Mind (Edinburgh, 1812), Vol. 2, p. 408.

CHAPTER XX

2001. Kant's Doctrine of Time.

I. Time is not an empirical concept deduced from any experience, for neither co-existence nor succession would enter into our perception, if the representation of time were not given *a priori*. Only when this representation *a priori* is given, can we imagine that certain things happen at the same time (simultaneously) or at different times (successively).

II. Time is a necessary representation on which all intuitions depend. We cannot take away time from phenomena in general, though we can well take away phenomena out of time. In time alone is reality of phenomena possible. All phenomena may vanish, but time itself (as the general condition of their possibility) cannot be done away with.

III. On this *a priori* necessity depends also the possibility of apodictic principles of the relations of time, or of axioms of time in general. Time has one dimension only; different times are not simultaneous, but successive, while different spaces are never successive, but simultaneous. Such principles cannot be derived from experience, because experience could not impart to them absolute universality nor apodictic certainty. . . .

IV. Time is not a discursive, or what is called a general concept, but a pure form of sensuous intuition. Different times are parts only of one and the same time. . . .

V. To say that time is infinite means no more than that every definite quantity of time is possible only by limitations of one time which forms the foundation of all times. The original representation of time must therefore be given as unlimited. But when the parts themselves and every quantity of an object can be represented as determined by limitation only, the whole representation cannot be given by concepts (for in that case the partial representation comes first), but must be founded on immediate intuition.—KANT, I.

Critique of Pure Reason [*Max Müller*] (*New York, 1900*), *pp. 24–25.*

2002. Kant's Doctrine of Space.

I. Space is not an empirical concept which has been derived from external experience. For in order that certain sensations should be referred to something outside myself, i. e. to something in a different part of space from that where I am; again, in order that I may be able to represent them as side by side, that is, not only as different, but as in different places, the representation of space must already be there. . . .

II. Space is a necessary representation *a priori*, forming the very foundation of all external intuitions. It is impossible to imagine that there should be no space, though one might very well imagine that there should be space without objects to fill it. Space is therefore regarded as a condition of the possibility of phenomena, not as a determination produced by them; it is a representation *a priori* which necessarily precedes all external phenomena.

III. On this necessity of an *a priori* representation of space rests the apodictic certainty of all geometrical principles, and the possibility of their construction *a priori*. For if the intuition of space were a concept gained *a posteriori*, borrowed from general external experience, the first principles of mathematical definition would be nothing but perceptions. They would be exposed to all the accidents of perception, and there being but one straight line between two points would not be a necessity, but only something taught in each case by experience. Whatever is derived from experience possesses a relative generality only, based on induction. We should therefore not be able to say more than that, so far as hitherto observed, no space has yet been found having more than three dimensions.

IV. Space is not a discursive or so-called general concept of the relations of things in general, but a pure intuition. For, first of all, we can imagine one space only, and if we speak of many spaces, we mean parts only of one and the same space. Nor can these parts be considered as antecedent to the one and all-embracing space and, as it were, its component parts out of which an aggregate is formed, but they can be thought of as existing within it only. Space is essentially one; its multiplicity, and therefore the general concept of spaces in general, arises entirely from limitations. Hence it follows that, with respect to space, an intuition *a priori*, which is not empirical, must form the foundation of all conceptions of space. . . .

V. Space is represented as an infinite given quantity. Now it is quite true that every concept is to be thought as a representation, which is contained in an infinite number of different possible representations (as their common characteristic), and therefore comprehends them: but no concept, as such, can be thought as if it contained in itself an infinite number of representations. Nevertheless, space is so thought (for all parts of infinite space exist simultaneously). Consequently, the original representation of space is an *intuition a priori*, and not a concept.—KANT, I.

Critique of Pure Reason [*Max Müller*] (*New York, 1900*), pp. 18–20 and Supplement 8.

2003. *Schopenhauer's Predicabilia a priori.**

OF TIME	OF SPACE
1. There is but *one time*, all different times are parts of it.	1. There is but *one space*, all different spaces are parts of it.
2. Different times are not simultaneous but successive.	2. Different spaces are not successive but simultaneous.
3. Everything in time may be thought of as non-existent, but not time.	3. Everything in space may be thought of as non-existent, but not space.
4. Time has three divisions: past, present and future, which form two directions with a point of indifference.	4. Space has three dimensions: height, breadth, and length.
5. Time is infinitely divisible.	5. Space is infinitely divisible.
6. Time is homogeneous and a continuum: i. e. no part is different from another, nor separated by something which is not time.	6. Space is homogeneous and a continuum: i. e. no part is different from another, nor separated by something which is not space.

* Schopenhauer's table contains a third column headed "of matter" which has here been omitted.

7. Time has no beginning nor end, but all beginning and end is in time.
8. Time makes counting possible.
9. Rhythm exists only in time.

10. The laws of time are *a priori* conceptions.
11. Time is perceptible *a priori*, but only by means of a line-image.
12. Time has no permanence but passes the moment it is present.
13. Time never rests.
14. Everything in time has duration.
15. Time has no duration, but all duration is in time; time is the persistence of what is permanent in contrast with its restless course.
16. Motion is only possible in time.
17. Velocity, the space being the same, is in the inverse ratio of the time.
18. Time is not directly measurable by means of itself but only by means of motion which takes place in both space and time. . . .
19. Time is omnipresent: each part of it is everywhere.
20. In time alone all things are successive.

7. Space has no limits [Gränzen], but all limits are in space.
8. Space makes measurement possible.
9. Symmetry exists only in space.

10. The laws of space are *a priori* conceptions.
11. Space is immediately perceptible *a priori*.
12. Space never passes but is permanent throughout all time.
13. Space never moves.
14. Everything in space has position.
15. Space has no motion, but all motion is in space; space is the change in position of that which moves in contrast to its imperturbable rest.
16. Motion is only possible in space.
17. Velocity, the time being the same, is in the direct ratio of the space.
18. Space is measurable directly through itself and indirectly through motion which takes place in both time and space. . . .
19. Space is eternal: each part of it exists always.
20. In space alone all things are simultaneous.

21. Time makes possible the change of accidents.

21. Space makes possible the endurance of substance.

22. Each part of time contains all substance.

22. No part of space contains the same substance as another.

23. Time is the *principium individuationis.*

23. Space is the *principium individuationis.*

24. The now is without duration.

24. The point is without extension.

25. Time of itself is empty and indeterminate.

25. Space is of itself empty and indeterminate.

26. Each moment is conditioned by the one which precedes it, and only so far as this one has ceased to exist. (Principle of sufficient reason of being in time.)

26. The relation of each boundary in space to every other is determined by its relation to any one. (Principle of sufficient reason of being in space.)

27. Time makes Arithmetic possible.

27. Space makes Geometry possible.

28. The simple element of Arithmetic is unity.

28. The element of Geometry is the point.

SCHOPENHAUER, A.
Die Welt als Vorstellung und Wille; Werke (Frauenstädt) (Leipzig, 1877), Bd. 2, p. 55.

2004. The clear possession of the Idea of Space is the first requisite for all geometrical reasoning; and this clearness of idea may be tested by examining whether the axioms offer themselves to the mind as evident.—WHEWELL, WILLIAM.
The Philosophy of the Inductive Sciences, Part 1, Bk. 2, chap. 4, sect. 4 (London, 1858).

2005. Geometrical axioms are neither synthetic *a priori* conclusions nor experimental facts. They are conventions: our choice, amongst all possible conventions, is guided by experimental facts; but it remains free, and is only limited by the necessity of avoiding all contradiction. . . . In other words, axioms of geometry are only definitions in disguise.

That being so what ought one to think of this question: Is the Euclidean Geometry true?
The question is nonsense. One might as well ask whether the metric system is true and the old measures false; whether Cartesian co-ordinates are true and polar co-ordinates false.

POINCARÉ, H.
Non-Euclidean Geometry; Nature, Vol. 45 (1891-1892), p. 407.

2006. I do in no wise share this view [that the axioms are arbitrary propositions which we assume wholly at will, and that in like manner the fundamental conceptions are in the end only arbitrary symbols with which we operate] but consider it the death of all science: in my judgment the axioms of geometry are not arbitrary, but reasonable propositions which generally have the origin in space intuition and whose separate content and sequence is controlled by reasons of expediency.—KLEIN, F.
Elementarmathematik vom höheren Standpunkte aus (Leipzig, 1909), Bd. 2, p. 384.

2007. Euclid's Postulate 5 [The Parallel Axiom].
That, if a straight line falling on two straight lines make the interior angles on the same side less than two right angles, the two straight lines, if produced indefinitely, meet on that side on which are the angles less than the two right angles.—EUCLID.
The Thirteen Books of Euclid's Elements [T. L. Heath] Vol. 1 (Cambridge, 1908), p. 202.

2008. It must be admitted that Euclid's [Parallel] Axiom is unsatisfactory as the basis of a theory of parallel straight lines. It cannot be regarded as either simple or self-evident, and it therefore falls short of the essential characteristics of an axiom. . . . —HALL, H. S. and STEVENS, F. H.
Euclid's Elements (London, 1892), p. 55.

2009. We may still well declare the parallel axiom the simplest assumption which permits us to represent spatial relations, and so it will be true generally, that concepts and axioms are not immediate facts of intuition, but rather the idealizations of these facts chosen for reasons of expediency.—KLEIN, F.
Elementarmathematik vom höheren Stanfpunkte aus (Leipzig, 1909), Bd. 2, p. 382.

2010. The characteristic features of our space are not necessities of thought, and the truth of Euclid's axioms, in so far as they specially differentiate our space from other conceivable spaces, must be established by experience and by experience only.—BALL, R. S.

> *Encyclopedia Britannica, 9th Edition; Article "Measurement."*

2011. Mathematical and physiological researches have shown that the space of experience is simply an *actual* case of many conceivable cases, about whose peculiar properties experience alone can instruct us.—MACH, ERNST.

> *Popular Scientific Lectures (Chicago, 1910), p. 205.*

2012. The familiar definition: An axiom is a self-evident truth, means if it means anything, that the proposition which we call an axiom has been approved by us in the light of our experience and intuition. In this sense mathematics has no axioms, for mathematics is a formal subject over which formal and not material implication reigns.—WILSON, E. B.

> *Bulletin American Mathematical Society, Vol. 2 (1904–1905), p. 81.*

2013. The proof of self-evident propositions may seem, to the uninitiated, a somewhat frivolous occupation. To this we might reply that it is often by no means self-evident that one obvious proposition follows from another obvious proposition; so that we are really discovering new truths when we prove what is evident by a method which is not evident. But a more interesting retort is, that since people have tried to prove obvious propositions, they have found that many of them are false. Self-evidence is often a mere will-o'-the-wisp, which is sure to lead us astray if we take it as our guide.

> RUSSELL, BERTRAND.
> *Recent Work on the Principles of Mathematics; International Monthly, Vol. 4 (1901), p. 86.*

2014. The problem [of Euclid's Parallel Axiom] is now at a par with the squaring of the circle and the trisection of an angle by means of ruler and compass. So far as the mathematical public

is concerned, the famous problem of the parallel is settled for all time.—YOUNG, JOHN WESLEY.
Fundamental Concepts of Algebra and Geometry (New York, 1911), p. 32.

2015. If the Euclidean assumptions are true, the constitution of those parts of space which are at an infinite distance from us, "geometry upon the plane at infinity," is just as well known as the geometry of any portion of this room. In this infinite and thoroughly well-known space the Universe is situated during at least some portion of an infinite and thoroughly well-known time. So that here we have real knowledge of something at least that concerns the Cosmos; something that is true throughout the Immensities and the Eternities. That something Lobatchewsky and his successors have taken away. The geometer of to-day knows nothing about the nature of the actually existing space at an infinite distance; he knows nothing about the properties of this present space in a past or future eternity. He knows, indeed, that the laws assumed by Euclid are true with an accuracy that no direct experiment can approach, not only in this place where we are, but in places at a distance from us that no astronomer has conceived; but he knows this as of Here and Now; beyond this range is a There and Then of which he knows nothing at present, but may ultimately come to know more.—CLIFFORD, W. K.
Lectures and Essays (New York, 1901), Vol. 1, pp. 358–359.

2016. The truth is that other systems of geometry are possible, yet after all, these other systems are not spaces but other methods of space measurements. There is one space only, though we may conceive of many different manifolds, which are contrivances or ideal constructions invented for the purpose of determining space.—CARUS, PAUL.
Science, Vol. 18 (1903), p. 106.

2017. As I have formerly stated that from the philosophic side Non-Euclidean Geometry has as yet not frequently met with full understanding, so I must now emphasize that it is universally recognized in the science of mathematics; indeed, for many purposes, as for instance in the modern theory of functions, it is used as an extremely convenient means for the visual representation of highly complicated arithmetical relations.—KLEIN, F.

> Elementarmathematik vom höheren Standpunkte aus (Leipzig, 1909), Bd. 2, p. 377.

2018. Everything in physical science, from the law of gravitation to the building of bridges, from the spectroscope to the art of navigation, would be profoundly modified by any considerable inaccuracy in the hypothesis that our actual space is Euclidean. The observed truth of physical science, therefore, constitutes overwhelming empirical evidence that this hypothesis is very approximately correct, even if not rigidly true.

> RUSSELL, BERTRAND.
> Foundations of Geometry (Cambridge, 1897), p. 6.

2019. The most suggestive and notable achievement of the last century is the discovery of Non-Euclidean geometry.

> HILBERT, D.
> Quoted by G. D. Fitch in Manning's "The Fourth Dimension Simply Explained," (New York, 1910), p. 58.

2020. Non-Euclidean geometry—primate among the emancipators of the human intellect. . . .—KEYSER, C. J.

> The Foundations of Mathematics; Science History of the Universe, Vol. 8 (New York, 1909), p. 192.

2021. Every high school teacher [Gymnasial-lehrer] must of necessity know something about non-euclidean geometry, because it is one of the few branches of mathematics which, by means of certain catch-phrases, has become known in wider circles, and concerning which any teacher is consequently liable to be asked at any time. In physics there are many such matters—almost every new discovery is of this kind—which, through certain catch-words have become topics of common conversation, and about which therefore every teacher must of course be informed. Think of a teacher of physics who knows nothing of Roentgen rays or of radium; no better impression would be made by a mathematician who is unable to give information concerning non-euclidean geometry.—KLEIN, F.

Elementarmathematik vom höheren Standpunkte aus (Leipzig, 1909), Bd. 2, p. 378.

2022. What Vesalius was to Galen, what Copernicus was to Ptolemy, that was Lobatchewsky to Euclid. There is, indeed, a somewhat instructive parallel between the last two cases. Copernicus and Lobatchewsky were both of Slavic origin. Each of them has brought about a revolution in scientific ideas so great that it can only be compared with that wrought by the other. And the reason of the transcendent importance of these two changes is that they are changes in the conception of the Cosmos. . . . And in virtue of these two revolutions the idea of the Universe, the Macrocosm, the All, as subject of human knowledge, and therefore of human interest, has fallen to pieces.—CLIFFORD, W. K.

Lectures and Essays (New York, 1901), Vol. 1, pp. 356, 358.

2023. I am exceedingly sorry that I have failed to avail myself of our former greater proximity to learn more of your work on the foundations of geometry; it surely would have saved me much useless effort and given me more peace, than one of my disposition can enjoy so long as so much is left to consider in a matter of this kind. I have myself made much progress in this matter (though my other heterogeneous occupations have left me but little time for this purpose); though the course which I have pursued does not lead as much to the desired end, which you assure me you have reached, as to the questioning of the truth of geometry. It is true that I have found much which many would accept as proof, but which in my estimation proves *nothing*, for instance, if it could be shown that a rectilinear triangle is possible, whose area is greater than that of any given surface, then I could rigorously establish the whole of geometry. Now most people, no doubt, would grant this as an axiom, but not I; it is conceivable that, however distant apart the vertices of the triangle might be chosen, its area might yet always be below a certain limit. I have found several other such theorems, but none of them satisfies me.—GAUSS.

Letter to Bolyai (1799); Werke, Bd. 8 (Göttingen, 1900), p. 159.

2024. On the supposition that Euclidean geometry is not valid, it is easy to show that similar figures do not exist; in that case the angles of an equilateral triangle vary with the side in which I see no absurdity at all. The angle is a function of the side and the sides are functions of the angle, a function which, of course, at the same time involves a constant length. It seems somewhat of a paradox to say that a constant length could be given a priori as it were, but in this again I see nothing inconsistent. Indeed, it would be desirable that Euclidean geometry were not valid, for then we should possess a general a priori standard of measure.—GAUSS.

Letter to Gerling (1816); Werke, Bd. 8 (Göttingen, 1900), p. 169.

2025. I am convinced more and more that the necessary truth of our geometry cannot be demonstrated, at least not *by* the *human* intellect *to* the human understanding. Perhaps in another world we may gain other insights into the nature of space which at present are unattainable to us. Until then we must consider geometry as of equal rank not with arithmetic, which is purely a priori, but with mechanics.—GAUSS.

Letter to Olbers (1817); Werke, Bd. 8 (Göttingen, 1900), p. 177.

2026. There is no doubt that it can be rigorously established that the sum of the angles of a rectilinear triangle cannot exceed 180°. But it is otherwise with the statement that the sum of the angles cannot be less than 180°; this is the real Gordian knot, the rocks which cause the wreck of all. . . . I have been occupied with the problem over thirty years and I doubt if anyone has given it more serious attention, though I have never published anything concerning it. The assumption that the angle sum is less than 180° leads to a peculiar geometry, entirely different from the Euclidean, but throughout consistent with itself. I have developed this geometry to my own satisfaction so that I can solve every problem that arises in it with the exception of the determination of a certain constant which cannot be determined a priori. The larger one assumes this constant the more nearly one approaches the Euclidean geometry, an infinitely large value makes the two coincide. The theorems of this geometry seem in part paradoxical, and to the unpracticed absurd; but on a closer and calm reflection it is found that in themselves they contain nothing impossible. . . . All my efforts to discover some contradiction, some inconsistency in this Non-Euclidean geometry have been fruitless, the one thing in it that seems contrary to reason is that space would have to contain a *definitely determinate* (though to us unknown) linear magnitude. However, it seems to me that notwithstanding the meaningless word-wisdom of the metaphysicians we know really too little, or nothing, concerning the true nature of space to confound what appears unnatural with the *absolutely impossible*. Should Non-Euclidean geometry be true, and this constant bear some relation to magnitudes which come within the domain of terrestrial or celestial measurement, it could be determined a posteriori.—GAUSS.

> *Letter to Taurinus (1824); Werke, Bd. 8 (Göttingen, 1900), p. 187.*

2027. There is also another subject, which with me is nearly forty years old, to which I have again given some thought during leisure hours, I mean the foundations of geometry. . . . Here, too, I have consolidated many things, and my conviction has, if possible become more firm that geometry cannot be completely established on a priori grounds. In the mean time I shall probably not for a long time yet put my *very extended* investigations concerning this matter in shape for publication, possibly not while I live, for I fear the cry of the Bœotians which would arise should I express my whole view on this matter.—It is curious too, that besides the known gap in Euclid's geometry, to fill which all efforts till now have been in vain, and which will never be filled, there exists another defect, which to my knowledge no one thus far has criticised and which (though possible) it is by no means easy to remove. This is the definition of a plane as a surface which wholly contains the line joining any two points. This definition contains more than is necessary to the determination of the surface, and tacitly involves a theorem which demands proof.—GAUSS.

Letter to Bessel (1829); Werke, Bd. 8 (Göttingen, 1900), p. 200.

2028. I will add that I have recently received from Hungary a little paper on Non-Euclidean geometry, in which I rediscover all *my own ideas* and *results* worked out with great elegance, . . . The writer is a very young Austrian officer, the son of one of my early friends, with whom I often discussed the subject in 1798, although my ideas were at that time far removed from the development and maturity which they have received through the original reflections of this young man. I consider the young geometer v. Bolyai a genius of the first rank.—GAUSS.

Letter to Gerling (1832); Werke, Bd. 8 (Göttingen, 1900), p. 221.

2029. Think of the image of the world in a convex mirror. . . . A well-made convex mirror of moderate aperture represents the objects in front of it as apparently solid and in fixed positions behind its surface. But the images of the distant horizon and of the sun in the sky lie behind the mirror at a limited distance, equal to its focal length. Between these and the surface of the mirror are found the images of all the other objects before it, but the images are diminished and flattened in proportion to the distance of their objects from the mirror. . . . Yet every straight line or plane in the outer world is represented by a straight [?] line or plane in the image. The image of a man measuring with a rule a straight line from the mirror, would contract more and more the farther he went, but with his shrunken rule the man in the image would count out exactly the same number of centimeters as the real man. And, in general, all geometrical measurements of lines and angles made with regularly varying images of real instruments would yield exactly the same results as in the outer world, all lines of sight in the mirror would be represented by straight lines of sight in the mirror. In short, I do not see how men in the mirror are to discover that their bodies are not rigid solids and their experiences good examples of the correctness of Euclidean axioms.

But if they could look out upon our world as we look into theirs without overstepping the boundary, they must declare it to be a picture in a spherical mirror, and would speak of us just as we speak of them; and if two inhabitants of the different worlds could communicate with one another, neither, as far as I can see, would be able to convince the other that he had the true, the other the distorted, relation. Indeed I cannot see that such a question would have any meaning at all, so long as mechanical considerations are not mixed up with it.—HELMHOLTZ, H.

On the Origin and Significance of Geometrical Axioms; Popular Scientific Lectures, second series (New York, 1881), pp. 57–59.

2030. That space conceived of as a locus of points has but three dimensions needs no argument from the mathematical point of view; but just as little can we from this point of view prevent the assertion that space has really four or an infinite number of dimensions though we perceive only three. The theory of multiply-extended manifolds, which enters more and more into the foreground of mathematical research, is from its very nature perfectly independent of such an assertion. But the form of expression, which this theory employs, has indeed grown out of this conception. Instead of referring to the individuals of a manifold, we speak of the points of a higher space, etc. In itself this form of expression has many advantages, in that it facilitates comprehension by calling up geometrical intuition. But it has this disadvantage, that in extended circles, investigations concerning manifolds of any number of dimensions are considered singular alongside the above-mentioned conception of space. This view is without the least foundation. The investigations in question would indeed find immediate geometric applications if the conception were valid but its value and purpose, being independent of this conception, rests upon its essential mathematical content.

KLEIN, F.
Mathematische Annalen, Bd. 43 (1893), p. 95.

2031. We are led naturally to extend the language of geometry to the case of any number of variables, still using the word *point* to designate any system of values of n variables (the coördinates of the point), the word *space* (of n dimensions) to designate the totality of all these points or systems of values, *curves* or *surface* to designate the spread composed of points whose coördinates are given functions (with the proper restrictions) of one or two parameters (the *straight line* or *plane*, when they are linear fractional functions with the same denominator), etc. Such an extension has come to be a necessity in a large number of investigations, in order as well to give them the greatest generality as to preserve in them the intuitive character of geometry. But it has been noted that in such use of geometric language we are no longer constructing truly a geometry, for the forms that we have been considering are essentially analytic, and that, for example, the general projective geometry constructed in this way is in substance nothing more than the algebra of linear transformations.

SEGRE, CORRADI.
Rivista di Matematica, Vol. 1 (1891), p. 59.
[*J. W. Young.*]

2032. Those who can, in common algebra, find a square root of -1, will be at no loss to find a fourth dimension in space in which ABC may become ABCD: or, if they cannot find it, they have but to imagine it, and call it an *impossible* dimension, subject to all the laws of the three we find possible. And just as $\sqrt{-1}$ in common algebra, gives all its *significant* combinations *true*, so would it be with any number of dimensions of space which the speculator might choose to call into *impossible* existence —DE MORGAN, A.
Trigonometry and Double Algebra (London, 1849), Part 2, chap. 3.

2033. The doctrine of non-Euclidean spaces and of hyperspaces in general possesses the highest intellectual interest, and it requires a far-sighted man to foretell that it can never have any practical importance.—SMITH, W. B.
Introductory Modern Geometry (New York, 1893), p. 274.

2034. According to his frequently expressed view, Gauss considered the three dimensions of space as specific peculiarities of the human soul; people, which are unable to comprehend this, he designated in his humorous mood by the name Bœotians. We could imagine ourselves, he said, as beings which are conscious of but two dimensions; higher beings might look at us in a like manner, and continuing jokingly, he said that he had laid aside certain problems which, when in a higher state of being, he hoped to investigate geometrically.

SARTORIUS, W. v. WALTERSHAUSEN.
Gauss zum Gedächtniss (Leipzig, 1856), p. 81.

2035. *There is many a rational logos,* and the mathematician has high delight in the contemplation of *inconsistent systems* of *consistent relationships.* There are, for example, a Euclidean geometry and more than one species of non-Euclidean. As theories of a given space, these are not compatible. If our universe be, as Plato thought, and nature-science takes for granted, a space-conditioned, geometrised affair, one of these geometries may be, none of them may be, not all of them can be, valid in it. But in the vaster world of thought, all of them are valid, there they co-exist, and interlace among themselves and others, as differing component strains of a higher, strictly supernatural, hypercosmic, harmony.—KEYSER, C. J.
The Universe and Beyond; Hibbert Journal, Vol. 3 (1904–1905), p. 313.

2036. The introduction into geometrical work of conceptions such as the infinite, the imaginary, and the relations of hyperspace, none of which can be directly imagined, has a psychological significance well worthy of examination. It gives a deep insight into the resources and working of the human mind. We arrive at the borderland of mathematics and psychology.

MERZ, J. T.
History of European Thought in the Nineteenth Century (Edinburgh and London, 1903), p. 716.

2037. Among the splendid generalizations effected by modern mathematics, there is none more brilliant or more inspiring or more fruitful, and none more commensurate with the limitless immensity of being itself, than that which produced the great concept designated . . . hyperspace or multidimensional space.—KEYSER, C. J.

Mathematical Emancipations; Monist, Vol. 16 (1906), p. 65.

2038. The great generalization [of hyperspace] has made it possible to enrich, quicken and beautify analysis with the terse, sensuous, artistic, stimulating language of geometry. On the other hand, the hyperspaces are in themselves immeasurably interesting and inexhaustibly rich fields of research. Not only does the geometrician find light in them for the illumination of otherwise dark and undiscovered properties of ordinary spaces of intuition, but he also discovers there wondrous structures quite unknown to ordinary space. . . . It is by creation of hyperspaces that the rational spirit secures release from limitation. In them it lives ever joyously, sustained by an unfailing sense of infinite freedom.—KEYSER, C. J.

Mathematical Emancipations; Monist, Vol. 16 (1906), p. 83.

2039. Mathematicians who busy themselves a great deal with the formal theory of four-dimensional space, seem to acquire a capacity for imagining this form as easily as the three-dimensional form with which we are all familiar.—OSTWALD, W.

Natural Philosophy [Seltzer], (New York, 1910), p. 77.

2040. Fuchs. Was soll ich nun aber denn studieren?
    Meph. Ihr könnt es mit *analytischer Geometrie* probieren.
        Da wird der Raum euch wohl dressiert,
        In Coordinaten eingeschnürt,
        Dass ihr nicht etwa auf gut Glück
        Von der Figur gewinnt ein Stück.
        Dann lehret man euch manchen Tag,
        Dass, was ihr sonst auf einen Schlag
        Construiertet im Raume frei,
        Eine Gleichung dazu nötig sei.
        Zwar war dem Menschen zu seiner Erbauung
        Die dreidimensionale Raumanschauung,

Dass er sieht, was um ihn passiert,
Und die Figuren sich construiert—
Der Analytiker tritt herein
Und beweist, das könnte auch anders sein.
Gleichungen, die auf dem Papiere stehn,
Die müsst' man auch können im Raume sehn;
Und könnte man's nicht construieren,
Da müsste man's anders definieren.
Denn was man formt nach Zahlengesetzen
Müsst' uns auch geometrisch erletzen.
Drum in den unendlich fernen beiden
Imaginären Punkten müssen sich schneiden
Alle Kreise fein säuberlich,
Auch Parallelen, die treffen sich,
Und im Raume kann man daneben
Allerlei Krümmungsmasse erleben.
Die Formeln sind alle wahr und schön,
Warum sollen sie nicht zu deuten gehn?
Da preisen's die Schüler aller Orten,
Dass das Gerade ist krumm geworden.
Nicht-Euklidisch nennt's die Geometrie,
Spotted ihrer selbst, und weiss nicht wie.

Fuchs. Kann euch nicht eben ganz verstehn.
Meph. Das soll den Philosophen auch so gehn.
Doch wenn ihr lernt alles reducieren
Und gehörig transformieren,
Bis die Formeln den Sinn verlieren,
Dann versteht ihr mathematish zu spekulieren.

LASSWITZ, KURD.

Der Faust-Tragödie (-n)ter Teil; Zeitschrift für den math-naturw. Unterricht, Bd. 14 (1888), p. 316.

[Fuchs. To what study then should I myself apply?
Meph. Begin with *analytical geometry*.
There all space is properly trained,
By coördinates well restrained,
That no one by some lucky assay
Carry some part of the figure away.

Next thou'll be taught to realize,
Constructions won't help thee to geometrize,
And the result of a free construction
Requires an equation for proper deduction.
Three-dimensional space relation
Exists for human edification,
That he may see what about him transpires,
And construct such figures as he requires.
Enters the analyst. Forthwith you see
That all this might otherwise be.
Equations, written with pencil or pen,
Must be visible in space, and when
Difficulties in construction arise,
We need only define it otherwise.
For, what is formed after laws arithmetic
Must also yield some delight geometric.
Therefore we must not object
That all circles intersect
In the circular points at infinity.
And all parallels, they declare,
If produced must meet somewhere.
So in space, it can't be denied,
Any old curvature may abide.
The formulas are all fine and true,
Then why should they not have a meaning too?
Pupils everywhere praise their fate
That that now is crooked which once was
    straight.
Non-Euclidean, in fine derision,
Is what it's called by the geometrician.
Fuchs. I do not fully follow thee.
Meph. No better does philosophy.
To master mathematical speculation,
Carefully learn to reduce your equation
By an adequate transformation
Till the formulas are devoid of interpretation.]

CHAPTER XXI

2101. The pseudomath is a person who handles mathematics as a monkey handles the razor. The creature tried to shave himself as he had seen his master do; but, not having any notion of the angle at which the razor was to be held, he cut his own throat. He never tried it a second time, poor animal! but the pseudomath keeps on in his work, proclaims himself clean shaved, and all the rest of the world hairy.

The graphomath is a person who, having no mathematics, attempts to describe a mathematician. Novelists perform in this way: even Walter Scott now and then burns his fingers. His dreaming calculator, Davy Ramsay, swears "by the bones of the immortal Napier." Scott thought that the philomaths worshipped relics: so they do in one sense.—DE MORGAN, A. *Budget of Paradoxes (London, 1872), p. 473.*

2102. Proof requires a person who can give and a person who can receive. . . .

> A blind man said, As to the Sun,
> I'll take my Bible oath there's none;
> For if there had been one to show
> They would have shown it long ago.
> How came he such a goose to be?
> Did he not know he couldn't see?
> Not he.

> DE MORGAN, A.
> *Budget of Paradoxes (London, 1872), p. 262.*

2103. Mathematical research, with all its wealth of hidden treasure, is all too apt to yield nothing to our research: for it is haunted by certain *ignes fatui*—delusive phantoms, that float before us, and seem so fair, and are *all but* in our grasp, so nearly that it never seems to need more than *one* step further, and the prize shall be ours! Alas for him who has been turned

364

aside from real research by one of these spectres—who has found a music in its mocking laughter—and who wastes his life and energy in the desperate chase!—DODGSON, C. L.
A new Theory of Parallels (London, 1895), Introduction.

2104. As lightning clears the air of impalpable vapours, so an incisive paradox frees the human intelligence from the lethargic influence of latent and unsuspected assumptions. Paradox is the slayer of Prejudice.—SYLVESTER, J. J.
On a Lady's Fan etc. Collected Mathematical Papers, Vol. 3, p. 36.

2105. When a paradoxer parades capital letters and diagrams which are as good as Newton's to all who know nothing about it, some persons wonder why science does not rise and triturate the whole thing. This is why: all who are fit to read the refutation are satisfied already, and can, if they please, detect the paradoxer for themselves. Those who are not fit to do this would not know the difference between the true answer and the new capitals and diagrams on which the delighted paradoxer would declare that he had crumbled the philosophers, and not they him.
DE MORGAN, A.
A Budget of Paradoxes (London, 1872), p. 484.

2106. Demonstrative reason never raises the cry of *Church in Danger!* and it cannot have any Dictionary of heresies except a Budget of Paradoxes. Mistaken claimants are left to Time and his extinguisher, with the approbation of all non-claimants: there is no need of a succession of exposures. Time gets through the job in his own workmanlike manner.—DE MORGAN, A.
A Budget of Paradoxes (London, 1872), p. 485.

2107. D'Israeli speaks of the "six follies of science,"—the quadrature, the duplication, the perpetual motion, the philosopher's stone, magic, and astrology. He might as well have added the trisection, to make the mystic number seven; but had he done so, he would still have been very lenient; only seven follies in all science, from mathematics to chemistry! Science might have said to such a judge—as convicts used to say who got seven years, expecting it for life, "Thank you, my Lord, and may you sit there until they are over,"—may the Curiosities of Literature outlive the Follies of Science!

DE MORGAN, A.
A Budget of Paradoxes (London, 1872), p. 71.

2108. Montucla says, speaking of France, that he finds three notions prevalent among cyclometers: 1. That there is a large reward offered for success; 2. That the longitude problem depends on that success; 3. That the solution is the great end and object of geometry. The same three notions are equally prevalent among the same class in England. No reward has ever been offered by the government of either country. The longitude problem in no way depends upon perfect solution; existing approximations are sufficient to a point of accuracy far beyond what can be wanted. And geometry, content with what exists, has long passed on to other matters. Sometimes a cyclometer persuades a skipper who has made land in the wrong place that the astronomers are at fault, for using a wrong measure of the circle; and the skipper thinks it a very comfortable solution! And this is the utmost that the problem has to do with longitude.—DE MORGAN, A.

A Budget of Paradoxes (London, 1872), p. 96.

2109. Gregory St. Vincent is the greatest of circle-squarers, and his investigations led him into many truths: he found the property of the arc of the hyperbola which led to Napier's logarithms being called hyperbolic. Montucla says of him, with sly truth, that no one ever squared the circle with so much genius, or, excepting his principal object, with so much success.

DE MORGAN, A.
A Budget of Paradoxes (London, 1872), p. 70.

2110. When I reached geometry, and became acquainted with the proposition the proof of which has been sought for centuries, I felt irresistibly impelled to try my powers at its discovery. You will consider me foolish if I confess that I am still earnestly of the opinion to have succeeded in my attempt.

BOLZANO, BERNARD.
Selbstbiographie (Wien, 1875), p. 19.

2111. The Theory of Parallels.

It is known that to complete the theory it is only necessary to demonstrate the following proposition, which Euclid assumed as an axiom:

Prop. If the sum of the interior angles ECF and DBC which two straight lines EC and DB make with a third line CP is less than two right angles, the lines, if sufficiently produced, will intersect.

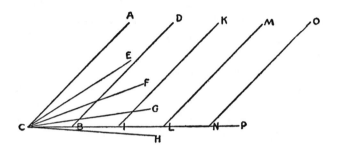

Proof. Construct PCA equal to the supplement PBD of CBD, and ECF, FCG, etc. each equal to ACE, so that ACF = 2.ACE, ACG = 3.ACE, etc. Then however small the angle ACE may be, there exists some number n such that n.ACE = ACH will be equal to or greater than ACP.

Again, take BI, IL, etc. each equal to CB, and draw IK, LM, etc. parallel to BD, then the figures ACBD, DBIK, KILM, etc. are congruent, and ACIK = 2.ABCD, ACLM = 3.ACBD, etc.

Take ACNO =n.ACBD, n having the same value as in the expression ACH = n.ACE, then ACNO is certainly less than ACP, since ACNO must be increased by ONP to be equal to ACP. It follows that ACNO is also less than ACH, and by taking the nth part of each of these, that ACBD is less than ACE.

But if ACE is greater than ACBD, CE and BD must intersect, for otherwise ACE would be a part of ACBD.

Journal für Mathematik, Bd. 2 (1834), p. 198.

2112. Are you sure that it is impossible to trisect the angle by *Euclid?* I have not to lament a single hour thrown away on the attempt, but fancy that it is rather a tact, a feeling, than a proof, which makes us think that the thing cannot be done. But would *Gauss's* inscription of the regular polygon of seventeen sides have seemed, a century ago, much less an impossible thing, by line and circle?—HAMILTON, W. R.

Letter to De Morgan (1852).

2113. One of the most curious of these cases [geometrical paradoxers] was that of a student, I am not sure but a graduate, of the University of Virginia, who claimed that geometers were in error in assuming that a line had no thickness. He published a school geometry based on his views, which received the endorsement of a well-known New York school official and, on the basis of this, was actually endorsed, or came very near being endorsed, as a text-book in the public schools of New York.

NEWCOMB, SIMON.
The Reminiscences of an Astronomer (Boston and New York, 1903), p. 388.

2114. What distinguishes the straight line and circle more than anything else, and properly separates them for the purpose of elementary geometry? Their self-similarity. Every inch of a straight line coincides with every other inch, and off a circle with every other off the same circle. Where, then, did Euclid fail? In not introducing the third curve, which has the same property—the *screw*. The right line, the circle, the screw—the representations of translation, rotation, and the two combined—ought to have been the instruments of geometry. With a screw we should never have heard of the impossibility of trisecting an angle, squaring the circle, etc.

DE MORGAN, A.
Quoted in Graves' Life of Sir W. R. Hamilton, Vol. 3 (New York, 1889), p. 342.

2115. Mad Mathesis alone was unconfined,
Too mad for mere material chains to bind,
Now to pure space lifts her ecstatic stare,
Now, running round the circle, finds it square.

POPE, ALEXANDER.
The Dunciad, .Bk. 4, lines 31–34.

2116. Or is't a tart idea, to procure
An edge, and keep the practic soul in ure,
Like that dear Chymic dust, or puzzling quadrature?

QUARLES, PHILIP.
Quoted by De Morgan: Budget of Paradoxes
(London, 1872), p. 436.

2117. Quale è'l geometra che tutto s' affige
Per misurar lo cerchio, e non ritruova,
Pensando qual principio ond' egli indige.—DANTE.
Paradise, canto 33, lines 122–125.

[As doth the expert geometer appear
Who seeks to square the circle, and whose skill
Finds not the law with which his course to steer.*]
Quoted in Frankland's Story of Euclid (London,
1902), p. 101.

2118.   In *Mathematicks* he was greater
Than *Tycho Brahe*, or *Erra Pater:*
For he, by *Geometrick* scale,
Could take the size of *Pots of Ale;*
Resolve by Signs and Tangents streight,
If *Bread* or *Butter* wanted weight;
And wisely tell what hour o' th' day
The Clock doth strike, by *Algebra.*

BUTLER, SAMUEL.
Hudibras, Part 1, canto 1, lines 119-126.

2119. I have often been surprised that Mathematics, the quintessence of truth, should have found admirers so few and so languid. Frequent considerations and minute scrutiny have at length unravelled the cause; viz. that though Reason is feasted, Imagination is starved; whilst Reason is luxuriating in its proper Paradise, Imagination is wearily travelling on a dreary desert.—COLERIDGE, SAMUEL.
A Mathematical Problem.

2120. At last we entered the palace, and proceeded into the chamber of presence where I saw the king seated on his throne,

* For another rendition of these same lines see 1858.

attended on each side by persons of prime quality. Before the throne, was a large table filled with globes and spheres, and mathematical instruments of all kinds. His majesty took not the least notice of us, although our entrance was not without sufficient noise, by the concourse of all persons belonging to the court. But he was then deep in a problem, and we attended an hour, before he could solve it. There stood by him, on each side, a young page with flaps in their hands, and when they saw he was at leisure, one of them gently struck his mouth, and the other his right ear; at which he started like one awaked on the sudden, and looking toward me and the company I was in, recollected the occasion of our coming, whereof he had been informed before. He spake some words, whereupon immediately a young man with a flap came to my side, and flapt me gently on the right ear, but I made signs, as well as I could, that I had no occasion for such an instrument; which, as I afterwards found, gave his majesty, and the whole court, a very mean opinion of my understanding. The king, as far as I could conjecture, asked me several questions, and I addressed myself to him in all the languages I had. When it was found, that I could neither understand nor be understood, I was conducted by his order to an apartment in his palace, (this prince being distinguished above all his predecessors, for his hospitality to strangers) where two servants were appointed to attend me. My dinner was brought, and four persons of quality, did me the honour to dine with me. We had two courses of three dishes each. In the first course, there was a shoulder of mutton cut into an equilateral triangle, a piece of beef into a rhomboides, and a pudding into a cycloid. The second course, was, two ducks trussed up in the form of fiddles; sausages and puddings, resembling flutes and haut-boys, and a breast of veal in the shape of a harp. The servants cut our bread into cones, cylinders, parallelograms, and several other mathematical figures.—SWIFT, JONATHAN.

Gulliver's Travels; A Voyage to Laputa, Chap. 2.

2121. Those to whom the king had entrusted me, observing how ill I was clad, ordered a taylor to come next morning, and take measure for a suit of cloaths. This operator did his office after a different manner, from those of his trade in Europe. He first took my altitude by a quadrant, and then, with rule and compasses, described the dimensions and outlines of my whole body, all which he entered upon paper; and in six days, brought my cloaths very ill made, and quite out of shape, by happening to mistake a figure in the calculation. But my comfort was, that I observed such accidents very frequent, and little regarded.

SWIFT, JONATHAN.
Gulliver's Travels; A Voyage to Laputa, Chap. 2.

2122. The knowledge I had in mathematics, gave me great assistance in acquiring their phraseology, which depended much upon that science, and music; and in the latter I was not unskilled. Their ideas are perpetually conversant in lines and figures. If they would, for example, praise the beauty of a woman, or any other animal, they describe it by rhombs, circles, parallelograms, ellipses, and other geometrical terms, or by words of art drawn from music, needless here to repeat. I observed in the king's kitchen all sorts of mathematical and musical instruments, after the figures of which, they cut up the joints that were served to his majesty's table.

SWIFT, JONATHAN.
Gulliver's Travels; A Voyage to Laputa, Chap. 2.

2123. I was at the mathematical school, where the master taught his pupils, after a method, scarce imaginable to us in Europe. The propositions, and demonstrations, were fairly written on a thin wafer, with ink composed of a cephalic tincture. This, the student was to swallow upon a fasting stomach, and for three days following, eat nothing but bread and water. As the wafer digested, the tincture mounted to his brain, bearing the proposition along with it. But the success has not hitherto been answerable, partly by some error in the *quantum* or composition, and partly by the perverseness of lads; to whom this bolus is so nauseous, that they generally steal aside, and discharge it upwards, before it can operate; neither have they been yet persuaded to use so long an abstinence as the prescription requires.—SWIFT, JONATHAN.

Gulliver's Travels; A Voyage to Laputa, Chap. 5.

2124. It is worth observing that some of those who disparage some branch of study in which they are deficient, will often affect more contempt for it than they really feel. And not unfrequently they will take pains to have it thought that they are themselves well versed in it, or that they easily might be, if they thought it worth while;—in short, that it is not from hanging too high that the grapes are called sour.

Thus, Swift, in the person of Gulliver, represents himself, while deriding the extravagant passion for Mathematics among the Laputians, as being a good mathematician. Yet he betrays his utter ignorance, by speaking " of a pudding in the *form of a cycloid:* " evidently taking the cycloid for a *figure*, instead of a *line*. This may help to explain the difficulty he is said to have had in obtaining his Degree.—WHATELY, R.

Annotations to Bacon's Essays, Essay L.

2125. It is natural to think that an abstract science cannot be of much importance in the affairs of human life, because it has omitted from its consideration everything of real interest. It will be remembered that Swift, in his description of Gulliver's voyage to Laputa, is of two minds on this point. He describes the mathematicians of that country as silly and useless dreamers, whose attention has to be awakened by flappers. Also, the mathematical tailor measures his height by a quadrant, and deduces his other dimensions by a rule and compasses, producing a suit of very ill-fitting clothes. On the other hand, the mathematicians of Laputa, by their marvellous invention of the magnetic island floating in the air, ruled the country and maintained their ascendency over their subjects. Swift, indeed, lived at a time peculiarly unsuited for gibes at contemporary mathematicians. Newton's *Principia* had just been written, one of the great forces which have transformed the modern world. Swift might just as well have laughed at an earthquake.

WHITEHEAD, A. N.

An Introduction to Mathematics (New York, 1911), p. 10.

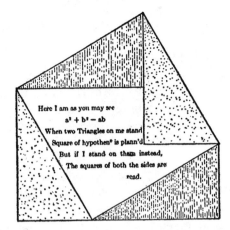

Here I am as you may see
a² + b² — ab
When two Triangles on me stand
Square of hypothen⁰ is plann'd
But if I stand on them instead,
The squares of both the sides are
read.

AIRY, G. B.
Quoted in Graves' Life of Sir W. R. Hamilton,
Vol. 3 (New York, 1889), p. 502.

2127. π = 3.141 592 653 589 793 238 462 643 383 279 . . .

3 1 4 1 5 9
Now I, even I, would celebrate
2 6 5 3 5
In rhymes inapt, the great
8 9 7 9
Immortal Syracusan, rivaled nevermore,
3 2 3 8 4
Who in his wondrous lore,
6 2 6
Passed on before,
4 3 3 8 3 2 7 9
Left men his guidance how to circles mensurate.

ORR, A. C.
Literary Digest, Vol. 32 (1906), p. 84.

2128. I take from a biographical dictionary the first five
names of poets, with their ages at death. They are

Aagard, died at 48.
Abeille, " " 76.
Abulola, " " 84.
Abunowas, " " 48.
Accords, " " 45.

These five ages have the following characters in common:—

1. The difference of the two digits composing the number, divided by *three*, leaves a remainder of *one*.

2. The first digit raised to the power indicated by the second, and then divided by *three*, leaves a remainder of *one*.

3. The sum of the prime factors of each age, including *one* as a prime factor, is divisible by *three*.—PEIRCE, C. S.

> *A Theory of Probable Inference; Studies in Logic (Boston, 1883), p. 163.*

2129. In view of the fact that the offered prize [for the solution of the problem of Fermat's Greater Theorem] is about $25,000 and that lack of marginal space in his copy of Diophantus was the reason given by Fermat for not communicating his proof, one might be tempted to wish that one could send credit for a dime back through the ages to Fermat and thus secure this coveted prize, if it actually existed. This might, however, result more seriously than one would at first suppose; for if Fermat had bought on credit a dime's worth of paper even during the year of his death, 1665, and if this bill had been drawing compound interest at the rate of six per cent. since that time, the bill would now amount to more than seven times as much as the prize.

MILLER, G. A.

> *Some Thoughts on Modern Mathematical Research; Science, Vol. 35 (1912), p. 881.*

2130. *If the Indians hadn't spent the $24.* In 1626 Peter Minuit, first governor of New Netherland, purchased Manhattan Island from the Indians for about $24. The rate of interest on money is higher in new countries, and gradually decreases as wealth accumulates. Within the present generation the legal rate in the state has fallen from 7% to 6%. Assume for simplicity a uniform rate of 7% from 1626 to the present, and suppose that the Indians had put their $24 at interest at that rate (banking facilities in New York being always taken for granted!) and had added the interest to the principal yearly. What would be the amount now, after 280 years? $24 \times (1.07)^{280}$ =more than 4,042,000,000.

The latest tax assessment available at the time of writing gives the realty for the borough of Manhattan as $3,820,754.181.

This is estimated to be 78% of the actual value, making the actual value a little more than $4,898,400,000.

The amount of the Indians' money would therefore be more than the present assessed valuation but less than the actual valuation.—WHITE, W. F.

A Scrap-book of Elementary Mathematics
(Chicago, 1908), pp. 47–48.

2131. See Mystery to Mathematics fly!—POPE, ALEXANDER.
The Dunciad, Bk. 4, line 647.

2132. The Pythagoreans and Platonists were carried further by this love of simplicity. Pythagoras, by his skill in mathematics, discovered that there can be no more than five regular solid figures, terminated by plane surfaces which are all similar and equal; to wit, the tetrahedron, the cube, the octahedron, the dodecahedron, and the eicosihedron. As nature works in the most simple and regular way, he thought that all elementary bodies must have one or other of those regular figures; and that the discovery of the properties and relations of the regular solids must be a key to open the mysteries of nature.

This notion of the Pythagoreans and Platonists has undoubtedly great beauty and simplicity. Accordingly it prevailed, at least to the time of Euclid. He was a Platonic philosopher, and is said to have wrote all the books of his Elements, in order to discover the properties and relations of the five regular solids. The ancient tradition of the intention of Euclid in writing his elements, is countenanced by the work itself. For the last book of the elements treats of the regular solids, and all the preceding are subservient to the last.—REID, THOMAS.

Essays on the Powers of the Human Mind
(Edinburgh, 1812), Vol. 2, p. 400.

2133. In the Timæus [of Plato] it is asserted that the particles of the various elements have the forms of these [the regular] solids. Fire has the Pyramid; Earth has the Cube; Water the Octahedron; Air the Icosahedron; and the Dodecahedron is the plan of the Universe itself. It was natural that when Plato had learnt that other mathematical properties had a bearing upon the constitution of the Universe, he should suppose that the singular property of space, which the existence of this limited and varied class of solids implied, should have some corresponding property in the Universe, which exists in space.

WHEWELL, W.
History of the Inductive Sciences, 3rd Edition, Additions to Bk. 2.

2134. The orbit of the earth is a circle: round the sphere to which this circle belongs, describe a dodecahedron; the sphere including this will give the orbit of Mars. Round Mars describe a tetrahedron; the circle including this will be the orbit of Jupiter. Describe a cube round Jupiter's orbit; the circle including this will be the orbit of Saturn. Now inscribe in the earth's orbit an icosahedron; the circle inscribed in it will be the orbit of Venus. Inscribe an octahedron in the orbit of Venus; the circle inscribed in it will be Mercury's orbit. This is the reason of the number of the planets.—KEPLER.

Mysterium Cosmographicum [Whewell].

2135. It will not be thought surprising that Plato expected that Astronomy, when further advanced, would be able to render an account of many things for which she has not accounted even to this day. Thus, in the passage in the seventh Book of the *Republic*, he says that the philosopher requires a reason for the proportion of the day to the month, and the month to the year, deeper and more substantial than mere observation can give. Yet Astronomy has not yet shown us any reason why the proportion of the times of the earth's rotation on its axis, the moon's revolution round the earth, and the earth's revolution round the sun, might not have been made by the Creator quite different from what they are. But in asking Mathematical Astronomy for reasons which she cannot give, Plato was only doing what a great astronomical discoverer, Kepler, did at a later period. One of the questions which Kepler especially wished to have answered was, why there are five planets, and why at such particular distances from the sun? And it is still more curious that he thought he had found the reason of these things, in the relation of those five regular solids which Plato was desirous of introducing into the philosophy of the universe. . . .

Kepler regards the law which thus determines the number and magnitude of the planetary orbits by means of the five regular solids as a discovery no less remarkable and certain than the Three Laws which give his name its imperishable place in the history of astromomy.—WHEWELL, W.

History of the Inductive Sciences, 3rd Edition, Additions to Bk. 3.

2136. Pythagorean philosophers . . . maintained that of two combatants, he would conquer, the sum of the numbers expressed by the characters of whose names exceeded the sum of those expressed by the other. It was upon this principle that they explained the relative prowess and fate of the heroes in Homer, Πατροκλος, Ἑκτωρ and Αχιλλευς, the sum of the numbers in whose names are 861, 1225, and 1276 respectively.

PEACOCK, GEORGE.

Encyclopedia of Pure Mathematics (London, 1847); Article "Arithmetic," sect. 38.

2137. Round numbers are always false.—JOHNSON, SAMUEL.

Johnsoniana; Apothegms, Sentiment, etc.

2138. Numero deus impare gaudet [God in number odd rejoices.]—VIRGIL.

Eclogue, 8, 77.

2139. Why is it that we entertain the belief that for every purpose odd numbers are the most effectual?—PLINY.

Natural History, Bk. 28, chap. 5.

2140. "Then here goes another," says he, "to make sure, Fore there's luck in odd numbers," says Rory O'Moore.

LOVER, S.

Rory O'Moore.

2141. This is the third time; I hope, good luck lies in odd numbers. . . . They say, there is divinity in odd numbers, either in nativity, chance, or death.—SHAKESPEARE.

The Merry Wives of Windsor, Act 5, scene 1.

2142. To add to golden numbers, golden numbers.

DECKER, THOMAS.
Patient Grissell, Act 1, scene 1.

2143. I've read that things inanimate have moved,
And, as with living souls, have been inform'd,
By magic numbers and persuasive sound.

CONGREVE, RICHARD.
The Morning Bride, Act 1, scene 1.

2144. . . . the Yancos on the Amazon, whose name for
three is

Poettarrarorincoaroac,

of a length sufficiently formidable to justify the remark of
La Condamine: Heureusement pour ceux qui ont à faire avec
eux, leur Arithmetique ne va pas plus loin.—PEACOCK, GEORGE.
*Encyclopedia of Pure Mathematics (London,
1847); Article "Arithmetic," sect. 32.*

2145. There are three principal sins, avarice, luxury, and
pride; three sorts of satisfaction for sin, fasting, almsgiving, and
prayer; three persons offended by sin, God, the sinner himself,
and his neighbour; three witnesses in heaven, *Pater, verbum,* and
spiritus sanctus; three degrees of penitence, contrition, confession, and satisfaction, which Dante has represented as the
three steps of the ladder that lead to purgatory, the first marble,
the second black and rugged stone, and the third red porphyry.
There are three sacred orders in the church militant, *sub-
diaconati, diaconiti,* and *presbyterati;* there are three parts, not
without mystery, of the most sacred body made by the priest
in the mass; and three times he says *Agnus Dei,* and three times,
Sanctus; and if we well consider all the devout acts of Christian
worship, they are found in a ternary combination; if we wish
rightly to partake of the holy communion, we must three times
express our contrition, *Domine non sum dignus;* but who can
say more of the ternary number in a shorter compass, than what
the prophet says, *tu signaculum sanctae trinitatis.*   There are
three Furies in the infernal regions; three Fates, Atropos, Lach-
esis, and Clotho.   There are three theological virtues: *Fides,*

spes, and *charitas. Tria sunt pericula mundi: Equum currere; navigare, et sub tyranno vivere.* There are three enemies of the soul: the Devil, the world, and the flesh. There are three things which are of no esteem: the strength of a porter, the advice of a poor man, and the beauty of a beautiful woman. There are three vows of the Minorite Friars: poverty, obedience, and chastity. There are three terms in a continued proportion. There are three ways in which we may commit sin: *corde, ore, ope.* Three principal things in Paradise: glory, riches, and justice. There are three things which are especially displeasing to God: an avaricious rich man, a proud poor man, and a luxurious old man. And all things, in short, are founded in three; that is, in number, in weight, and in measure.

> PACIOLI, *Author of the first printed treatise on arithmetic.*
> *Quoted in Encyclopedia of Pure Mathematics*
> *(London, 1847); Article "Arithmetic," sect. 90.*

2146. Ah! why, ye Gods, should two and two make four?

> POPE, ALEXANDER.
> *The Dunciad, Bk. 2, line 285.*

2147. By him who stampt *The Four* upon the mind,—
The Four, the fount of nature's endless stream.

> *Ascribed to* PYTHAGORAS.
> *Quoted in Whewell's History of the Inductive*
> *Sciences, Bk. 4, chap. 3.*

2148. Along the skiey arch the goddess trode,
And sought Harmonia's august abode;
The universal plan, the mystic Four,
Defines the figure of the palace floor.
Solid and square the ancient fabric stands,
Raised by the labors of unnumbered hands.

> NONNUS.
> *Dionysiac, 41, 275–280.* [*Whewell*].

2149. The number seventy-seven figures the abolition of all sins by baptism. . . . The number ten signifies justice and beatitude, resulting from the creature, which makes seven with the Trinity, which is three: therefore it is that God's commandments are ten in number. The number eleven denotes sin, because it *transgresses* ten. . . . This number seventy-seven is the product of eleven, figuring sin, multiplied by seven, and not by ten, for seven is the number of the creature. Three represents the soul, which is in some sort an image of Divinity; and four represents the body, on account of its four qualities. . . .

St. Augustine.
Sermon 41, art. 23.

2150. Heliodorus says that the Nile is nothing else than the year, founding his opinion on the fact that the numbers expressed by the letters Νεῖλος, Nile, are in Greek arithmetic, $N = 50$; $E = 5$; $I = 10$; $\Lambda = 30$; $O = 70$; $\Sigma = 200$; and these figures make up together 365, the number of days in the year.

Littell's Living Age, Vol. 117, p. 380.

2151. In treating 666, Bungus [Petri Bungi Bergomatis Numerorum mysteria, Bergamo, 1591] a good Catholic, could not compliment the Pope with it, but he fixes it on Martin Luther with a little forcing. If from A to I represent 1–10, from K to S 10–90, and from T to Z 100–500, we see—

M	A	R	T	I	N		L	U	T	E	R	A
30	1	80	100	9	40		20	200	100	5	80	1

which gives 666. Again in Hebrew, *Lulter* [Hebraized form of Luther] does the same:—

ר	ה	ל	י	ל
200	400	30	6	30

De Morgan, A.
Budget of Paradoxes (London, 1872), p. 37.

2152. Stifel, the most acute and original of the early mathematicians of Germany, . . . relates . . . that whilst a monk at Esslingen in 1520, and when infected by the writings of Luther, he was reading in the library of his convent the 13th Chapter of *Revelations*, it struck his mind that the *Beast* must signify the Pope, Leo X.; He then proceeded in pious hope to make the calculation of the sum of the numeral letters in *Leo decimus*, which he found to be M, D, C, L, V, I; the sum which these formed was too great by M, and too little by X; but he bethought him again, that he has seen the name written Leo X., and that there were ten letters in *Leo decimus*, from either of which he could obtain the deficient number, and by interpreting the M to mean *mysterium*, he found the number required, a discovery which gave him such unspeakable comfort, that he believed that his interpretation must have been an immediate inspiration of God.—PEACOCK, GEORGE.

> *Encyclopedia of Pure Mathematics (London, 1847); Article "Arithmetic," sect. 89.*

2153. Perhaps the best anagram ever made is that by Dr. Burney on Horatio Nelson, so happily transformed into the Latin sentence so truthful of the great admiral, *Honor est a Nilo*. Reading this, one is almost persuaded that the hit contained in it has a meaning provided by providence or fate.

This is also amusingly illustrated in the case of the Frenchman André Pujom, who, using j as i, found in his name the anagram, Pendu à Riom. Riom being the seat of justice for the province of Auvergne, the poor fellow, impelled by a sort of infatuation, actually committed a capital offence in that province, and was hanged at Riom, that the anagram might be fulfilled.

> *New American Cyclopedia, Vol. 1; Article "Anagram."*

2154. The most remarkable pseudonym [of transposed names adopted by authors] is the name of "Voltaire," which the celebrated philosopher assumed instead of his family name, "François Marie Arouet," and which is now generally allowed to be an anagram of "Arouet, l. j.," that is, Arouet the younger.

> *Encyclopedia Britannica, 11th Edition; Article "Anagram."*

2155. Perhaps the most beautiful anagram that has ever been composed is by Jablonsky, a former rector of the school at Lissa. The occasion was the following: When while a young man king Stanislaus of Poland returned from a journey, the whole house of Lescinsky assembled to welcome the family heir. On this occasion Jablonsky arranged for a school program, the closing number of which consisted of a ballet by thirteen pupils impersonating youthful heroes. Each of them carried a shield on which appeared in gold one of the letters of the words *Domus Lescinia*. At the end of the first dance the children were so arranged that the letters on their shields spelled the words *Domus Lescinia*. At the end of the second dance they read: *ades incolumis* (sound thou art here). After the third: *omnis es lucida* (wholly brilliant art thou); after the fourth: *lucida sis omen* (bright be the omen). Then: *mane sidus loci* (remain our country's star); and again: *sis columna Dei* (be a column of God); and finally: *I! scande solium* (Proceed, ascend the throne). This last was the more beautiful since it proved a true prophecy.

Even more artificial are the anagrams which transform one verse into another. Thus an Italian scholar beheld in a dream the line from Horace: *Grata superveniet, quae non sperabitur, hora*. This a friend changed to the anagram: *Est ventura Rhosina parataque nubere pigro*. This induced the scholar, though an old man, to marry an unknown lady by the name of Rosina.

HEIS, EDUARD.
Algebraische Aufgaben (Köln, 1898), p. 331.

2156. The following verses read the same whether read forward or backward:—

> Aspice! nam raro mittit timor arma, nec ipsa
> Si se mente reget, non tegeret Nemesis; *

also,　　　　Sator Arepo tenet opera rotas.

HEIS, EDUARD.
Algebraische Aufgaben (Köln, 1898), p. 328.

2157. There is a certain spiral of a peculiar form on which a point may have been approaching for centuries the center, and have nearly reached it, before we discover that its rate of approach is accelerated. The first thought of the observer, on seeing the acceleration, would be to say that it would reach the center sooner than he had before supposed. But as the point comes near the center it suddenly, although still moving under the same simple law as from the beginning, makes a very short turn upon its path and flies off rapidly almost in a straight line,

---

* The beginning of a poem which Johannes a Lasco wrote on the count Karl von Südermanland.

out to an infinite distance. This illustrates that apparent breach of continuity which we sometimes find in a natural law; that apparently sudden change of character which we sometimes see in man.—HILL, THOMAS.

Uses of Mathesis; Bibliotheca Sacra, Vol. 32, p. 521.

2158. One of the most remarkable of Babbage's illustrations of miracles has never had the consideration in the popular mind which it deserves; the illustration drawn from the existence of isolated points fulfilling the equation of a curve. . . . There are definitions of curves which describe not only the positions of every point in a certain curve, but also of one or more perfectly isolated points; and if we should attempt to get by induction the definition, from the observation of the points on the curve, we might fail altogether to include these isolated points; which, nevertheless, although standing alone, as miracles to the observer of the course of the points in the curve, are nevertheless rigorously included in the law of the curve.—HILL, THOMAS.

Uses of Mathesis; Bibliotheca Sacra, Vol. 32, p. 516.

2159. Pure mathematics is the magician's real wand.

NOVALIS.

Schriften, Zweiter Teil (Berlin, 1901), p. 223.

2160. Miracles, considered as antinatural facts, are amathematical, but there are no miracles in this sense, and those so called may be comprehended by means of mathematics, for to mathematics nothing is miraculous.—NOVALIS.

Schriften, Zweiter Teil (Berlin, 1911), p. 222.

INDEX

Black-faced numbers refer to authors

Abbreviations:—m. = mathematics, math. = mathematical,
math'n. = mathematician.

Abbott, **1001**.
Abstract method, Development
of, 729.
Abstract nature of m., Reason
for, 638.
Abstractness, math., Compared
with logical, 1304.
Abstract reasoning, Objection to,
1941.
Adams, Henry, M. and history,
1599.
Math'ns practice freedom, **208**,
805.
Adams, John, Method in m., **226**.
Aeneid, Euler's knowledge of,
859.
Aeschylus. On number, 1606.
Aim in teaching m., 501–508, 517,
844.
Airy, Pythagorean theorem,
2126.
Akenside, **1532**.
Alexander, 901, 902.
Algebra, Chapter XVII.
Definitions of, 110, 1714, 1715.
Problems in, 320, 530, 1738.
Of use to grown men, 425.
And geometry, 525–527, 1610,
1707.
Advantages of, 1701, 1703,
1705.
Laws of, 1708–1710.
As an art, 1711.
Review of, 1713.
Designations of, 1717.
Origin of, 1736.
Burlesque on modern, 1741.
Hume on, 1863.
Algebraic notation, value of,
1213, 1214.

Algebraic treatises, How to read,
601.
Amusements in m., 904, 905.
Anagrams, On De Morgan, 947.
On Domus Lescinia,
2155.
On Flamsteed, 968.
On Macaulay, 996.
On Nelson, 2153.
On Newton, 1028.
On Voltaire, 2154.
Analysis, Invigorates the faculty
of resolution, 416.
Relation of geometry to, 1931.
Analytical geometry, 1889, 1890,
1893.
Method of, 310.
Importance of, 949.
Burlesque on, 2040.
Ancient geometry,
Characteristics of, 712, 714.
Compared with modern, 1711–
1716.
Method of, 1425, 1873–1875.
Ancients, M. among the, 321.
Anecdotes, Chapters, IX, X.
Anger, M. destroys predisposi-
tion to, 458.
Angling like m., 739.
Anglo-Danes, Aptitude for m.,
836.
Anglo-Saxons, Aptitude for m.,
837.
Newton as representative of,
1014.
Anonymous, Song of the screw,
1894.
Appolonius, 712, 714.
Approximate m., Why not suffi-
cient, 1518.

385

394 INDEX

Group, Notion of, 1751.
Growth of m., 209, 211, 703.

Hall, G. S., M. the ideal and norm of all careful thinking, **304**.
Hall and Stevens, On the parallel axiom, **2008**.
Haller, On the infinite, **1968**.
Halley, On Cartesian geometry, 716.
Halsted, On Bolyai, **924–926**.
On Sylvester, **1030, 1039**.
And Slyvester, **1031, 1032**.
On m. as logic, **1305**.
Definition of geometry, **1815**.
Hamilton, Sir William, His ignorance of m., 978.
Hamilton, W. R., Importance of his quaternions, 333.
Estimate of Comte's ability, **943**.
To the memory of Fourier, **969**.
Discovery in light, 1558.
On algebra as the science of time, **1715, 1716**.
On quaternions, **1718**.
On trisection of an angle, **2112**.
Hankel, Definition of m., **114**.
On freedom in m., **206**.
On the permanency of math. knowledge, **216**.
On aim in m., **508**.
On isolated theorems, **621**.
On tact in m., **622**.
On geometry, 714.
Ancient and modern m. compared, **718, 720**.
Variability the central idea in modern m., **720**.
Characteristics of modern m., **728**.
On Descartes, **949**.
On Euler's work, **956**.
On philosophy and m., **1404**.
On the origin of m., **1412**.
On irrationals and imaginaries, **1729**.
On the origin of algebra, **1736**.
Euclid the only perfect model, **1822**.

Modern geometry a royal road, **1878**.
Harmony, 326, 1208.
Harris, M. gives command over nature, **434**.
Hathaway, On Sylvester, **1036**.
Heat, M. and the theory of, **1552. 1553**.
Heath, Character of Archimedes' work, **913**.
Heaviside, The place of Euclid, **1828**.
Hebrew and Latin races, Aptitude for m., 838.
Hegel, **1417**.
Heiss, Famous anagrams, **2055**.
Reversible verses, **2056**.
Helmholtz, M. the purest form of logical activity, **231**.
M. requires perseverance and great caution, **240**.
M. should take more important place in education, **441**.
Clifford on, **979**.
M. the purest logic, **1302**.
M. and applications, **1445**.
On geometry, **1836**.
On the importance of the calculus, **1939**.
A non-euclidean world, **2029**.
Herbart, Definition of m., **117**.
M. the predominant science, **209**.
On the method of m., **212, 1576**.
M. the priestess of definiteness and clearness, **217**.
On the importance of checks, **230**.
On imagination in m, **257**.
M. and invention, **406**.
M. the chief subject for common schools, **432**.
On aptitude for m., **509**.
On the teaching of m., **516**.
M. the greatest blessing, **1401**.
M. and philosophy, **1408**.
If philosophers understood m., **1415**.
M. indispensable to science, **1502**.

The universe in a single formula, **1920**.

On probability, **1963, 1969, 1971**.

Laputa, Math'ns of, 2120–2122, Math. school of, 2123.

Lasswitz, On modern algebra, **1741**.

On function theory, **1934**.

On non-euclidean geometry, **2040**.

Latin squares, 252.

Latta, On Leibnitz's logical calculus, **1317**.

Law and m., 1597, 1598.

Laws of thought, 719, 1318.

Leadership, M. as training for, 317.

Lefevre, M. hateful to weak minds, **733**.

Logic and m., **1309**.

Leibnitz, On difficulties in m., **241**.

His greatness, 987.

His influence, 988.

The nature of his work, 989.

His math. tendencies, 990.

His binary arithmetic, 991.

On Newton, **1010**.

On demonstrations outside of m., **1312**.

Ars characteristica, **1316**.

His logical calculus, 1317.

Union of philosophical and m. productivity, 1404.

M. and philosophy, **1435**.

On the certainty of math. knowledge, **1442**.

On controversy in geometry, **1859**.

His differential calculus, 1902.

His notation of the calculus, 1904.

On necessary and contingent truth, **1966**.

Lecture, Preparation of, 540.

Leverrier, Discovery of Neptune, 1559.

Lewes, On the infinite, **1953**.

Lie, On central conceptions in modern m., **727**.

Endowment of math'ns, **818**.

The comparative anatomist, 992.

Aim of his work, 993.

His genius, 994.

On groups, **1752**.

On the origin of the calculus, **1901**.

On differential equations, **1924**.

Liliwati, Origin of, 995.

Limitations of math. science, 1437.

Limits, Method of, 1905, 1908, 1909, 1940.

Lindeman, On m. and science, **1523**.

Lobatchewsky, **2022**.

Locke, On the method of m., **214, 235**.

On proofs and demonstrations, **236**.

On the unpopularity of m., **271**.

On m. as a logical exercise, **423, 424**.

M. cures presumption, **425**.

Math. reasoning of universal application, **426**.

On reading of classic authors, **604**.

On Aristotle, **914**.

On m. and philosophy, **1433**.

On m. and moral science, **1439, 1440**.

On the certainty of math. knowledge, **1440, 1441**.

On unity, **1607**.

On number, **1608**.

On demonstrations in numbers, **1630**.

On the advantages of algebra, **1705**.

On infinity, **1955, 1957**.

On probability, **1965**.

Logarithmic spiral, 922.

Logarithmic tables, 602.

Logarithms, 1526, 1614, 1616.

Logic and m., Chapter XIII. See also 423–430, 442.

Logical calculus, 1316, 1317.

Longevity of math'ns, 839.

Liouville, 822.

God geometrizes, 1635, 1636. 1702.

On geometry, 429, 1803, 1804, **1806, 1844, 1845.**

Pleasure, Element of in m., 1622, 1629, 1848, 1850, 1851.

Pliny, **2039.**

Plus and minus signs, 1727.

Plutarch, On Archimedes, **903, 904, 908–910, 912.**

God geometrizes, **1802.**

Poe, **417.**

Poetry and m.,
Weierstrass on, 802.
Pringsheim on, 1108.
Wordsworth on, 1117.
Milner on, 1118.
Workman on, 1120.
Pollock on, 1121.
Hoffman on, 1122.
Thoreau on, 1123.
Emerson on, 1124.
Hill on, 1125, 1126.
Shakespeare on, 1127.

Poincaré, On elegance in m., **640.**
M. has a triple end, **1102.**
M. as a language, **1208.**
Geometry not an experimental science, **1867.**
On geometrical axioms, **2005.**

Point, 1816.

Politics, Math'ns and, 814.

Political science, M. and, 1201, 1324.

Pollock, On Clifford, **938–941, 1121.**

Pope, **907, 2015, 2031, 2046.**

Precision in m., 228, 639, 728.

Precocity in m., 835.

Predicabilia a priori, 2003.

Press, M. ignored by daily, 731, 732.

Price, Characteristics of m., **247.**
On m. and physics, **1550.**

Prime numbers, Sylvester on, 1648.

Principia Mathematica, 1326.

Pringsheim, M. the science of the self-evident, **232.**
M. should be studied for its own sake, **439.**

On the indirect value of m., **448.**

On rigor in m., **535.**

On m. and journalism, **732.**

On math'ns in public service, **824.**

Math'n somewhat of a poet, **1108.**

On music and m., **1132.**

On the language of m., **1211.**

On m. and physics, **1548.**

Probabilities, 442, 823, 1589, 1590–1592, 1962–1972, 1975.

Problems, In m., 523, 534.
In arithmetic, 528.
In algebra, 530.
Should be simple, 603.
In Cambridge texts, 608.
On solution of, 611.
On importance of, 624, 628.
What constitutes good, 629.
Aid to research, 644.
Of modern m., 1926.

Problem solving, 531, 532.

Proclus, Ptolemy and Euclid, **951.**
On characteristics of geometry, **1869.**

Progress in m., 209, 211, 212, 216, 218, 702–705, 708.

Projective geometry, 1876, 1877, 1879, 1880.

Proportion, Euclid's doctrine of, 1834.
Euclid's definition of, 1835.

Proposition, 1219, 1419.

Prussia, M. in, 513.

Pseudomath, Defined, 2101.

Ptolemy and Euclid, 951.

Publications, Math. of present day, 702, 703.

Public service, M. and, 823, 824, 1303, 1574.

Public speaking, M. and, 420, 829, 830.

Pure M., Bacon's definition of, 106.
Whewell's definition of, 107.
On the object of, 111, 129.
Novalis' conception of, 112.
Hobson's definition of, 118.

Geometry not an inductive science, 1830.

On limits, 1909.

On the idea of space, 2004.

On Plato and the regular solids, **2133, 2135.**

White, H. S., On the growth of m., **211.**

White, W. F., Definition of m., **131, 1203.**

M. as a prerequisite for public speaking, **420.**

On beauty in m., **1119.**

The place of the math'n, **1529.**

On m. and social science, **1586.**

The cost of Manhattan island, **2130.**

Whitehead, On the ideal of m., **119.**

Definition of m., **122.**

On the scope of m., **126.**

On the nature of m., **233.**

Precision necessary in m., **639.**

On practical applications, **655.**

On theoretical investigations, **659.**

Characteristics of ancient geometry, **713.**

On the extent of m., **737.**

Archimedes compared with Newton, **911.**

On the Arabic notation, **1217.**

Difficulty of math. notation, **1218.**

On symbolic logic, **1320.**

Principia Mathematica, 1326.

On philosophy and m., **1403.**

On obscurity in m. and philosophy, **1407.**

On the laws of algebra, **1708.**

On + and − signs, **1727.**

On universal algebra, **1753.**

On the Cartesian method, **1890.**

On Swift's ignorance of m., **2125.**

Whitworth, On the solution of problems, **611.**

Williamson, On the value of m., **1575.**

Infinitesimals and limits, **1905.**

On infinitesimals, **1946.**

Wilson, E. B., On the social value of m., **1588.**

On m. and economics, **1593.**

On the nature of axioms, **2012.**

Wilson, John, On Newton and Shakespeare, **1012.**

Newton and Linnæus, **1013.**

Woodward, On probabilities, **1589.**

On the theory of errors, **1973, 1974.**

Wordsworth, W., On Archimedes, **906.**

On poetry and geometric truth, **1117.**

On geometric rules, **1418.**

On geometry, **1840, 1848.**

M. and solitude, **1859.**

Workman, On the poetic nature of m., **1120.**

Young, C. A., On the discovery of Neptune, **1559.**

Young, C. W., Definition of m., **124.**

Young, J. W. A., On m. as type a of thought, **404.**

M. as preparation for science study, **421.**

M. essential to comprehension of nature, **435.**

Development of abstract methods, **729.**

Beauty in m., **1110.**

On Euclid's axiom, **2014.**

Zeno, His problems, 1938.

Zero, 1948, 1954.